KU-196-788

THE NATURAL RUBBER FORMULARY
and Property Index

Malaysian Rubber Producers' Research Association
a unit of the Malaysian Rubber Research and Development Board
An agency responsible to the Ministry of Primary Industries

First published 1984

ISBN 0-9504401-3-2

Technical enquiries concerning natural rubber are welcomed by the MRRDB Technical Advisory Service located at each Malaysian Rubber Bureau and at the MRPRA and RRIM laboratories. Addresses for all these organizations will be found inside the back cover.

Printed in England by **Inprint of Luton Limited**
95-115 Windmill Road, Luton, Beds.

Price £8.00

CONTENTS

Preface 2

General notes 3

Part A Dry Rubber Formulary 5

Grades of Malaysian rubber 6
Protective systems for natural rubber 8
Vulcanization systems for natural rubber 15
Hardness adjustment of natural rubber vulcanizates 23

Section
1 Adhesives, solution 25
2 Belting, conveyor 31
3 Chemical plant linings 43
4 Ebonite 47
5 Engineering rubbers 51
6 Extrusions 83
7 Footwear 107
8 Hose 121
9 Mouldings, classified by hardness 141
10 Mouldings, classified by application 179
11 Printing and stationery 197
12 Seals and gaskets 205
13 Tyres and associated components 219
14 Miscellaneous 241

Part B Latex Formulary 251

Natural rubber latex concentrate 252
Preparation of dispersions and emulsions 253

Section
15 Adhesives 257
16 Carpet backing applications 265
17 Dipped products 277
18 Latex foam 289
19 Prevulcanized latices 295
20 Miscellaneous 301

Part C Dry rubber vulcanizate property index 315

Notes on property index 316

Section
21 Dry rubber vulcanizate property index 317

Part D Additional information and applications indexes 325

Physical test methods 326
Conversion table for stress values 330
Temperature equivalents of saturated steam 331
Useful conversion factors 332
Densities of rubber and compounding ingredients 333
Physical constants of vulcanized rubber 334
Abbreviations 335
Trade Names index 336
Applications index, dry rubber 340
Applications index, latex 344

Preface

This Formulary is an aid to the successful use of natural rubber in a wide range of industrial applications: it contains some 300 dry rubber and 80 latex formulations. Some modifications to these formulations may be necessary to meet individual factory requirements, particularly in ease of processing, and when using local variations of ingredients. The Technical Advisory Service of the Malaysian Rubber Research and Development Board is pleased to assist in any aspect of the use of natural rubber.

Many of the formulations for specific applications have been published in Natural Rubber Technical Information Sheets, the quarterly journal *NR Technology*, or in Natural Rubber Engineering Data Sheets, and in these cases the reference source is given. In this Formulary, additional data, which may not be relevant to the original application, have been included to enable the formulation to be considered for wider use.

Applications indexes are provided for both dry rubber and latex formulations. The dry rubber physical property index lists formulations in order of increasing hardness and increasing tensile strength; this should aid selection of formulations to meet particular needs.

The information contained in this Formulary is believed to be reliable but the Board does not accept any responsibility for it. Users are reminded that it may contain matter the subject of patent protection and they should therefore satisfy themselves as to the position and obtain any necessary licences before employing processes described. Users should inform themselves of any health and safety requirements in the use of ingredients in these formulations.

General notes

References given to previously published formulations may contain further information on compound design, mixing, processing or vulcanizate properties.

Rubber grades

Notes on the selection of appropriate dry rubber grades and latices are given in the introductions to Parts A and B.

Dry rubber formulations

Quantities are expressed as parts of ingredient by weight per hundred parts of rubber (parts phr), or in a few cases per hundred parts of rubber plus extender oil. The nominal hardness value given for each formulation is for guidance only.

Latex formulations

Ingredients are listed in recommended order of addition to the mix. Dispersions are prefixed by the concentration of the ingredient and the quantities are based on the wet weight. Latex is assumed to be 60 per cent dry rubber content. Vulcanizing ingredients are usually added as aqueous dispersions, surfactants as aqueous solutions and oils as aqueous emulsions. The preparation of dispersions and emulsions is described in Part B. Distilled or de-ionized water should be used.

Formulations containing thiourea are not recommended for medical or food-contact applications.

Ingredients

Where ingredients are designated by trade names this indicates only that they are examples or the materials used to develop the formulation and does not imply recommendation of specific trade materials. Chemically equivalent materials would be expected to give similar results. Part D contains an index of trade names used.

Abbreviations

A list of abbreviations used is given in Part D.

Carbon blacks

Designation is by ASTM D1765 number codes, but where appropriate the type is also indicated by the conventional letter code.

Test data

Unless otherwise stated, tests were conducted on specially-moulded sheets or test pieces prepared from laboratory-scale mixes by vulcanization in a platen press. Appropriate International Standard (ISO) or British Standard (BS) test methods were normally used. Details of test methods, including any modifications to the standard procedures, are given in Part D. Results are expressed in SI units; Part D also contains conversion factors and tables for metric and Imperial units.

Part A

Dry rubber formulary

Grades of Malaysian Rubber

With certain obvious exceptions such as oil-extended natural rubber, all grades are virtually 100% *cis*-1,4-polyisoprene and inter-grade differences are far smaller than for many types of synthetic rubber. Nevertheless, characteristic differences do exist and these should be recognized if natural rubber is to be used to full advantage. Some general background and guidance is given here.

Malaysian rubber is obtained by coagulation of latex obtained from the *Hevea brasiliensis* tree. The highest quality grades are obtained by deliberate coagulation of latex, usually by acidification, under carefully controlled conditions in a processing factory. These are often called the latex grades.

Other grades contain cup lump and other rubber materials produced by natural coagulation of latex which exudes from the tree after the main bulk has been collected. These field coagula are collected at the next tapping.

The different source materials undergo essentially the same processing, either by crumb routes into Standard Malaysian Rubber (SMR) grades, or by traditional processes into sheet or crepe. Currently a very minor amount of sheet is marketed under the SMR scheme as SMR 5 (RSS). The general-purpose grade, SMR GP, consists of a blend of latex and field coagula; it is chemically treated (usually with hydroxylamine salts) to prevent viscosity increase during shipping and storage. A latex grade viscosity-stabilized rubber, SMR CV, is also produced. These viscosity-stabilized rubbers should not be confused with normal grades of rubber selected for low initial viscosity.

The main grades available are summarized in Table 1.

The quality of raw natural rubber depends on several factors, principally

1 freedom from particulate contamination (*eg* sand and bark) which is detrimental to high strength and fatigue resistance,

2 a normal level of naturally-occurring antioxidants; removal of these materials by overwashing can result in inadequate ageing resistance,

3 freedom from contamination with active metals or pro-oxidants resulting from undue exposure to heat and light during production,

4 presence of a balanced level of non-rubber materials which give normal cure activity; overwashing of coagula can reduce cure activity.

These factors affect all grades of natural rubber. Only Standard Malaysian Rubbers give an assurance of quality through specification of minimum levels of dirt, oxidizability and, for top quality grades, cure behaviour. Furthermore, the small bales are relatively easy to handle. Further information on SMR grades is given in Technical Information Sheets D60–69 and SMR Bulletins 9 and 10.

Table 1 SMR and International Grades

Quality	Viscosity stabilized grades	Latex grades		Field coagulum grades
High		Pale crepe[a]		
	SMR CV	SMR L[b]		
			RSS1	
		SMR WF		
		SMR 5	RSS2	
Good	SMR GP		RSS3	SMR 10
				Estate Brown Crepes
				SMR 20
				No 2, 3 Remilled crepes
Moderate			RSS5	
				No 3, 4 Blanket crepes

a. Whitest pale crepe is obtained by fractional coagulation and/or chemical bleaching.
b. A light-coloured grade.

The formulations given here use an appropriate grade of SMR or special-purpose rubber. The use of other grades or rubbers may give slightly different results; in injection moulding, in which consistency of viscosity and cure behaviour are critical, it is believed that SMR CV gives the best results. The special-purpose rubbers used are briefly described below.

Special-purpose grades

Oil-extended natural rubber (OENR) is prepared by addition of oil either to latex prior to coagulation or to dried field coagulum. Grades containing aromatic (A) or non-staining naphthenic (N) oils are available. The ratio of raw rubber to oil and oil type is denoted by a code, *eg* OENR 75/25N. For further information see Technical Information Sheet D33.

Deproteinized natural rubber (DPNR) is prepared by enzyme treatment of latex, and is normally available in viscosity-stabilized form. For further information see Technical Information Sheet D6.

Superior Processing rubbers (SP and PA rubbers) are prepared by coagulating prevulcanized latex mixed with normal latex. The proportion of prevulcanized rubber varies from 20 to 80% and is indicated by a numerical grade code. Among the advantages of SP rubbers are improved calendering, better finish, lower die swell and higher dimensional stability, especially in soft, lightly-filled mixes. SP rubbers may be used as complete or partial replacement for normal grades. Similar vulcanizate properties are obtained provided that curative levels are properly adjusted. Premastication of the SP or PA rubber is always advisable. An oil-extended grade, PA 57, contains 57% prevulcanized rubber and 29% oil. For further information see Technical Information Sheet D47.

Methacrylate graft (MG) rubbers are prepared by polymerizing 30–49 parts of methyl methacrylate in the latex before coagulation. They are sold under the trade name *Heveaplus MG*. Some pre-mastication is necessary prior to use. MG rubbers may be blended with normal grades to produce vulcanizates with high stiffness and manageable compound viscosities at normal processing temperature. MG rubbers are also used in adhesives. For further information see Technical Information Sheet D101.

Protective systems for natural rubber

In this formulary, protective agents have usually been chosen for general-purpose use, rather than for particular applications. Changes may be necessary for specific service conditions, which may vary widely even for a single product. Such changes will usually have little effect on unaged physical properties, but may alter the effect of anti-flex-cracking agents on fatigue life. Advice is given here on the selection of systems for protection against ozone, flex-cracking and trace metal-catalysed oxidation.

The major factors involved in ageing of natural rubber vulcanizates are:

Agency	Effect	Protective agent
1 anaerobic ageing	reversion, network maturing reactions	heat-resistant vulcanization system
2 oxygen + heat	oxidation	antioxidant
3 oxygen + heavy metals	metal-catalysed oxidation	metal deactivator
4 oxygen + flexing	flex-cracking	anti-flex-cracking agent
5 ozone + stress	ozone cracking	chemical antiozonant or wax
6 light or uv light	crazing, photo-oxidation	antioxidant and uv absorber

Agencies 1–3 generally affect bulk physical properties as well as the surface, whereas 4–6 usually affect only the surface and require special consideration, *eg* in the ability of a protective wax to form a protective surface bloom.

Anaerobic ageing generally results in decreases in stiffness, resilience and tensile, tear and fatigue properties; the extent is mainly determined by the type of vulcanization system.

Oxidative ageing generally causes a decrease in tensile, tear and fatigue properties. The effect on stiffness depends on the formulation and the temperature of ageing: lower temperatures favour an increase in stiffness, particularly in the early stages. At high temperatures, oxidative ageing affects only the surface as essentially all the oxygen is consumed by reaction with antioxidant or rubber before it can diffuse into the bulk. A resinous skin is formed and high-temperature ageing in the centre of a large component is essentially anaerobic. Extreme care must be used in interpreting ageing data obtained from tests on thin strips.

Many applications require protection against more than one of the agencies listed above, and blends of protective agents are often used. The acceptability of staining and discolouration and the risk of loss by volatilization or by extraction with water, oils and solvents must be considered.

Protective agents for natural rubber may be categorized as:

1 staining antidegradants protecting against oxygen, ozone and flex-cracking
2 staining antioxidants with flex-cracking protection
3 low-staining antioxidants
4 non-staining antioxidants
5 waxes
6 metal deactivators
7 hydroperoxide decomposers
8 uv absorbers.

1 Staining antidegradants giving protection against oxidation, ozone and flex cracking
The *p*-phenylenediamines are by far the most effective types of antidegradant used in natural rubber. Trade examples are shown in Table 2. There are 3 main classes: N-alkyl-N′-phenyl-, N,N′-dialkyl- and N,N′-diaryl-*p*-phenylenediamines. Those having lowest molecular weight are the most reactive, but are also the most volatile, most easily extracted and worst staining.

Table 2 Antidegradants

Antidegradant	Abbreviation	Comments	Trade examples
p-Phenylenediamines			
Alkyl-phenyl			
N-isopropyl-N′-phenyl	IPPD	high overall antidegradant activity	*Flexzone 3C* *Permanax IPPD* *Santoflex IP* *Vulkanox 4010NA*
N-(1,3-dimethylbutyl)-N′-phenyl	HPPD or 6PPD	as IPPD but more resistant to leaching, less volatile.	*Antiozite 67* *Permanax 6PPD* *Santoflex 13* *UOP 588*
Dialkyl			
N,N′-bis-(1,4-dimethyl-pentyl)	7PPD	high antiozonant activity under static strain	*Eastozone 33* *Flexzone 4L* *Santoflex 77* *Vulkanox 4030*
N,N′-di(1-ethyl-3-methylpentyl)	DOPPD	high antiozonant activity under static strain	*Antiozite 2* *Flexzone 8L* *Santoflex 17* *UOP 88*
Diaryl			
mixed diaryl		lowest antiozonant activity, but most resistant to aqueous leaching; least staining; low volatility	*Akroflex AZ* *Antigene D* *Wingstay 100*
Hydroquinoline			
6-ethoxy-2,2,4-trimethyl-1,2-dihydroquinoline		less effective than IPPD or HPPD	*Anox W* *Permanax ETMQ* *Santoflex AW* *Vulkanox EC*

Alkyl-phenyl- and dialkyl-*p*-phenylenediamines reduce the rate of growth of ozone-induced cracks under both static and dynamic conditions. The dialkyl compounds also increase the threshold strain for static ozone cracking; they may therefore be used alone. Alkyl-phenyl compounds need an additional antiozonant or wax for static protection; the synergistic (greater than additive) effect obtained with such blends allows lower loadings of each constituent to be used. This may be beneficial in reducing staining.

6-Ethoxy-2,2,4-trimethyl-1,2-dihydroquinoline is less effective than *p*-phenylenediamines. It is highly staining and reduces only the crack growth rate. It does not protect against static cracking unless blended with waxes, when a synergistic effect is also obtained.

Typical protective systems	Comments
2 parts phr IPPD or HPPD + 2–3 parts phr wax	static and dynamic protection
3–4 parts phr DOPPD	static and dynamic protection
1 part phr IPPD or HPPD + 1 part phr diaryl PPD + 2–3 parts phr wax	static and dynamic protection, more resistance to extraction and volatilization

The systems shown may be used without additional antioxidant, but dialkyl-*p*-phenylene diamines are weaker antioxidants than alkyl-phenyl compounds and their antiozonant activity is less well retained after heat ageing; for the best oxidation resistance an antioxidant should also be included with them. Diaryl-*p*-phenylenediamines are most resistant to chemical and physical losses in activity, but are weaker antiozonants. Replacement of up to half the loading of alkyl-phenyl compound with a diaryl compound will often confer greater resistance to extraction and more long-term protection under severe conditions.

It should be noted that the antiozonant system required to pass a specification is not always appropriate for long-term protection against ozone, particularly if the ozone concentration in the test is high and/or if the pre-conditioning time is low.

For further information on ozone protection see *NR Technology*, 1972, **3**, Part 1, No 1.

2 Staining antioxidants with anti-flex-cracking protection only Diphenylamine-acetone condensates and naphthylamine derivatives are good anti-flex-cracking agents, but they are not as effective as *p*-phenylenediamines. Table 3 lists some of the more common examples.

Table 3 Staining antioxidants giving flex-cracking resistance

Type of antioxidant	Comments	Trade examples
acetone/diphenylamine condensates	general-purpose including tyre components	*Agerite Superflex* *BLE 25*, *Cyanoflex* *Permanax B*
naphthylamine derivatives		
phenyl-ß-naphthylamine	not recommended for high temperatures	*Agerite Powder* *Antigene D* *Vulkanox PBN*

3 Low-staining amine antioxidants These include polymerized 2,2,4-trimethyl-1,2-dihydroquinoline (TMQ), di-ß-naphthyl-*p*-phenylenediamine and some substituted diphenylamines; see Table 4 for trade examples. They provide good protection against heat and oxygen, and the *p*-phenylenediamine is also very effective as a metal deactivator. Substituted diphenylamines also confer some resistance to flex-cracking. All stain less than most other amine antioxidants.

Table 4 Low-staining antioxidants with no flex-cracking or ozone protection

Type of antioxidant	Comments	Trade examples
Polymerized 2,2,4-trimethyl-1,2-dihydroquinoline	general purpose	*Agerite Resin D* *Flectol H* *Permanax TQ* *Vulkanox HS*
Di-ß-naphthyl-*p*-phenylenediamine	metal deactivator	*Agerite White* *Antigene F*
Alkylated or aralkylated diphenylamines	minimal stain	*Agerite Stalite* *Octamine* *Permanax CD* *Permanax OD* *Vulkanox DDA* *Wingstay 29*

4 Non-staining antioxidants The least staining and discolouration is given by phenolic antioxidants; the more important types are shown in Table 5. The most effective in natural rubber are phenol-alkanes, in particular hindered *o*-methylene-bis-phenols, but they are susceptible to pinking on exposure to light. Better resistance to pinking is given by some of the more complex phenol-alkanes.

Most simple phenolic antioxidants are much cheaper than phenol-alkanes, and many are more resistant to discolouration. Hindered thio-bis-phenols and hydroquinone derivatives are also available; the latter are often used in unvulcanized compositions and adhesives.

Table 5 Non-staining antioxidants

Type of antioxidant	Comments	Trade examples
Phenol-alkanes		
o-methylene-bis-phenols	good antioxidant protection, some pinking	*Antioxidant 425* *Antioxidant 2246* *Naugawhite* *Permanax WSP* *Vulkanox BKF* *Vulkanox ZKF*
complex phenol-alkanes	more resistant to pinking	*Lowinox 22IB46* *Wingstay L*
Hindered phenols		
styrenated phenols		*Montaclere* *Permanax SP* *Wingstay S*
other phenolics[a]		*Permanax WSL* *Santowhite 54* *Wingstay T* *Vulkanox KSM*
thio-bis-phenols		*Ethyl Antioxidant 736*
Hydroquinones		*Agerite Alba* *Santovar A*

a. *eg* Alkylated and aralkylated phenols

5 Waxes These provide non-staining protection against ozone attack under static conditions, and increase the threshold strain. The type and level of wax used depends on the service and storage temperature and the product specification test temperatures. As a general guide, the melting temperature of the wax should not be less than 20°C above the maximum surface temperature of the product. To be effective, the wax must bloom to the surface of the vulcanizate and form a coherent layer. The diffusion rate of a wax in rubber increases dramatically with temperature, but its solubility also rises. Since these factors govern the rate of blooming, differences will be found between various waxes. For year-round protection and retention of activity over a wide tèmperature range, proprietary blends containing the so-called 'microcrystalline' waxes are recommended.

Waxes are more soluble in oil-extended vulcanizates and higher levels are required to give the same level of protection to the vulcanizate.

Some types of wax are given in Table 6.

Table 6 Waxes for ozone resistance

Temperature	Trade examples
below 20°C	*Antilux, Antilux L* *Okerin 444, 587*
15–40°C	*Antilux 654* *Sunolite 666*
0–40°C	*Antilux 600* *Sunolite 127, 154, 240* *Sunproof Improved*

6 Metal deactivation Trace quantities of certain metals such as copper, manganese, iron, *etc* may act as catalysts for the oxidation of natural rubber vulcanizates. Many amines and some phenolics are effective inhibitors of metal-catalysed oxidation and, provided that staining and discolouration are acceptable, *p*-phenylenediamines are particularly suitable for this purpose. Di-ß-naphthyl-*p*-phenylenediamine is recommended where minimum staining is required.

Blends of antioxidants and the synergist MBI or its zinc salt are highly effective; those incorporating phenolic antioxidants are recommended for protection of light-coloured goods. Trade examples of non-staining metal deactivators are given in Table 7, and blends containing some of the these deactivators are commercially available.

Table 7 Metal deactivators and hydroperoxide decomposers, non-staining

Metal deactivator	Trade examples
2-mercaptobenzimidazole	*Permanax MBI* *Vulkanox MB*
zinc 2-mercaptobenzimidazole	*Permanax ZMBI* *Vulkanox ZMB*

7 Hydroperoxide decomposers Resistance to thermal oxidation is primarily determined by the vulcanization system, but the best protection is given by the synergism between antioxidants and the hydroperoxide decomposer MBI or its zinc salt. Trade examples are given in Table 7. For black-filled vulcanizates, blends of TMQ or diphenylamines with MBI (2 parts phr of each) are recommended. In the absence of MBI or ZMBI certain bis-phenols can be less effective in semi-EV and EV vulcanizates.

8 Light resistance Protection against photo-oxidation is only necessary in light-coloured articles. Combinations of a phenolic antioxidant with a UV absorber such as a benztriazole derivative, *eg Tinuvin P* or *Tinuvin 327* (Ciba Geigy), are recommended, particularly for transparent articles which are most at risk.

Further information For further information on the effects of ageing on natural rubber see:

The Chemistry and Physics of Rubber-like Substances, Ed. Bateman, L. London, Maclaren; New York, Wiley, 1963.

Protecting natural rubber against ozone cracking, *NR Technology*, 1972, **3,** Part 1, No 1.

Factors influencing high temperature ageing of large natural rubber components, *Proc. Int. Rubb. Conf. 1975*, Kuala Lumpur: Rubber Research Institute of Malaysia, 1978, 5, 57.

Vulcanization systems for natural rubber

Vulcanization converts rubber from a linear polymer to a three-dimensional network by crosslinking the polymer chains; resilience, stiffness and resistance to creep are increased. Natural rubber is usually vulcanized with sulphur and organic accelerators, although other reagents such as the *Novor* urethanes and organic peroxides may be used.

Sulphur vulcanization

The chemistry of vulcanization is complex, and the physical properties obtained depend on the types of crosslink formed and the extent of main-chain modification by side reactions. The crosslinks may be mono-, di-, tri- or higher poly-sulphides, the proportion of each being largely determined by the vulcanization system, although cure time and temperature also have an important effect.

Activators and organic accelerators are used in sulphur vulcanization systems. The activators, usually zinc oxide and stearic acid, increase the number of crosslinks, and hence stiffness, but amounts used are not critical provided that certain minimum levels are exceeded. The accelerator increases the rate of cure and the efficiency with which sulphur is used in crosslinking compared to side reactions. The sulphur/accelerator ratio is particularly important in determining the type of crosslink formed. High sulphur levels, *ie* 2–3.5 parts phr, and low levels of accelerator, typically 0.3–1 part phr, are called 'conventional' systems. At optimum cure the vulcanizates contain mostly polysulphidic crosslinks with a relatively high level of chain modification. Low sulphur levels, typically 0.25–0.7 parts phr, with high accelerator levels, typically 2.5–5 parts phr, will give mainly monosulphidic crosslinks and much less chain modification; they are therefore known as 'efficient' vulcanization (EV) systems. Semi-EV systems, with intermediate sulphur levels of 1–2 parts phr and 2.5–1 parts phr of accelerator are often used.

Physical properties Polysulphide networks generally have good tensile, tear and fatigue properties and excellent resistance to low-temperature crystallization. However, they are susceptible to reversion, *ie* loss of properties on overcure, and to oxidative ageing. Other drawbacks include high compression set and high rates of secondary creep and stress relaxation at elevated temperatures, owing in part to exchange reactions between polysulphidic crosslinks.

Because of the higher thermal stability of monosulphidic crosslinks, EV systems give vulcanizates which are more resistant to reversion, oxidative ageing and high-temperature compression set. However, resistance to tearing, fatigue and wear and, to a lesser extent, tensile strength, are generally lower than for conventional vulcanizates. Resistance to low-temperature crystallization is poor and rubber-to-metal bonding may be difficult. EV systems are used for the vulcanization of thick articles and those used at elevated service temperatures.

For best resistance to oxidative ageing, efficient vulcanizates should be protected by a combination of a hydroperoxide decomposer, *eg* MBI or ZMBI, and a powerful antioxidant such as TMQ (see previous section).

Soluble EV systems are designed for lowest compression set, lowest rates of creep and stress relaxation and high precision of stiffness. Stearic acid is replaced by the rubber-soluble activator, zinc 2-ethylhexanoate (ZEH), and rubber-soluble accelerators which give soluble vulcanization products are used with normal levels of zinc oxide. The vulcanizates are particularly suitable for engineering applications. A rubber-soluble activator also improves resistance to primary creep and stress relaxation in conventional vulcanizates.

Semi-EV vulcanizates have physical properties intermediate between those of conventional and EV vulcanizates. They give some improvement in reversion, ageing resistance and compression set compared with conventional vulcanizates, but resistance to fatigue and low-temperature crystallization is impaired. Scorch safety can be high, particularly with sulphenamide accelerators.

Cure time also has an important effect on crosslink structure and hence on physical properties. Undercured vulcanizates, particularly conventional and semi-EV, have higher polysulphide levels. Overcure gives lower polysulphide levels, accompanied by some loss of modulus and tensile properties. However, compression set of overcured conventional and semi-EV vulcanizates may be considerably reduced by the improved anaerobic stability of networks with higher proportions of monosulphidic crosslinks. Unfortunately, their oxidative ageing resistance is reduced by the increased level of chain modification.

Some typical sulphur vulcanization systems are listed below, the amounts being shown in parts phr. All require appropriate levels of activators.

(a) conventional
Sulphur 2–3.5 + 0.5–1 sulphenamide
Sulphur 2–3.5 + 0.5–1 thiazole + 0.1–0.5 DPG or TMTM
Sulphur 2–3 + 0.3 thiuram or dithiocarbamate

(b) semi-EV range
Sulphur 2 + 1 sulphenamide
Sulphur 1.5 + 1.5 sulphenamide
Sulphur 1.0 + 2 sulphenamide
Sulphur 1.5 + 0.6 DTDM + 0.6 sulphenamide
Sulphur 1.2 + 1.0 thiocarbamylsulphenamide
Sulphur 1 + 1 MBTS + 1 zinc dialkyldithiophosphate

(c) EV systems
low sulphur systems
Sulphur 0.7 + 1.7 MBS + 0.7 TBTD, soluble EV
Sulphur 0.6 + 1.6 DTDM + 1.0 sulphenamide
Sulphur 0.6 + 1.1 MBS + 1.1 thiocarbamylsulphenamide
Sulphur 0.5 + 6 CBS
Sulphur 0.3 + 3 CBS + 2 TMTD, high modulus
Sulphur 0.25 + 1.8 CBS + 1.2 TMTD, lower modulus

(d) sulphurless
3 TMTD
1.5 DTDM + 2 MBTS, for light colours, non-copper staining
1 DTDM + 1 CBS + 1 TMTD
1.5 MBD + 1.5 CdDMC

Accelerators for sulphur vulcanization

Guanidines These are very slow, inefficient accelerators. They are used with high sulphur levels (>3 parts phr) for thick articles, *eg* roll covers; the vulcanizates may discolour on exposure to light.

Their main use is as secondary accelerators for thiazoles and sulphenamides. Typical examples are diphenylguanidine (DPG) or di-*o*-tolylguanidine (DOTG).

Thiazoles Slow accelerators when used alone, thiazoles are mainly used with secondary accelerators such as DPG, TMTM, TMTD, ZDMC, *etc* to give very fast-curing mixed accelerator systems. Typical examples are 2-mercaptobenzothiazole (MBT) and 2,2′-dibenzothiazyl disulphide (MBTS).

MBTS/TMTM combinations are recommended for the best compromise of scorch safety, fast cure and resistance to light discolouration, but the ageing resistance obtained is inferior to that given by MBTS/DPG. The latter combination may give better reversion and ageing resistance than sulphenamide accelerators. MBTS/hexamine combinations are often used for light-coloured vulcanizates.

Sulphenamides These fast-curing, delayed-action accelerators are used extensively in carbon black-filled vulcanizates. Low levels of thiurams or dithiocarbamates are used as secondary accelerators in conventional systems to shorten cure times, although scorch safety is reduced. Sulphenamide accelerators are also widely used in semi-EV and EV systems in combination with thiuram disulphides and other sulphur donors. Typical examples in order of increasing scorch safety are: N-cyclohexylbenzothiazole-2-sulphenamide (CBS), N-t-butylbenzothiazole-2-sulphenamide (TBBS), and morpholinylbenzothiazole-2- sulphenamide (MBS).

Dithiocarbamates These are the fastest accelerators and give least processing safety. They are mainly used as secondary accelerators, the zinc dithiocarbamates particularly in light coloured goods. Zinc dibutyldithiocarbamate is particularly suited for the production of transparent goods because of its higher solubility in rubber. Other dithiocarbamates bloom to the rubber surface even at low levels. Dithiocarbamates are powerful antioxidants in heat-resistant EV or peroxide vulcanizates, but may act as pro-oxidants in conventional vulcanizates. Typical examples are zinc dimethyldithiocarbamate (ZDMC), zinc diethyldithiocarbamate (ZDEC), zinc dibutyldithiocarbamate (ZDBC), bismuth dimethyldithiocarbamate (BiDMC) and cadmium diethyldithiocarbamate (CdDEC).

Thiurams These are also ultra-fast accelerators, the disulphides and polysulphides also acting as sulphur donors. They are generally slower than dithiocarbamates and give greater scorch safety. Zinc dithiocarbamates are formed during vulcanization. Typical examples are tetramethylthiuram disulphide (TMTD), tetra-ethylthiuram disulphide (TETD), tetrabutylthiuram disulphide (TBTD) and tetramethylthiuram monosulphide (TMTM).

Thiurams may be used as primary accelerators with intermediate to high sulphur levels to give very fast cures, particularly for light colours. Resistance to ageing may be poor, particularly at high sulphur levels. TBTD is used in the 'soluble EV' system which takes advantage of the high solubility of the zinc dibutyldithiocarbamate formed during vulcanization. TMTD is used at about 3 parts phr in heat-resistant 'sulphurless' vulcanizates.

Other accelerators Some new types of accelerator have become available over the last decade or so. These include zinc dialkyl-dithiophosphates (*eg Rhenocure TP* or *Vocol*), triazines (*eg Triacit 20*), and a thiocarbamyl sulphenamide (*Cure-rite 18*). The last two types of accelerator give improved scorch safety in fast-curing conventional and semi-EV systems.

Sulphur donors These are used to replace part or all of the elemental sulphur in semi-EV or EV systems. Typical examples are dithiodimorpholine (DTDM), 4-morpholinyl-2-benzothiazyldisulphide (MBD), thiuram disulphides (see above), a caprolactam disulphide (*Rhenocure S*) and a bis-alkylphenyldisulphide (*Vultac*).

Accelerator combinations

Many combinations of accelerators show synergism in rates of vulcanization and state of cure. This synergism may be exploited to obtain higher stiffness and faster rates of cure, or to reduce overall accelerator loadings in EV systems. However, scorch safety must also be considered. There is also considerable synergism between urethane and conventional sulphur curing systems, as in mixed *Novor* cure systems (see later). The largest synergistic effects are given by blends of dissimilar accelerators, and many proprietary synergistic blends are commercially available. Some examples of synergistic mixtures are:

Accelerator pair	Approximate ratio for maximum modulus
Conventional and semi–EV	
MBTS/DPG	50/50
MBT/TMTD	60/40
MBT/DPG	50/50
Low sulphur systems	
TMTD/MBTS	80/20
TMTD/MBS	50/50
ZDMC/DPG	40/60
CBS/ZDMC	50/50
TMTD/DTDM	

Retarders and prevulcanization inhibitors

Retarders such as N-nitrosodiphenylamine (NDPA), phthalic anhydride and salicylic and benzoic acids increase scorch safety, but also increase cure times. They are not very effective with thiurams or dithiocarbamates. NDPA stains badly and is normally only used in carbon black-filled vulcanizates.

Prevulcanization inhibitors were introduced relatively recently. The most widely used is N-cyclohexylthiophthalimide (CTP) *eg Santogard PVI* or *Vulkalent G*. It is very effective in increasing scorch safety in sulphenamide cure systems, and at low levels has no effect on rate of cure or modulus. A new pre-vulcanization inhibitor is now available; N,N′,N″-tris (isopropylthio)-N,N′,N″-triphenylphosphoric triamide (*Vulcatard PRS*). This inhibitor is considerably more effective than CTP.

Novor vulcanizing systems

Novor is the trade name of urethane vulcanizing agents developed by MRPRA and now being used increasingly in a variety of applications, in particular those demanding high temperature vulcanization or high temperature service. The principal benefits of the new systems are outstanding reversion resistance and good ageing resistance coupled with good initial vulcanizate properties: a combination that cannot be achieved by established sulphur vulcanization systems. Another feature is that the urethane agents can be blended with sulphur vulcanizing systems to give a family of systems designed to vary in cost, cure behaviour and other properties. These mixed systems can also be devised to give vulcanizates with properties virtually unaffected by cure temperature – something which sulphur systems alone cannot provide.

Novor vulcanizing agents are marketed by Durham Chemicals Ltd, Birtley, County Durham, UK and their European agents, and by Akron Chemicals in North America.

All-*Novor* vulcanizing systems The outstanding feature of the all-*Novor 924* vulcanizing system is its
ability to give vulcanizates having exceptional reversion resistance. Typical formulation are shown.

Ingredient	Parts phr	Function
Novor 924	6.7	crosslinking agent
ZDMC	2	activator/catalyst
Calcium oxide	3	drying agent

The best heat-ageing resistance is given by the incorporation of a blend of TMQ and zinc 2-mercaptobenzimidazole (ZMBI), each at 2 parts phr. The best resistance to fatigue cracking is obtained with a *p*-phenylenediamine type antidegradant without a drying agent. Ageing resistance will be inferior to that obtained with the TMQ/ZMBI system, although it is still better than that of a well-protected high sulphur vulcanizate.

Mixed *Novor*/sulphur systems Adding a conventional sulphur vulcanizing system to *Novor 924* reduces cost and gives a much faster cure rate, whilst retaining many of the desirable features of the urethane system. The two systems can be blended in any proportion, but formulations having less than 50% *Novor* are not generally recommended since they do not offer any advantage over semi-EV systems. Resistance to reversion decreases as the *Novor*/sulphur ratio is reduced but 90/10 and 80/20 *Novor 924*/sulphur systems are still able to match EV systems. With certain mixed systems the same modulus/strength/resilience properties are obtained whether curing takes place at 140°C or 200°C. Mixed systems, like the all-*Novor* system, give vulcanizates whose fatigue resistance can improve upon ageing.

A blend of a *Novor* and a sulphur system will give a higher crosslink density than that expected from the two components, and the overall levels must be adjusted to maintain modulus. In the following formulations the levels of *Novor*, catalyst, sulphur and accelerator have been reduced by 20% (*ie* to 80% vulcanization potential).

	Novor/sulphur ratio				
	90/10	80/20	70/30	60/40	50/50
	Parts phr				
Novor 924	4.8	4.2	3.8	3.2	2.7
TMTM[a]	1.4	1.3	1.2	1.1	1.0
Zinc oxide	5	5	5	5	5
Stearic acid	1	1	1	1	1
Sulphur	0.2	0.4	0.6	0.8	1.0
TBBS	0.04	0.08	0.12	0.16	0.20

a. Activator for *Novor* providing better scorch safety than ZDMC.

Mixed *Novor*/sulphur systems are particularly useful in high-temperature curing, *eg* continuous vulcanization and injection moulding, where advantage can be taken of the combination of high reversion resistance, fast cure rate and insensitivity of properties to cure temperature. Optimum cures of 2–4 minutes at 180°C, 1–3 minutes at 190°C and 0.5–1 minute at 200°C have been obtained in injection moulding with an 80/20 system (see *NR Technology*, 1980, **11**, 36). They are also useful in the high-temperature curing of conveyor belting and, because of their reversion resistance, give more uniform vulcanization of rubber-covered rollers.

Peroxide vulcanization

Peroxide vulcanizates have the best heat resistance when suitable antioxidants are included. However, cure rates are slow and scorch safety is low. Long cure times, *ie* about 6 times the half-life of the peroxide, are needed to ensure its complete decomposition so that resistance to oxidative ageing is not reduced. Many antioxidants, particularly *p*-phenylenediamines, interfere with peroxide vulcanization. For highest resistance to oxidative degradation and least inference with vulcanization, a combination of MBI or ZMBI with TMQ and ZDMC is recommended. ZDMC is a very effective antioxidant for peroxide vulcanizates. The addition of calcium hydroxide is recommended, but is not always essential.

The most commonly used peroxide is dicumyl peroxide, but the vulcanizates possess a distinct odour. An alternative is bis-(*t*-butylperoxy-isopropylbenzene), which is slower curing. Trade examples and half-lives are shown.

Chemical name	Trade example	Half-lives, min at	
		160°C	180°C
dicumyl peroxide	*Dicup* *Luperco 500* *Perkadox BC*	8.7	*ca* 1.3
bis-(*t*-butylperoxy-isopropylbenzene)	*Perkadox 14* *Retilox* *VulCup*	*ca* 12	*ca* 2

Coagents increase the efficiency of the organic peroxide, but do not affect the rate of cure. They are used either to obtain higher moduli or to reduce the level of peroxide required. Coagents include methacrylates (*Saret* or *ATM*), triallylcyanurate (*Aktivator OC*), and a bismalemide (*HVA2*).

The scorch safety of peroxides may be improved by the addition of a free-radical trap, but the level of peroxide or coagent must be increased to compensate for a loss of crosslinks. Low levels of *p*-phenylenediamines are used for this purpose, and coagents containing a trap are available *eg Saret 500* or *ATM16*.

Peroxide vulcanizates have poor resistance to low-temperature crystallization and inferior strength properties compared with sulphur vulcanizates, although resistance to primary stress relaxation, creep and compression set is good. Protection against ozone attack, especially under dynamic conditions, is not easily achieved, as chemical anti-ozonants interfere with vulcanization. However, peroxide vulcanizates from blends of natural rubber with ozone-resistant rubbers such as EPDM are sometimes useful.

Peroxides are not suitable for hot-air or steam-pan curing, as peroxy radicals can initiate oxidation. Sticky mould flash often causes mould fouling in press cures, but less trouble is experienced when antioxidants are present.

Bibliography

Elliott,D.J. and Tidd, B.K., Developments in curing systems for natural rubber, *Prog. Rubber Technol.*, 1973/4, **37**, 83.

Vulcanization with urethane reagents, NR Technical Bulletin, MRPRA.

Articles in *NR Technology*:
NR and the LCM process, 1970, **1**, Part 2, No 6.
Compounding natural rubber for microwave heating and curing, 1975, **6**, 13.
Vulcanization time with peroxide cure systems, 1976, **7**, 61.
Use of secondary accelerators with MBTS/S system, 1981, 12, 68.
Novor vulcanization systems – a guide to types, properties and applications, 1983, **14**, 17.
Improved methods of vulcanization of natural rubber, 1973, **4**, 76.

Elliott, D.J., Developments with natural rubber, *Developments in Rubber Technology*, Volume 1, Eds Whelan, A. and Lee, K.S. London, Applied Science Publishers, 1979.

Hardness adjustment of natural rubber vulcanizates

Variation of filler loading

The hardness of natural rubber vulcanizates is usually controlled by the level of filler used. Table 8 gives the approximate loading of various fillers required to give a 10 point increase in hardness on the IRHD scale.

Table 8 Filler loadings

Filler	ASTM designation	Loading parts phr
Carbon blacks		
MT	N990	40–50
SRF	N762, N774	25–30
GPF	N660	25
FEF,GPF–HS	N550, N650	20–25
HAF–LS	N326	20–25
HAF	N330	20
HAF–HS	N347	15–20
Inorganic fillers		
Silica, precipitated		20
Clays		45–55
Whiting		60–70

Interchange of carbon blacks at constant hardness

In many formulations the type of carbon black used is not critical and other grades may be substituted for those shown, provided that (a) the hardness is maintained, and (b) abrasion grades (*ie* N100–N300 series) are not replaced by semi-reinforcing (N500–N700 series) or thermal grades, or *vice versa*.

If the grade of black is changed, the loading of replacement black may require adjustment in order to obtain the same hardness. Where the ASTM number and dibutyl phthalate absorption (DBP) of the two blacks are known, the approximate loading required can be calculated from the conversion factors given in Table 9. If black A is to be replaced by black B, the following formula is used:

$$\text{Loading of B} = \text{loading of A} \times L_B/L_A$$

where L_A and L_B are the L values for blacks A and B.

The table serves as a guideline only, as the hardness obtained in a factory depends to some extent on processing equipment and procedures.

Table 9 Carbon black interchange

Black types	ASTM designation	DBP range	L[a]	Examples of types
Abrasion furnace	N100, N200 and N300	60–90	0.50	HAF–LS
		90–110	0.45	HAF, ISAF–LS
		110–130	0.40	HAF–HS,ISAF,SAF
Semi-reinforcing furnace	N500, N600 and N700	50–80	0.67	SRF–LM
		80–100	0.60	GPF
		100–130	0.55	FEF, GPF–HS
Thermal	N990	30–40	1.0	MT

a. A single L value serves for a range of ASTM and DBP numbers.

Example To replace 60 parts phr of SRF (N762, DBP = 65) by FEF (N500, DBP = 120), the loading of FEF would be: $60 \times 0.55/0.67 = 50$ parts phr.

Section 1: Solution adhesives

1.1 General-purpose pressure-sensitive adhesive
1.2 Packaging and surgical tape pressure-sensitive adhesive
1.3 Vulcanizable general-purpose adhesive
1.4 Vulcanizable 2-part adhesive

See also: Latex adhesives (Section 15)

1.1 General-purpose pressure-sensitive adhesive

Applications include electrical insulation tapes, identification tapes and masking tapes for paint spraying

Formulation

NR[a]	100
Tackifier[b]	50–100
Plasticizer[c]	0–50
Antioxidant[d]	1–2
Filler[e]	0–100
Solvent[f]	to give 25–30% solution

a. Pale crepe for lightest colours. SMR L is suitable for less critical applications, *eg* paper-backed masking tape.
b. *eg* Wood rosin derivatives, coumarone-indene resins, synthetic phenolic or hydrocarbon resins.
c. *eg* Non-staining process oil or lanolin (wool fat).
d. Non-staining phenolic type, *eg Permanax WSL* (Vulnax Int), *Santovar A* (Monsanto) or *Wingstay L* (Goodyear).
e. Calcium carbonate, zinc oxide, clay or aluminium hydrate.
f. Toluene, naphtha or trichlorethylene.

Notes on mix procedure

Initial shredding or granulation of the rubber aids dissolution. Alternatively, swell the rubber in part of the solvent then mix the swollen rubber with the remainder.

Reference: Technical Information Sheet D59:1979

1.2 Packaging and surgical pressure-sensitive adhesive

Formulations

	packaging tape	surgical tape
NR[a]	100	100
Ester gum[b]	175	100
Lanolin (wool fat)	25	25
Antioxidant[c]	1	1
Zinc oxide[d]	50	100
Solvent[e]	400	200

a. Pale crepe for lightest colours; SMR CV is not recommended for surgical tape.
b. Tackifier.
c. Non-staining phenolic type, *eg Permanax WSL* (Vulnax Int). For surgical tape, the antioxidant must be non-toxic and must not cause skin irritation.
d. Zinc oxide is recommended for surgical tape because it acts as an antiseptic. Fillers such as calcium carbonate, aluminium hydrate or clay may be substituted for zinc oxide in packaging tape.
e. Toluene, naphtha or trichlorethylene.

Notes on mix procedure

Initial shredding or granulation of the rubber aids dissolution. Alternatively, lightly mill the rubber and zinc oxide then add solvent. Blend the swollen mixture in a Z-blade mixer until homogeneous, then add the ester gum, antioxidant and finally lanolin.

Reference: Technical Information Sheet D59:1979

1.3 Vulcanizable general-purpose adhesive

Formulation

SMR WF	100
Zinc oxide	10
Antioxidant[a]	1
Sulphur	1
Solvent[b]	800
10% Accelerator solution[c]	40

Cure: 3–4 days at room temperature

a. Non-staining phenolic type.
b. Toluene, naphtha or trichlorethylene.
c. Activated dithiocarbamate, *eg Butyl Eight* (Vanderbilt).

Notes on mix procedure

Initial shredding or granulation of the rubber aids dissolution. Alternatively, lightly mill the rubber and zinc oxide then add solvent. Blend the swollen mixture in a Z-blade mixer until homogeneous then add sulphur and antioxidant. Immediately before use, add the accelerator solution and mix thoroughly.

Reference: *NR Technology*, 1972, **3**, Part 2, No 2.

1.4 Vulcanizable 2-part adhesive

For bonding vulcanized rubber

Formulation

	Part A	Part B
SMR 5	100	100
Zinc oxide	5	5
Stearic acid	0.5	0.5
Antioxidant[a]	1	1
Solvent[b]	1000	1000
Sulphur	4	
Accelerator, ZIX[c]		1.5
Accelerator[d]		0.5

a. *eg* Phenol condensation product.
b. *eg* Aliphatic petroleum spirit, 123–155°C.
c. Zinc isopropyl xanthate.
d. Diethylammonium diethyldithiocarbamate.

Notes on mix procedure

Initial shredding or granulation of the rubber aids dissolution. Alternatively, lightly mill the rubbber and zinc oxide then add solvent. Blend the swollen mixture in a Z-blade mixer until homogeneous then add remaining ingredients. Solutions A and B should be mixed immediately before use.

Bond stength data

Bonding vulcanized natural rubber to itself
Cure: 7 days at room temperature
Test temperature 23°C

Pre–treatment	None	Pretreatment Air-oven aged[a]	Flexed[b]	Immersed in water[c]
		Peel strength, kN/m		
Unfilled	2.4	2.8	2.6	2.9
Aluminimum silicate-filled	2.8	2.1	3.7	4.6
HAF black-filled	1.8	1.7	2.0	2.2

a. 28 days at 70°C.
b. 50kc.
c. 56 days at 23°C.

Reference: Technical Information Sheet D49:1979

Section 2 Conveyor belting

2.1 High-quality conveyor belt covers
2.2 General-purpose conveyor belt covers
2.3 White covers for food-contact conveyors
2.4 Friction formulations
2.5 Friction formulations for synthetic fabrics

2.1 High quality conveyor belt covers — 60–65 IRHD

These formulations meet the requirements of BS 490 Part 1:1972 for high quality M24 grade, which specifies minimum tensile strength and elongation at break as 24.0MPa and 450% with a maximum change on ageing 7 days at 70°C of ±25%. Formulation 1 is for use at ambient temperatures and formulation 2 is heat-resistant. Both are suitable for use with very abrasive materials, *eg* metal ores or gravel.

Formulations

	1	2
SMR 20	100	100
N330, HAF black	45	45
Aromatic oil[a]	4	4
Zinc oxide	5	5
Stearic acid	2	2
Antidegradant, HPPD[b]	1	2
Sulphur	2.5	0.35
CBS	0.5	
MBS		1.4
TMTD		0.4

a. *eg Dutrex 729UK* (Shell).
b. *eg Santoflex 13* (Monsanto).

Rheological properties

	1	2
Mooney viscosity, 100°C	55	57
Mooney scorch, 120°C, min	24	18
Monsanto *Rheometer*, 140°C		
M_{HR}, torque units	37	30
M_L, torque units	19.5	9.5
scorch, t_{s1}, min	7.2	6.8
cure, $t_c'(95)$, min	22	24
cure, $t_c'(100)$, min	33	60

Reference: Technical Information Sheets D57 and D58:1979

2.1 (cont.)

Vulcanizate properties, unaged

Formulation	1	2
Cure time at 140°C, min	30	35
Hardness, IRHD	65	58
Density, Mg/m^3	1.11	1.11
MR100, MPa	2.06	1.31
Resilience, Lupke, %	64	61
Abrasion, DIN, mm^3	207	275
Tensile properties		
M100, MPa	2.0	1.5
M300, MPa	11	8.3
TS, MPa	29	30
EB, %	575	645
Tear, ISO trouser		
23°C, median, kN/m	20	32
high/low ratio	3.3	3.6
100°C, median, kN/m	14	23
high/low ratio	2	3.2
Ring fatigue life, 0–100% strain		
median, kc	160	56
high/low ratio	1.5	1.6
Compression set, %		
1 day at −26°C	13	24
1 day at 0°C	5	14
3 days at 23°C	9	14
1 day at 70°C	34	17
1 day at 100°C	60	34
1 day at 125°C		53

2.1 (cont)

Environmental ageing data

Formulation	1	2
Air-oven ageing for 3 days at 70°C		
change in hardness, IRHD	+3	+2
change in M100, %	+40	+10
change in M300, %	+30	+10
change in TS, %	−5	−5
change in EB, %	−10	−5
Air-oven ageing for 7 days at 70°C		
change in hardness, IRHD	+4	+3
change in M100, %	+50	+15
change in M300, %	+35	+10
change in TS, %	−10	−5
change in EB, %	−15	−5
Air-oven ageing for 3 days at 100°C		
change in hardness, IRHD	+1	+6
change in M100, %	+60	+16
change in M300, %	+40	+15
change in TS, %	−55	−10
change in EB, %	−50	−10
Low-temperature storage at −26°C		
time to		
5 point IRHD rise, days	28	2

2.2 General-purpose conveyor belt covers **60 IRHD**

Oil-extended formulations

These formulations meet physical property requirements of BS 490 Part 1:1972 for general-purpose N17 grade, which specifies minimum tensile strength and elongation at break as 17.0MPa and 400% with a maximum change on ageing 7 days at 70°C of ±25%. They are suitable for use with moderately abrasive materials, *eg* sand, cement or coal.

Formulations

	1	2	3
SMR 10	100		40
OENR 75/25A[a]		133	
SBR 1712[b]			60
N326, HAF-LS black	80		
Vulcan J N375 black[c]		75	50
Aromatic oil[d]	27	21	15
Zinc oxide	6	6	5
Stearic acid	2	2	2
Antidegradant, HPPD[e]	2	2	2
Sulphur	2.5	3	1.7
CBS	0.5	0.6	0.9
DPG			0.25

a. Oil-extended natural rubber, 25% aromatic oil.
b. Oil-extended SBR.
c. HAF Improved (Cabot Carbon).
d. *eg Dutrex 729UK* (Shell).
e. *eg Santoflex 13* (Monsanto).

Rheological properties

	1	2	3
Mooney viscosity, 100°C	58	35	51
Mooney scorch, 120°C, min	13	19	20
Monsanto *Rheometer*, 140°C			
M_{HR}, torque units	33	24.5	30
M_L, torque units	8.5	5	7.5
scorch, t_{s1}, min	6.1	7.0	8.5
cure, $t_c'(95)$, min	29	32	26
cure, $t_c'(100)$, min	45	47	45

Reference: Technical Information Sheet D112:1982

2.2 (cont.)

Vulcanizate properties, unaged

Formulation	1	2	3
Cure: 30min at 140°C			
Hardness, IRHD	66	59	66
Density, Mg/m^3	1.18	1.14	1.14
MR100, MPa	1.80	1.30	1.49
Resilience, Lupke,%	45	44	45
Abrasion, DIN, mm^3	271	301	243
Tensile properties			
M100, MPa	2.1	1.5	1.7
M300, MPa	10	7.3	8.2
TS, MPa	21.5	19.5	20
EB, %	550	595	545
Tear, ISO trouser			
23°C, median, kN/m	36	34	23
high/low ratio	1.2	1.7	1.8
100°C, median, kN/m	29	32	15
high/low ratio	1.4	1.3	1.3
Ring fatigue life, 0–100% strain			
median, kc	255	285	178
high/low ratio	1.8	1.7	2.1
Compression set, %			
1 day at −26°C	25	28	34
3 days at 23°C	11	12	13
1 day at 70°C	43	58	32
1 day at 100°C	71	86	55

2.2 (cont.)

Environmental ageing data

Formulation	1	2	3
Air-oven ageing for 3 days at 70°C			
change in hardness, IRHD	+3	+4	+3
change in M100, %	+40	+35	+30
change in M300, %	+25	+25	+23
change in TS, %	+5	+5	−5
change in EB, %	−5	−5	−15
Air-oven ageing for 7 days at 70°C			
change in hardness, IRHD	+5	+8	+5
change in M100, %	+30	+30	+40
change in M300, %	+25	+25	+35
change in TS, %	−5	−5	−15
change in EB, %	−10	−10	−20
Low-temperature storage at −26°C			
time to			
5 point IRHD rise, days	3	5	3
10 point IRHD rise, days	10	>28	>28

2.3 White covers for food-contact conveyors **50–60 IRHD**

These formulations meet the physical property requirements of BS 490 Part 1:1972 for the general-purpose N17 grade, which specifies minimum tensile strength and elongation at break as 17.0MPa and 400% with a maximum change on ageing 7 days at 70°C of ±25%. The aluminium silicate filler provides abrasion resistance. Requirements of the USA Food and Drugs Administration for dry food contact are met.

Formulation

	1	2
Nominal hardness	50	60
SMR L	100	100
Aluminium silicate[a]	30	60
Light oil[b]	5	5
Zinc oxide	5	5
Stearic acid	1	1
Antioxidant[c]	2	2
Wax blend[d]	5	5
Sulphur	3	3
CBS	0.8	0.8
DPG	0.2	

a. *eg Silteg AS7* (Degussa).
b. *eg Fina Process Oil 2059* (Petrofina).
c. *eg Antioxidant 2246* (Cyanamid).
d. *eg Antilux L* (Rhein-Chemie)

Rheological properties

Mooney viscosity, 100°C	50	64
Mooney scorch, 120°C, min	12	10
Monsanto *Rheometer*, 140°C		
M_{HR}, torque units	29.5	36
M_L, torque units	10.5	12.5
scorch, t_{s1}, min	4.0	3.0
cure, $t_c'(95)$, min	19.5	30
cure, $t_c'(100)$, min	35	45

Reference: Technical Information Sheet D106:1982

2.3 (cont)

Vulcanizate properties, unaged

Formulation	1	2
Nominal hardness	50	60
Cure time at 140°C, min	20	30
Hardness, IRHD	53	59
Density, Mg/m^3	1.08	1.19
MR100, MPa	1.05	1.22
Resilience, Lupke, %	87	74
Abrasion, DIN, mm^3	225	300
Tensile properties		
M100, MPa	1.1	1.5
M300, MPa	3.5	4.8
TS, MPa	25	19
EB, %	665	640
Tear, ISO trouser		
23°C, median, kN/m	9	34
high/low ratio	1.7	1.7
100°C, median, kN/m	3.1	22
high/low ratio	1.4	1.7
Ring fatigue life, 0–100% strain		
median, kc	70	45
high/low ratio	1.7	1.5
Compression set, %		
1 day at −26°C	26	36
1 day at 0°C	12	17
3 days at 23°C	11	11
1 day at 70°C	45	42

2.3 (cont.)

Environmental ageing data

Formulation	1	2
Air-oven ageing for 3 days at 70°C		
change in hardness, IRHD	+2	+2
change in M100, %	+20	+20
change in M300, %	+20	+30
change in TS, %	+10	+10
change in EB, %	0	5
Air-oven ageing for 7 days at 70°C		
change in hardness, IRHD	+2	+3
change in M100, %	+15	+20
change in M300, %	+25	+30
change in TS, %	−5	+10
change in EB, %	0	−5
Air-oven ageing for 3 days at 100°C		
change in hardness, IRHD	0	0
change in M100, %	+5	+10
change in TS, %	−40	−40
change in EB, %	−15	−25
Volume swell in water		
3 days at 100°C, %	37	18

2.4 Friction formulations

General-purpose and heat-resistant

Black friction formulations 1 and 2 are for general-purpose and heat-resistant conveyor belts respectively. Formulation 3 is a general-purpose, light-coloured friction mix. All may be used with natural or synthetic fabrics; rayon, nylon and polyester textiles must be treated to promote adhesion.

Formulation

	1	2	3
SMR 20	100	100	100
N762, SRF-LM-NS black	18	20	
Coated calcium carbonate[a]	12	10	
Whiting			15
Coal tar oil	9		
Coumarone resin	15		3
Pine tar		7.5	
Sulphonated oil[b]			3
Titanium dioxide			8
Zinc oxide	10	15	5
Stearic acid	1	2	1
Antioxidant[c]	1	1	1
Sulphur	2.5	0.5	2.75
Activated thiazole[d]			1
CBS	1	0.5	
TMTD		0.5	

a. *eg Calofort S* (John & E Sturge).
b. *eg Plastogen* (Vanderbilt).
c. Formulations 1 and 2: *eg Flectol H* (Monsanto) Formulation 3: phenolic condensate, *eg Permanax EXP* (Vulnax Int).
d. A blend of MBTS and DPG, *Vulcafor 9* (Vulnax Int).

Properties

	1	2	3
Mooney viscosity, 100°C	15	11	18
Cure: 25min at 141°C			
Hardness, IRHD	50	40	52
Density, Mg/m^3	1.12	1.15	1.09
Tensile properties			
M300,MPa	5.25	2.6	4.0
TS, MPa	21	18	17
EB, %	595	680	675

Reference: Technical Information Sheet D80:1979

2.5 Friction formulations for synthetic fabrics
For nylon and other synthetic fabrics

A proprietary bonding agent containing resorcinol and silica, *eg Cofill 11*, together with a formaldehyde donor such as hexamine improves adhesion of rubber to untreated synthetic fabric; treated fabrics give further improvements. Hexamine should be added towards the end of the mixing cycle with the accelerators.

Formulation

	1	2
SMR CV	80	50
SBR 1714[a]		40
N762, SRF-LM-NS black	25	25
Whole tyre reclaim	40	20
Process oil[b]	10	10
Zinc oxide	10	10
Stearic acid	3	3
Silica[c]	12	12
Bonding agent[d]	6	6
Amine antioxidant	1	1
Sulphur	2.5	2.25
CBS	1.5	2
Hexamine[e]	1.5	1.5

a. Oil-extended SBR.
b. Aromatic or naphthenic oil.
c. Fine-particle precipitated silica.
d. *eg* Blend of resorcinol and silica, *Cofill 11* (Degussa).
e. *Vulkacit H30* (Bayer).

Properties

Mooney viscosity, 100°C	21	24
Cure: 25min at 141°C		
Hardness, IRHD	73	62
Density, Mg/m³	1.17	1.15
Tensile properties		
M300, MPa	11.1	7.1
TS, MPa	12.5	11.5
EB, %	335	430

Reference: Technical Information Sheet D81:1979.

Section 3 Chemical plant linings

3.1 Ebonite lining
3.2 Ebonite lining adhesive
3.3 Soft rubber lining

3.1 Ebonite lining

Typical applications include battery boxes, containers, valves, pumps, filters, pipes, trays, bowls and rollers.

Formulation

SMR WF	100
Peptizer	0.3
Ebonite dust	25
China clay[a]	75
SRF black	3
Process oil	5
Light calcined magnesium oxide	5
MC sulphur[b]	25
DPG	1

a. *eg Devolite* (English China Clays).
b. Sulphur surface-treated with magnesium carbonate.

Properties

Cure: 5h in steam or hot air, temperature increasing from 125°C to 150°C

Hardness, Shore D	70
Density, Mg/m^3	1.36

For further information on plant linings see *NR Technology*, 1971, **2**, Part 4, No 12.

3.2 Ebonite lining adhesive
Vulcanizable

Formulation

SMR WF	95
SRF black	1
Litharge	5
Ebonite dust	25
Heavy calcined magnesium oxide	10
China clay[a]	75
Linseed oil	3
DPG	1
MC Sulphur[b]	45
Petroleum solvent	To give 30% solution

a. *eg Devolite* (English China Clays).
b. Sulphur surface-treated with magnesium carbonate.

For further information on plant linings see *NR Technology*, 1971, **2**, Part 4, No 12.

3.3 Soft rubber lining **60 IRHD**

Applications include pickling and plating baths and railway tank cars.

Formulation

SMR WF	100
SRF black	20
Soft clay[a]	60
Barytes	30
Talc	30
Zinc oxide	5
Stearic acid	1
Antioxidant[b]	1
Sulphur	2.5
DPG	1

a. *eg Devolite* (English China Clays).
b. *eg Flectol H* (Monsanto).

Properties

Cure: up to 3h at temperatures not exceeding 140°C.

Hardness, IRHD	60
Density, Mg/m^3	1.5

Section 4 Ebonite

4.1 Battery plate separators
4.2 General-purpose ebonite
4.3 Injection-moulded ebonite

See also: Ebonite linings (Section 3)

4.1 Battery plate separators

Formulation

SMR WF	100
Ebonite dust	200
Paraffin wax	2
Stearic acid	1
DPG	1
Sulphur	50

Cure: press cure 25min at 153°C followed by 2h at 153°C in steam; or alternatively 4h at 153°C in a steam pan.

4.2 General-purpose ebonites

Suitable for a wide range of moulded, extruded and hand-built applications.

Formulations

	Moulded	Sheet/rod/tube	Hand-built
SMR WF	100	100	100
Ebonite dust[a]	100	150	150
China clay	50		
Reclaim[b]		30	50
Magnesium oxide	5	5	
Linseed oil	5		
Process oil		5	
Resin oil			10
Sulphur	45	60	60
DPG	3		
Accelerator, BA[c]		3	3.5

a. Reduces shrinkage and heat evolution during cure; improves calendering and extrusion; and increases dimensional stability in open steam curing.
b. Calendering aid.
c. Butyraldehyde-aniline condensate, *eg Vulcafor BA* (Vulnax)

Notes on processing

Moulding is normally carried out between 130°C and 160°C. Rods and tubes are usually embedded in chalk and autoclaved in steam; typically with a 2h rise followed by 6–8h at 0.31MPa (45lbf/in^2) steam pressure (143°C). Great care must be taken in selecting cure conditions since the reaction results in a temperature rise which can lead to porosity or even an explosion.

Reference: Technical Information Sheet D19:1976

4.3 Injection-moulded ebonite **90 Shore D**

Suitable for a range of injection moulded products, including battery boxes and lavatory cisterns.

Formulation

SMR 20[a]	100
N330, HAF black	18
China clay[b]	215
Mineral rubber[c]	38
Magnesium oxide	15
Sulphur	35
CBS	2.7
Prevulcanization inhibitor[d]	0.6

a. Use a high quality grade, *eg* SMR WF, for electrical purposes or for a highly polished surface finish.
b. *eg Devolite* (English China Clays).
c. *eg MRX* (Anchor).
d. *eg Santogard PVI* (Monsanto).

Rheological properties

Mooney viscosity, 120°C	30
Mooney scorch, 120°C, min	20

Vulcanizate properties

Injection moulded using *REP B43K* machine
Extruder temperature, 85°C; injection chamber temperature, 90°C

Cure: 4min at 190°C

Hardness, Shore D	87
Density, Mg/m^3	1.66
Flexural modulus, MPa	6700

Reference: Technical Information Sheet D25:1977

Section 5 Engineering Rubbers

5.1 Moderate damping rubbers
5.2 High damping, low creep rubbers
5.3 Engine mounts, general-purpose
5.4 Engine mounts, heat-resistant
5.5 General-purpose engineering rubbers
5.6 Low creep rubbers
5.7 Low creep rubbers, for injection moulding
5.8 Semi-EV vulcanizates
5.9 Suspension bushes
5.10 Tear- and abrasion-resistant rubbers

See also: Hardness-classified mouldings (Section 9)

5.1 Moderate damping rubbers **40–60 IRHD**

Damping is given by a high viscosity oil with high filler loading and a cure system to produce a low crosslink density. Not suitable for use at elevated temperatures.

Formulation

	1	2	3	4	5	6	7	8
Nominal hardness	40	40	40	50	50	50	60	60
SMR 10	100	100	100	100	100	100	100	100
N330, HAF black	10	30	50	25	45	75	45	65
Coated calcium carbonate[a]	20	20	20	20	20	20	20	20
High viscosity aromatic oil[b]	5	25	45	5	25	45	5	25
Zinc oxide	5	5	5	5	5	5	5	5
Stearic acid	2	2	2	2	2	2	2	2
Antidegradant, HPPD[c]	2	2	2	2	2	2	2	2
Sulphur	1.5	1.5	1.5	1.5	1.5	1.5	1.5	1.5
CBS	0.5	0.5	0.5	0.5	0.5	0.5	0.5	0.5

a. *eg Calofort S* (John & E Sturge).
b. *eg Dutrex 729UK* (Shell).
c. *eg Santoflex 13* (Monsanto).

Rheological properties

	1	2	3	4	5	6	7	8
Mooney viscosity, 100°C	32	36	31	34	30	42	60	39
Mooney scorch, 120°C, min	28	28	32	28	32	22	20	25
Monsanto *Rheometer*, 150°C								
M_{HR}, torque units	21.5	19	15	23.5	21	21.5	31	29
M_L, torque units	6.5	6	3.5	5.5	5	3	9	6.5
scorch, t_{s1}, min	5.5	4.8	5.2	5.6	5.5	5.0	4.5	5
cure, $t_c'(95)$, min	14	14	13	15	15	11.5	14	12
cure, $t_c'(100)$, min	17	18	18	19	18	16	19	17

Reference: Technical Information Sheet D110:1982

5.1 (cont)

Vulcanizate properties, unaged

Formulation	1	2	3	4	5	6	7	8
Cure: 14min at 150°C								
Hardness, IRHD	42	41	40	48	48	52	61	60
Density, Mg/m^3	1.08	1.12	1.16	1.13	1.16	1.19	1.19	1.20
MR100, MPa	0.65	0.65	0.61	0.90	0.85	0.91	1.40	1.15
Resilience, Lupke, %	78	66	54	70	52	40	58	43
Tensile properties								
M100, MPa	0.6	0.7	0.7	1.0	0.9	1.0	1.7	1.4
M300, MPa	1.8	3.0	3.0	4.4	4.6	5.3	8.0	7.6
TS, MPa	25	21	15.0	25	20	15.3	23	18
EB, %	785	725	690	715	705	615	560	590
Tear, ISO trouser								
23°C, median, kN/m	6	7.1	8.6	16	25	30	29	33
high/low ratio	3	2.2	1.8	1.5	1.6	1.5	1.7	1.6
100°C,median, kN/m	2.4	28	5.9	28	32	7.2	17	34
high/low ratio	2	1.4	1.2	2.9	1.4	1.2	4	2
Ring fatigue life, 0–100% strain								
median, kc	120	130	66	210	230	128	130	210
high/low ratio	2.7	2.4	3.2	2.2	3.2	5.6	2.4	2.3
Compression set, %								
1 day at −26°C	22	28	30	17	19	35	29	27
1 day at 0°C	10	14	14	8	12	16	13	12
3 days at 23°C	8	10	14	9	13	16	10	17
1 day at 70°C	39	50	61	44	50	54	44	50
Stress relaxation rate, 20% compression								
% per decade	2.1	2.3	3.9	2.6	3.9	4.2	3.4	4.3

5.1 (cont)

Environmental ageing data

Formulation	1	2	3	4	5	6	7	8
Air-oven ageing for 3 days at 70°C								
change in hardness, IRHD	+4	+4	+9	+2	+7	+8	+3	+7
change in M100, %	+20	+40	+35	+15	+30	+40	+15	+30
change in M300, %	+20	+40	+40	+30	+35	+40	+10	+20
change in TS, %	+5	+15	+20	+10	+10	+10	+5	−20
change in EB, %	−5	−5	−5	−5	−5	−10	0	−5
Air-oven ageing for 7 days at 70°C								
change in hardness, IRHD	+4	+6	+5	+7	+10	+8	+4	+9
change in M100, %	+30	+40	+40	+30	+45	+45	+30	+25
change in M300, %	+30	+50	+50	+40	+45	+40	+25	+20
change in TS, %	+5	+10	+15	+10	+10	+5	−5	−20
change in EB, %	−5	−10	−5	−5	−10	−10	−5	−5
Air-oven ageing for 3 days at 100°C								
change in hardness, IRHD	−2	0	+1	+2	+4	+2	+1	+5
change in M100, %	0	+10	0	0	+10	+5	+30	+10
change in M300, %	+10	+10		+5	+5	0	+10	−20
change in TS, %	−50	−65	−50	−45	−55	−45	−40	−65
change in EB, %	−20	−30	−20	0	−30	−20	−30	−30
Low-temperature storage at −26°C								
time to								
5 point IRHD rise, days	3	2	7	3	7	21	3	3
10 point IRHD rise, days	7	10	14	7	14	28	5	>28
20 point IRHD rise, days	10	21	28	10	28	>28	7	>28

5.1 (cont)

Dynamic test data in simple shear at 23°C

G* = Shear modulus, MPa
δ = Phase angle in degrees

Formulation		1		2		3		4	
Hardness, IRHD		42		41		40		48	
Frequency Hertz	Strain %	G*	δ	G*	δ	G*	δ	G*	δ
0.1	2	0.52	1.7	0.91	7.8	0.77	11.8	0.83	4.2
0.1	10	0.50	1.5	0.69	6.7	0.55	9.8	0.71	5.2
0.1	50	0.44	2.0	0.48	4.5	0.39	7.3	0.58	4.0
1	1	0.54	1.3	1.11	9.3	1.01	10.6	0.94	4.0
1	2	0.54	2.2	1.00	8.2	0.88	10.7	0.89	5.0
1	5	0.53	1.7	0.81	8.7	0.72	11.3	0.78	7.2
1	10	0.52	1.8	0.73	7.8	0.62	10.5	0.75	5.7
1	20	0.49	2.7	0.61	6.7	0.53	9.4	0.72	5.7
1	50	0.45	3.0	0.51	5.7	0.42	8.1	0.61	5.0
1	70	0.43	2.5	0.47	5.3	0.36	8.2	0.57	5.0
10	2	0.58	3.3	1.08	9.8			0.97	6.6
10	5	0.54	4.3	0.88	10.3			0.86	7.4
10	10	0.52	3.1	0.78	9.0			0.82	7.2

Formulation		5		6		7		8	
Hardness, IRHD		48		52		61		60	
Frequency Hertz	Strain %	G*	δ	G*	δ	G*	δ	G*	δ
0.1	2	1.04	9.3	1.71	18.5	1.72	10.5	2.02	17.5
0.1	10	0.74	8.3	1.0	14.5	1.26	8.5	1.16	14.2
0.1	50	0.57	5.8	0.59	8.9	0.83	7.2	0.70	9.0
1	1	1.28	8.5	2.52	14.4	2.13	9.8	3.23	15.0
1	2	1.13	10.7	1.98	16.3	1.90	10.8	2.29	18.8
1	5	0.92	10.8	1.40	16.8	1.55	10.7	1.62	17.3
1	10	0.8	9.3	1.07	14.8	1.35	9.3	1.29	15.0
1	20	0.67	8.7	0.85	12.6	1.11	8.5	0.96	10.3
1	50	0.54	7.0	0.62	10.5	0.87	8.0	0.74	10.8
1	70	0.50	7.0	0.55	10.1	0.78	7.7	0.57	9.8
10	2	1.25	11.6			2.02	11.0	2.60	19.5
10	5	1.00	11.6			1.44	11.4	1.81	18.1
10	10	0.80	10.7			1.44	10.3	1.42	15.9

5.2 High damping, low creep rubbers — 45 IRHD

Typical applications include vehicle suspensions and body insulators. A soluble EV system is used. For bonded bushes the proportion of acrylonitrile-isoprene copolymer should be restricted to 30 parts phr or less.

Formulation

	1	2	3	4	5	6
SMR CV	100	90	80	70	60	50
Krynac 833[a]		10	20	30	40	50
N660, GPF black	25	20	20	20	20	20
Zinc oxide	5	5	5	5	5	5
Zinc 2-ethylhexanoate[b]	2	2	2	2	2	2
Antioxidant, TMQ[c]	2	2	2	2	2	2
Antidegradant, HPPD[d]	2	2	2	2	2	2
Wax blend[e]	4	4	4	4	4	4
Sulphur	0.6	0.6	0.6	0.6	0.6	0.6
MBS	1.4	1.4	1.4	1.4	1.4	1.4
TBTD	0.6	0.6	0.6	0.6	0.6	0.6

a. Acrylonitrile-isoprene copolymer, 33% acrylonitrile (Polysar).
b. *eg Zinc Octoate* (Tenneco).
c. *eg Flectol H* (Monsanto).
d. *eg Santoflex 13* (Monsanto).
e. *eg Sunproof Improved* (Uniroyal).

Rheological properties

	1	2	3	4	5	6
Mooney viscosity, 100°C	35	31	32	30	30	32
Mooney scorch, 120°C, min	35	31	28	32	25	30
Monsanto *Rheometer*, 150°C						
M_{HR}, torque units	24	22.5	23.5	23	24.5	23
M_L, torque units	4	4	4	4	4	4
scorch, t_{s1}, min	7.0	6.0	5.2	6.0	5.5	6.0
cure, $t_c'(95)$, min	14	11.8	11.5	13	12.5	14.5
cure, $t_c'(100)$, min	30	30	30	30	40	45

Reference: Technical Information Sheet D124:1983

5.2 (cont)

Vulcanizate properties, unaged

Formulation	1	2	3	4	5	6
Cure time at 150°C, min	30	30	30	30	45	45
Hardness, IRHD	43	42	44	44	46	45
Density, Mg/m^3	1.04	1.03	1.04	1.06	1.07	1.07
MR100, MPa	0.91	0.81	0.84	0.77	0.93	0.81
Resilience, Lupke, %	72	53	42	32	25	20
Abrasion, DIN, mm^3	300	326	313	373	worn away	
Tensile properties						
M100, MPa	0.9	0.9	0.95	0.9	1.1	1.0
M300, MPa	4.1	2.9	3.2	2.9	3.6	3.1
TS, MPa	25	24	22	20	19.5	17
EB, %	655	705	675	700	645	665
Tear, ISO trouser						
23°C, median, kN/m	7	11	19	19	13	15
high/low ratio	1.8	4.1	1.7	1.4	3.2	2.4
100°C, median, kN/m	6.8	9	12	15	7.3	5.9
high/low ratio	3.1	1.5	1.3	1.3	1.8	2.5
Ring fatigue life, 0–100% strain						
median, kc	78	66	79	63	77	91
high/low ratio	1.8	1.8	1.7	6.2	2.4	2.8
Compression set, %						
1 day at 0°C	15	16	16	18	16	27
3 days at 23°C	9	9	10	12	15	15
1 day at 70°C	20	19	18	19	16	20
1 day at 100°C	39	27	35	40	31	34
1 day at 125°C	53	55	55	59	51	53
Stress relaxation rate, 20% compression, % per decade						
100–1000min	2.3	2.6	2.7	2.8	3.0	3.6
Rubber-to-mild steel bond strength, 90° peel test, kN/m[a]						
Chemlok 205/220	13	6.1	7.3	4.1	3.6	2.0
Chemlok 205/233	2.0	6.0	4.2	3.8	2.8	2.8

a. Improved bond strengths may be obtained from a 3-coat bonding system of *Chemlok 205* (primer), *Chemlok 220* and *Ty-Ply RC* (cover coat).

5.2 (cont)

Environmental ageing data

Formulation	1	2	3	4	5	6
Air-oven ageing for 7 days at 70°C						
change in hardness, IRHD	0	+2	+2	+1	0	0
change in M100, %	+20	+14	+18	+20	+12	+12
change in M300, %	+25	+25	+25	+27	+17	+15
change in TS, %	0	−6	+5	+15	+3	+9
change in EB, %	−7	−8	−4	−2	−4	0
Air-oven ageing for 3 days at 100°C						
change in hardness, IRHD	+2	+4	+4	+4	+4	+4
change in M100, %	+18	+17	+22	+25	+23	+17
change in M300, %	+31	+33	+33	+36	+31	+22
change in TS, %	−14	−11	−8	−6	−2	−9
change in EB, %	−10	−10	−9	−11	−8	−7
Air-oven ageing for 7 days at 100°C						
change in hardness, IRHD	+2	+5	+4	+5	+4	+2
change in M100, %	−4	0	+22	+30	+25	+21
change in TS, %	−25	−21	−14	−6	−13	−3
change in EB, %	−6	−11	−10	−11	−14	−9
Air-oven ageing for 3 days at 125°C						
change in hardness, IRHD	−3	0	+1	+1	+1	+1
change in M100, %	−25	−14	+9	+30	+35	+33
change in TS, %	−80	−75	−70	−60	−55	−25
change in EB, %	−50	−42	−60	−40	−35	−20
Volume swell, 3 days at 100°C						
ASTM No 1 oil, %	123	105	82	76	62	41
ASTM No 3 oil, %	250	223	198	175	150	120
Low-temperature storage at −26°C						
time to						
5 point IRHD rise, days	5	5	3	7	21	21
10 point IRHD rise, days	>28	>28	21	28	>28	>28
Ozone resistance, 50pphm, 40°C, 20% strain						
time to first crack, days	>14	>14	>14	>14	>14	>14

5.2 (cont.)

Dynamic test data in simple shear at 23°C;
Bonding system *Chemlok 205/220.*

G* = Shear modulus, MPa
δ = Phase angle in degrees

Formulation		1		2		3		4		5	
NR/NIR ratio		100/0		90/10		80/20		70/30		60/40	
Frequency Hertz	Strain %	G*	δ	G*	δ	G*	δ	G*	δ	G*	δ
0.1	2	0.71	4.5	0.70	5.5	0.78	6.8	0.84	7.9	0.86	6.8
0.1	10	0.71	4.5	0.54	6.4	0.68	5.8	0.70	6.6	0.76	6.3
0.1	50	0.52	4.2	0.48	4.2	0.57	5.2	0.56	5.7	0.62	6.2
1	1	0.81	3.3	0.83	5.9	0.93	7.2	1.02	8.6	1.04	7.9
1	2	0.75	4.8	0.76	6.6	0.87	8.2	0.97	9.5	0.98	8.7
1	5	0.71	5.0	0.70	7.3	0.81	8.6	0.89	9.0	0.92	9.0
1	10	0.66	4.3	0.59	7.4	0.76	8.2	0.79	8.6	0.86	8.5
1	20	0.62	4.3	0.56	6.3	0.70	8.0	0.72	8.6	0.80	9.2
1	50	0.54	4.2	0.54	5.7	0.62	7.8	0.62	7.8	0.70	8.2
1	100	0.58	3.7	0.46	5.3	0.55	7.3	0.56	7.1	0.60	8.6
15	1	0.91	4.7	1.02	9.4	1.21	13.1	1.39	16.6	1.40	15.9
15	2	0.83	5.5	0.92	10.0	1.13	14.1	1.31	16.8	1.31	16.7
15	5	0.77	6.0	0.77	11.9	1.00	13.9	1.18	16.7	1.21	16.8
15	10	0.70	5.6	0.65	11.5	0.96	13.7	1.01	15.7	1.09	16.4
25	1	0.93	4.9	1.08	9.2	1.30	14.2	1.52	17.9	1.50	17.2
25	2	0.84	6.0	0.96	11.3	1.21	14.8	1.43	18.4	1.42	19.0
50	1	0.94	4.9	1.10	10.5	1.45	15.0	1.68	18.8	1.68	19.1

5.3 General-purpose engine mounts **60 IRHD**

These formulations are for mounts operating at low and near-ambient temperatures. Almost any commercially-available grade of black may be used. Formulation 4 may give improved ageing resistance.

Formulation

	1	2	3	4
SMR 10	100	100	100	100
N550, FEF black	45	45	40	45
Light oil[a]	10	10	10	10
Zinc oxide	5	5	5	10
Stearic acid	2	2	2	2
Antioxidant, TMQ[b]	2	2	2	2
Antidegradant, HPPD[c]	2	2	2	2
Sulphur	2.5	2.25	2.25	1.5
MBTS	1	1	1	
DPG	0.1	0.2	0.2	
DTDM[d]			1	
CBS				1.2
TMTD				0.2

a. *eg Fina Process Oil 2059* (Petrofina).
b. *eg Flectol H* (Monsanto).
c. *eg Santoflex 13* (Monsanto).
d. *eg Sulfasan R* (Monsanto).

Rheological properties

	1	2	3	4
Mooney viscosity, 100°C	51	48	45	60
Mooney scorch, 120°C, min	9	8	10	12
Monsanto *Rheometer*, 150°C				
M_{HR}, torque units	37	37	45	40
M_L, torque units	7	6.5	6	9
scorch, t_{s1}, min	2.0	1.8	2.6	3.0
cure, $t_c'(95)$, min	9.0	7.5	7.5	7
cure, $t_c'(100)$, min	13	12	12	14
time to 5% reversion, min	20	20	30	30

5.3 (cont)

Vulcanizate properties, unaged

Formulation	1	2	3	4
Cure: 15min at 150°C				
Hardness, IRHD	59	60	64	64
Density, Mg/m³	1.10	1.10	1.09	1.13
MR100, MPa	1.81	2.01	2.58	2.50
Resilience, Lupke, %	79	80	85	74
Abrasion, DIN, mm³	220	215	210	
Tensile properties				
M100, MPa	1.9	2.1	2.8	2.0
M300, MPa	9.6	10	13	13.5
TS, MPa	22	23	21	24
EB, %	540	535	450	475
Tear, ISO trouser				
23°C, median, kN/m	12	9.2	7.2	10.5
high/low ratio	1.6	1.5	1.7	1.2
100°C, median, kN/m	6.8	8.1	4	4.4
high/low ratio	2.6	1.7	1.6	1.4
Ring fatigue life, 0–100% strain				
median, kc	150	120	65	65
high/low ratio	1.8	1.6	1.2	1.4
Compression set, %				
1 day at −26°C	10	10	10	16
1 day at 0°C	10	8	7	6
3 days at 23°C	6	7	6	7
1 day at 70°C	27	24	20	26
1 day at 100°C	48	47	53	46

5.3 (cont)

Environmental ageing data

Formulation	1	2	3	4
Air-oven ageing for 3 days at 70°C				
change in hardness, IRHD	+4	+3	+2	
change in M100, %	+35	+25	+20	
change in M300, %	+30	+20	+15	
change in TS, %	0	−5	+5	
change in EB, %	−10	−10	−5	
Air-oven ageing for 7 days at 70°C				
change in hardness, IRHD	+4	+5	+2	+4
change in M100, %	+55	+50	+20	+50
change in M300, %	+40	+30	+20	+12
change in TS, %	0	0	−10	−4
change in EB, %	−10	−10	−20	−10
Air-oven ageing for 3 days at 100°C				
change in hardness, IRHD	+5	+5	+4	+3
change in M100, %	+75	+55	−40	+50
change in TS, %	−30	−25	−35	−25
change in EB, %	−40	−30	−40	−17
Low-temperature storage at −26°C				
time to				
5 point IRHD rise, days	>28	28	10	10
10 point IRHD rise, days	>28	>28	>28	20

5.4 Heat-resistant engine mounts — 60–70 IRHD

For mounts which cannot easily be shielded from the engine and exhaust system. Formulation 4 should only be used if the mounts can be designed to eliminate dangerously high peak stresses.

Formulations

	1	2	3	4
Vulcanization system	Soluble EV	EV	*Novor*	Peroxide
SMR 10	100	100	100	100
N330, FEF black	50	50	45	50
Light oil[a]	10	10	10	10
Zinc oxide	5	5	5	
Stearic acid		2	1	
Zinc 2-ethylhexanoate[b]	1			
Antioxidant, TMQ[c]	2	2	2	2
Antidegradant, HPPD[d]	2	2		
Antioxidant, ZMBI[e]			2	2
Sulphur	0.6	0.25	0.4	
Novor 924[f]			4.2	
MBS	1.5			
TBBS		2.1	0.1	
TBTD	0.6			
TMTD		1		
TMTM			1.8	
ZDMC				2
Dicumyl peroxide				2.5
Calcium hydroxide				2

a. *eg Fina Process Oil 2059* (Petrofina).
b. *eg Zinc Octoate* (Tenneco).
c. *eg Flectol H* (Monsanto).
d. *eg Santoflex 13* (Monsanto).
e. *eg Vulkanox ZMB2* (Bayer).
f. Urethane crosslinker (Durham Chemicals). *Novor 950* will give substantially the same results.

Rheological properties

	1	2	3	4
Mooney viscosity, 100°C	66	41	61	70
Mooney scorch, 120°C, min	23	11	16	9
Monsanto *Rheometer*, °C	150	150	150	160
M_{HR}, torque units	35	33	34	34
M_L, torque units	8.5	8.5	9.5	10.5
scorch, t_{s1}, min	4.5	3.5	3.5	1.3
cure, $t_c'(95)$, min	10	19	13	25
cure, $t_c'(100)$, min	16	45	25	*ca* 60

5.4 (cont)

Vulcanizate properties, unaged

Formulation	1	2	3	4
Cure time, min	30	30	15	60
Cure temperature, °C	150	150	150	160
Hardness, IRHD	58	59	68	59
Density, Mg/m^3	1.11	1.11	1.10	1.08
MR100, MPa	1.92	1.46	1.69	1.67
Resilience, Lupke, %	73	67	69	72
Abrasion, DIN, mm^3	210	214	252	210
Tensile properties				
M100, MPa	2.2	1.6	1.5	1.7
M300, MPa	12	9.4	9.2	12.3
TS, MPa	23	23	23	18
EB, %	520	540	555	395
Tear, ISO trouser				
23°C, median, kN/m	11	10	10	1.6
high/low ratio	1.5	1.6	1.9	1.2
100°C, median, kN/m	4	4.5	1.8	1.8
high/low ratio	1.6	1.8	3	3
Ring fatigue life, 0–100% strain				
median, kc	60	55	36	56
high/low ratio	1.3	1.7	2.3	1.2
Compression set, %				
1 day at −26°C	23	77	43	85
1 day at 0°C	13	16	7	9
3 days at 23°C	7	18	9	6
1 day at 70°C	14	17	25	12
1 day at 100°C	28	31	41	20
1 day at 125°C	45	45	51	22

5.4 (cont)

Environmental ageing data

Formulation	1	2	3	4
Air-oven ageing for 7 days at 70°C				
change in hardness, IRHD	+3	0	+2	+3
change in M100, %	+5	+15	+55	−5
change in M300, %	+5	+10	+15	−5
change in TS, %	0	−5	−10	+5
change in EB, %	−5	−5	−10	0
Air-oven ageing for 3 days at 100°C				
change in hardness, IRHD	+5	+4	+2	+4
change in M100, %	+15	+85	+75	+5
change in M300, %	+10	+15	+25	+5
change in TS, %	−10	−15	−20	−5
change in EB, %	−10	−15	−25	−10
Air-oven ageing for 3 days at 125°C				
change in hardness, IRHD	−2	0	−3	+5
change in M100, %	−10	+15	+40	0
change in TS, %	−65	−50	−50	−30
change in EB, %	−50	−45	−40	−10
Low-temperature storage at −26°C				
time to				
5 point IRHD rise, days	4	2	3	1
10 point IRHD rise, days	7	3	5	2
20 point IRHD rise, days	10	7	10	3

5.5 Low temperature engineering rubbers **50–60 IRHD**

Compression set can be reduced by raising the crosslink density (formulations 2 and 4), but tensile, fatigue and ageing properties are reduced slightly. Formulations 2 and 4 pass physical property requirements of ASTM D4014, grade 5 for bridge bearings.

Formulation

	1	2	3	4
SMR CV60	100	100	100	100
N550, FEF black	20	20	40	40
Light oil[a]	2	2	4	4
Zinc oxide	5	5	5	5
Stearic acid	2	2	2	2
Antidegradant, HPPD[b]	3	3	3	3
Wax blend[c]	2	2	2	2
Sulphur	2.5	3.25	2.5	3.25
CBS	0.6	0.8	0.6	0.8

a. *eg Fina Process Oil 2059* (Petrofina).
b. *eg Santoflex 13* (Monsanto).
c. *eg Sunproof Improved* (Uniroyal).

Rheological properties

	1	2	3	4
Mooney viscosity, 100°C	27	29	34	35
Mooney scorch, 120°C, min	39	33	31	27
Monsanto *Rheometer*, 140°C				
scorch, t_{s1}, min	12	11.3	9.7	9.1
cure, $t_c'(95)$, min	29	28	27	25

Reference: Engineering Data Sheets 22, 23, 32, 33.

5.5 (cont)

Vulcanizate properties, unaged

Formulation	1	2	3	4
Cure: 45min at 140°C				
Hardness, IRHD	51	53	60	67
Density, Mg/m^3	1.04	1.04	1.09	1.10
MR100, MPa	1.12	1.36	1.80	2.06
Resilience, Lupke, %	78	84	73	77
Tensile properties				
M300, MPa	5.0	6.5	10.1	10.9
TS, MPa	30	25.5	26	23
EB, %	670	590	560	495
Tear, ISO trouser				
23°C, median, kN/m	11	8.5	14	9.7
Ring fatigue life, 0–100% strain				
median, kc	272	155	207	144
Compression set, %				
14 days at −26°C	26	18	32	20
1 day at −26°C	17	13	21	15
14 days at −10°C	11	10	14	11
1 day at 0°C	13	6	13	7
3 days at 23°C	2	4	6	5
1 day at 70°C	34	23	33	22
Goodrich *Flexometer*				
Static stress 1MPa (24lb), stroke 5.71mm (0.225in), start 100°C.				
Temp rise after 2h, deg C	7	6	17	15
Stress relaxation rate, 20% compression				
% per decade	1.8	1.4	2.8	2.5
Dynamic shear modulus and phase angle				
Frequency 0.1Hz, strain ±10%, 23°C				
Shear modulus, MPa	0.73	0.84	1.28	1.14
Phase angle, degrees	2.2	1.7	4.0	4.2

MRPRA Engineering Data Sheets give complete data on variation of fatigue life with strain and dependence of dynamic properties on temperature, frequency and strain.

5.5 (cont)

Environmental ageing data

Formulation	1	2	3	4
Air-oven ageing for 7 days at 70°C				
change in hardness, IRHD	+1	+2	+1	+3
change in M300, %	+26	+19	+18	+31
change in TS, %	−2	−8	−2	0
change in EB, %	−6	−10	−6	−11
Air-oven ageing for 14 days at 70°C				
change in hardness, IRHD	+1	+5	+2	+5
change in M300, %	+42	+36	+26	+38
change in TS, %	−5	−22	−9	−14
change in EB, %	−9	−19	−12	−21
Volume swell in water 3 days at 100°C, %	7.9	4.6	5.1	3.9
Low-temperature storage at −26°C time to 5 point IRHD rise, days	>28	>28	>28	>28
Impact brittleness, −40°C		no failures		
Ozone resistance, 100pphm, 40°C, 20% strain time to first crack, days	>7	>7	>7	>7

5.6 Low creep rubbers **45–65 IRHD**

Soluble EV systems give low creep, stress relaxation and compression set at elevated temperatures. Not suitable for service at low temperatures for prolonged periods.

Formulation

	1	2	3
Nominal hardness	45	55	65
SMR L	100	100	100
N762, SRF-LM-NS black	30	55	85
Zinc oxide	5	5	5
Zinc 2-ethylhexanoate[a]	1	1	1
Antioxidant, TMQ[b]	2	2	2
Antiozonant, DOPPD[c]	4	4	4
Sulphur	0.7	0.7	0.7
MBS	1.7	1.7	1.7
TBTD	0.7	0.7	0.7

a. *eg Zinc Octoate* (Tenneco).
b. *eg Flectol H* (Monsanto).
c. *eg UOP 88* (Universal Oil Products).

Rheological proerties

	1	2	3
Mooney viscosity, 100°C	47	61	80
Mooney scorch, 120°C, min	29	25	23
Monsanto *Rheometer*, 153°C			
scorch, t_{s1}, min	5.0	4.4	3.7
cure, $t_c'(95)$, min	8.7	8.3	7.2

Reference: Engineering Data Sheets 4, 5 and 6

5.6 (cont)

Vulcanizate properties, unaged

Formulation	1	2	3
Cure: 60min at 153°C			
Hardness, IRHD	45	56	66
Density, Mg/m^3	1.07	1.14	1.21
MR100, MPa	0.89	1.37	2.36
Resilience, Lupke, %	75	68	56
Tensile properties			
M300, MPa	4.4	9.1	14
TS, MPa	26	23	20
EB, %	650	550	455
Tear, ISO trouser			
23°C, median, kN/m	3.9	15	27
Ring fatigue life, 0–100% strain			
median, kc	83	63	46
Compression set, %			
1 day at −26°C	17	24	83
7 days at −10°C	74	30	87
1 day at 0°C	8	9	11
3 days at 23°C	5	5	5
1 day at 70°C	10	10	11
1 day at 100°C	21	21	20
3 days at 100°C	37	33	35
1 day at 125°C	36	29	30
Stress relaxation rate, 20% compression			
% per decade	1.5	2.2	2.7
Dynamic shear modulus and phase angle			
Frequency 0.1Hz, strain ±10%, 23°C			
Shear modulus, MPa	0.62	1.09	1.83
Phase angle, degrees	2.9	4.8	7.8

MRPRA Engineering Data Sheets give complete data on variation of fatigue life with strain and dependence of dynamic properties on temperature, frequency and strain.

5.6 (cont)

Environmental ageing data

Formulation	1	2	3
Air-oven ageing for 14 days at 70°C			
change in hardness, IRHD	+2	+3	+2
change in M300, %	+21	+17	+11
change in TS, %	0	−3	−1
change in EB, %	−4	−9	−5
Air-oven ageing for 3 days at 100°C			
change in hardness, IRHD	+2	+3	+3
change in M300, %	+15	+10	+1
change in TS, %	−8	−9	−13
change in EB, %	−5	−8	−12
Air-oven ageing for 7 days at 100°C			
change in hardness, IRHD	+2	+2	+2
change in M300, %	−2	−1	−8
change in TS, %	−24	−27	−26
change in EB, %	−7	−19	−19
Air-oven ageing for 1 day at 125°C			
change in hardness, IRHD	0	−1	0
change in M300, %	−5	+9	−1
change in TS, %	−19	−19	−18
change in EB, %	−8	−13	−18
Volume swell in water			
3 days at 100°C, %	4	4	−2
Low-temperature storage at −26°C			
time to			
5 point IRHD rise, days	>7	>7	3
10 point IRHD rise, days	10	<14	7
20 point IRHD rise, days	<14	<14	10
Impact brittleness, −40°C		no failures	
Ozone resistance, 200pphm, 40°C, 20% strain			
time to first crack, days	>7	>7	>7

5.7 Low creep rubbers, for injection moulding — 40–80 IRHD

Soluble EV systems give scorch safety and fast curing characteristics coupled with good reversion resistance. Vulcanizates are suitable for service at moderate to elevated temperatures. Typical applications are rubber springs, mountings, couplings and bushes.

Formulation

	1	2	3	4	5
Nominal hardness, IRHD	40	50	60	70	80
SMR CV	100	100	100	100	100
N762, SRF-LM-NS black	2	30	60	100	120
Zinc oxide	5	5	5	5	5
Zinc 2-ethylhexanoate[a]	1	1	1	1	1
Antioxidant, TMQ[b]	1	1	1	1	1
Sulphur	0.7	0.7	0.7	0.7	0.7
MBS	1.7	1.7	1.7	1.7	2
TBTD	0.7	0.7	0.7	0.7	0.4

a. Use stearic acid if resistance to primary stress relaxation or creep is not critical.
b. *eg Flectol H* (Monsanto).

Rheological properties

	1	2	3	4	5
Mooney viscosity, 135°C	35	41	46	53	109
Mooney scorch, 135°C, min	12	7.5	6.5	6	6
Monsanto *Rheometer*, °C	190	190	180	180	180
scorch, t_{s1}, min	0.75	0.5	1.0	0.75	1.0
cure, $t_c'(95)$, min	1.85	1.6	2.35	1.85	2.6
time to 5% reversion, min	5.0	4.0	8.7	6.75	7.0

Reference: Technical Information Sheet D24:1977.

5.7 (cont)

Vulcanizate properties, unaged

Injection moulded using *REP B43K* machine
extruder jacket temperature110°C (40 and 50 IRHR) and 100°C (60–80 IRHD)
injection chamber temperature 110°C (40 and 50 IRHD) and 100°C (60—80 IRHD).

Cure time, min	0.75	0.75	1.5	1.0	1.25
Cure temperature, °C	190	190	180	180	180
Hardness, IRHD	39	52	60	72	82
Density, Mg/m^3	0.97	1.07	1.16	1.25	1.28
Resilience, Dunlop, %	88	82	71	59	46
Tensile properties					
M300, MPa	1.4	5.4	10.3		
TS, MPa	17.5	23.5	18.4	16.5	14.5
EB, %	715	590	475	290	235

5.8 Semi-EV vulcanizates **50–70 IRHD**

Formulations giving improved compression set.

Semi-EV systems give improved resistance to reversion and compression set at elevated temperatures. The formulations are suitable for thick mouldings and meet the physical property requirements of BS 5400: Part 9 and ASTM D4014 (grades 2 and 3) for bridge bearings.

Formulation

	1	2	3
Nominal hardness	50	60	70
SMR CV60	100	100	100
N550, FEF black	20	40	60
Light oil[a]	2	4	6
Zinc oxide	5	5	5
Stearic acid	2	2	2
Antidegradant, HPPD[b]	3	3	3
Wax blend[c]	2	2	2
Sulphur	1.5	1.5	1.5
CBS	1.5	1.5	1.5

a. eg *Fina Process Oil 2059* (Petrofina).
b. eg *Santoflex 13* (Monsanto).
c. eg *Sunproof Improved* (Uniroyal).

Rheological properties

Mooney viscosity, 100°C	30	35	43
Mooney scorch, 120°C, min	34	31	25
Monsanto *Rheometer*, 140°C			
scorch, t_{s1}, min	11.6	9.4	7.2
cure, $t_c'(95)$, min	20	17	15

Reference: Engineering Data Sheets 36–38.

5.8 (cont)

Vulcanizate properties, unaged

Formulation	1	2	3
Cure: 45 min at 140°C			
Hardness, IRHD	51	62	70
Density, Mg/m^3	1.03	1.09	1.14
MR100, MPa	1.14	1.67	2.60
Resilience, Lupke, %	81	72	63
Tensile properties			
M300, MPa	4.7	9.3	14.2
TS, MPa	29	26	21.5
EB, %	640	565	445
Tear, ISO trouser			
23°C, median, kN/m	5.9	17	18
Ring fatigue life, 0–100% strain			
median, kc	187	104	120
Compression set, %			
1 day at −26°C	25	29	34
7 days at −10°C	12	15	18
1 day at 0°C	8	9	8
3 days at 23°C	8	8	9
1 day at 70°C	18	19	21
1 day at 100°C	44	44	44
Goodrich *Flexometer*			
Static stress 1MPa (24lb), stroke 5.71mm (0.225in), start 100°C			
Temp. rise after 2h, deg C	4	11	20
Stress relaxation rate, 20% compression			
% per decade	2.4	2.8	3.3
Dynamic shear modulus and phase angle			
Frequency 0.1Hz, strain ±10%, 23°C			
Shear modulus, MPa	0.73	1.13	1.41
Phase angle, degrees	2.4	5.5	6.8

MRPRA Engineering Data Sheets give complete data on the variation of fatigue life with strain and the dependence of dynamic properties on temperature, frequency and strain.

5.8 (cont)

Environmental ageing data

Formulation	1	2	3
Air-oven ageing for 7 days at 70°C			
change in hardness, IRHD	+3	+3	+3
change in M300, %	+40	+17	+11
change in TS, %	−2	−7	−3
change in EB, %	−8	−10	−9
Air-oven ageing for 14 days at 70°C			
change in hardness, IRHD	+4	+5	+5
change in M300, %	+49	+25	+18
change in TS, %	−4	−10	−8
change in EB, %	−9	−14	−19
Air-oven ageing for 3 days at 100°C			
change in hardness, IRHD	+4	+5	+3
change in M300, %	+31	+22	+13
change in TS, %	−18	−15	−18
change in EB, %	−12	−14	−25
Volume swell in water			
3 days at 100°C, %	4.1	4.1	3.5
Low-temperature storage at −26°C			
time to			
5 point IRHD rise, days	7	14	10
10 point IRHD rise, days	14	21	14
20 point IRHD rise, days	21	28	>28
Impact brittleness, −40°C		no failures	
Ozone resistance, 100pphm, 40°C, 20% strain			
time to first crack, days	>7	>7	>7

5.9 Suspension bushes — 60–65 IRHD

General-purpose and heat-resistant formulations

Formulations 1, 2 and 5 give good bond strengths to metal and are recommended for bonded bushes. Formulations 3 and 4 are recommended for unbonded bushes.

Formulation

	1	2	3	4	5
Vulcanization system	Conventional	Semi-EV	EV	Soluble EV	*Novor*
SMR 10	100	100	100	100	100
N326, HAF-LS black	40		40		
N550, FEF black		45		50	35
Zinc oxide	10	10	10	5	5
Stearic acid	2	2	2		1
Zinc 2-ethylhexanoate[a]				2	
Antidegradant, HPPD[b]	2	2	2	2	
Antioxidant, TMQ[c]					2
Antioxidant, ZMBI[d]					2
Sulphur	2.5	1.5	0.25	0.7	1
Novor 924[e]					2.7
CBS	0.7	1.5			
MBS			2.1	1.5	
TBBS					0.2
TMTD		0.1	1.0		
TBTD				1.0	
DPG					
TMTM					1

a. *eg Zinc Octoate* (Tenneco).
b. *eg Santoflex 13* (Monsanto).
c. *eg Flectol H* (Monsanto).
d. *eg Vulkanox ZMB2* (Bayer).
e. Urethane crosslinker (Durham Chemicals). *Novor 950* will give substantially the same results.

Rheological properties

	1	2	3	4	5
Mooney viscosity, 100°C	70	77	70	70	53
Mooney scorch, 120°C, min	20	10	12	14	21
Monsanto *Rheometer*, 150°C					
M_{HR}, torque units	41.5	36	35	42	36
M_L, torque units	10	12	11	9	9.5
scorch, t_{s1}, min	4	1.7	3	3.5	3.7
cure, $t_c'(95)$, min	13	6	18	9	9
cure, $t_c'(100)$, min	18	8	*ca* 60	*ca* 60	20
time to 5% reversion, min	31	20			

Reference: Technical Information Sheet D111:1982

5.9 (cont) **60–65 IRHD**

Vulcanizate properties, unaged

Formulation	1	2	3	4	5
Vulcanization system	Conventional	Semi-EV	EV	Soluble EV	*Novor*
Cure time at 150°C, min	20	15	20	30	10
Hardness, IRHD	66	63	64	65	66
Density, Mg/m³	1.15	1.13	1.14	1.13	1.10
MR100, MPa	1.92	2.04	1.62	2.00	1.84
Resilience, Lupke, %	66	73	64	74	73
Abrasion, DIN, mm³	179		197	215	235
Tensile properties					
M100, MPa	2.1	2.25	1.8	2.2	1.6
M300, MPa	12	12	10	13	10
TS, MPa	27	24.5	28.5	21	24.5
EB, %	515	515	560	445	530
Tear, ISO trouser					
23°C, median, kN/m	15.5	11.5	15	9.2	11
high/low ratio	1.6	1.4	1.4	2.4	2
100°C, median, kN/m	8	5.5	7.5	1.5	8
high/low ratio	1.4	3	2.6	1.7	2
Ring fatigue life, 0–100% strain					
median, kc	105	70	45	47	40
high/low ratio	2.8	1.5	1.5	1.4	1.4
Compression set, %					
1 day at −26°C	14	25	79	29	19
1 day at 0°C	7	6	16	4	6
3 days at 23°C	7	8	12	6	8
1 day at 70°C	30	19	14	12	24
1 day at 100°C	54	47	33	26	39
1 day at 125°C			44	40	52

5.9 (cont)

Environmental ageing data

Formulation	1	2	3	4	5
Vulcanization system	Conventional	Semi-EV	EV	Soluble EV	*Novor*
Air-oven ageing for 3 days at 70°C					
change in hardness, IRHD	+2		+2		+3
change in M100, %	+10	0	+10		+20
change in M300, %	+15	0	+10		+20
change in TS, %	−10	−5	0		−5
change in EB, %	−10	−5	0		−10
Air-oven ageing for 7 days at 70°C					
change in hardness, IRHD	+4	0	+2	+3	+6
change in M100, %	+15	0	+10	+15	+35
change in M300, %	+18	0	+15	+12	+30
change in TS, %	−10	−5	+5	+10	0
change in EB, %	−10	−5	0	0	−15
Air-oven ageing for 3 days at 100°C					
change in hardness, IRHD	+3	+3	+5	+3	+4
change in M100, %	+55	+10	+35	0	+40
change in TS, %	−50	−40	−10	0	−15
change in EB, %	−45	−30	−15	+5	−25
Low-temperature storage at −26°C					
time to					
5 point IRHD rise, days	>28	3	<3	4	7
10 point IRHD rise, days	>28	5	<3	7	17
20 point IRHD rise, days	>28	10	10	10	23

5.10 Tear- and abrasion-resistant rubbers **50–70 IRHD**

A reinforcing carbon black is desirable when high resistance to tearing and wear is needed. Formulation 3 uses an alternative protective system, but is otherwise similar to formulation 2.

Formulation

	1	2	3	4
Nominal hardness	50	60	60	70
SMR CV60	100	100	100	100
N330, HAF black	15	30	30	45
Light oil[a]	1.5	3	3	4.5
Zinc oxide	5	5	5	5
Stearic acid	2	2	2	2
Antidegradant, HPPD[b]	3	3		3
Antiozonant, DOPPD[c]			4	
Antioxidant, TMQ[d]			2	
Wax blend[e]	2	2		2
Sulphur	2.5	2.5	2.5	2.5
CBS	0.6	0.6	0.6	0.6

a. *eg Fina Process Oil 2059* (Petrofina).
b. *eg Santoflex 13* (Monsanto).
c. *eg UOP 88* (Universal Oil Products).
d. *eg Flectol H* (Monsanto).
e. *eg Sunproof Improved* (Uniroyal).

Rheological properties

	1	2	3	4
Mooney viscosity, 100°C	47	47	48	57
Mooney scorch, 120°C, min	21	36	23	22
Monsanto *Rheometer*, 140°C				
scorch, t_{s1}, min	8.8	10.4	6.8	7.3
cure, $t_c'(95)$, min	29	28	25	28

Reference: Engineering Data Sheets 14–16 and 21.

5.10 (cont)

Vulcanizate properties, unaged

Formulation	1	2	3	4
Cure: 45min at 140°C				
Hardness, IRHD	52	60	55	71
Density, Mg/m^3	1.02	1.07	1.06	1.10
MR100, MPa	1.02	1.38	1.28	2.02
Resilience, Lupke, %	83	74	74	63
Tensile properties				
M300, MPa	4.0	6.8	6.6	10.8
TS, MPa	29	29	29	27
EB, %	690	640	650	550
Tear, ISO trouser				
23°C, median, kN/m	8.2	20	16	24
Ring fatigue life, 0–100% strain				
median, kc	236	197	134	218
Compression set, %				
28 days at −26°C	33	44	61	57
1day at −26°C	23	30	24	31
1day at 0°C	10	12	11	12
3days at 23°C	6	8	8	9
1day at 70°C	32	28	27	29
1day at 100°C	51	47	49	48
Goodrich *Flexometer*				
Static stress 1MPa (24lb), stroke 5.71mm (0.225in), start 100°C				
Temp. rise after 2h, deg C	10	19	19	fail
Stress relaxation rate, 20% compression				
% per decade	2.4	3.3	3.8	3.6
Dynamic shear modulus and phase angle				
Frequency 0.1Hz, strain +10%, 23°C				
Shear modulus, MPa	0.66	1.18	1.02	1.77
Phase angle, degrees	2.8	5.0	4.8	7.7

MRPRA Engineering Data Sheets give complete data on the variation of fatigue life with strain and the dependence of dynamic properties on temperature, frequency and strain.

5.10 (cont)

Environmental ageing data

Formulation	1	2	3	4
Air-oven ageing for 7 days at 70°C				
change in hardness, IRHD	0	+3	+3	+3
change in M300, %	+37	+26	+19	+25
change in TS, %	−2	−4	−2	−2
change in EB, %	−9	−8	−8	−9
Air-oven ageing for 14 days at 70°C				
change in hardness, IRHD	+2	+3	+4	+4
change in M300, %	+40	+35	+38	+32
change in TS, %	−3	−6	−2	−6
change in EB, %	−10	−8	−9	−13
Volume swell in water				
3 days at 100°C, %	6.5	6.9	5.8	5.3
Low-temperature storage at −26°C				
time to				
5 point IRHD rise, days	28	28	>28	21
Impact brittleness, −40°C		no failures		
Ozone resistance, 100pphm, 40°C, 20% strain				
time to first crack, days	>7	>7	>7	>7

Section 6 Extrusions

6.1	Hard compounds
6.2	Light-coloured compounds
6.3	EPDM blends, LCM vulcanization
6.4	General-purpose, LCM vulcanization
6.5	Heat-resistant, LCM vulcanization
6.6	Light-coloured, LCM vulcanization
6.7	Seals, LCM vulcanization
6.8	Sponge rubber, LCM vulcanization
6.9	Microwave vulcanization, black-filled
6.10	Tubing, laboratory
6.11	Tubing, transparent

See also: Mouldings meeting ASTM D2000 (Sections 9.9–9.14).

6.1 Hard compounds **90 IRHD**

Blending natural rubber with *trans*-polyoctenamer lowers mix viscosity, increases extrusion rate and raises vulcanizate hardness.

Formulation

	1	2	3
SMR 20[a]	100	70	70
Vestenamer 8012[b]		30	30
N330, HAF black	80	80	60
Process oil[c]	10	10	10
Zinc oxide	5	5	5
Stearic acid	2	2	2
Tackifying resin[d]	5	5	5
Antioxidant[e]	1	1	1
Phenol-formaldehyde resin[f]	5	5	5
Sulphur	3.5	3.5	3.5
MBS	0.7	1	1
Hexamine[g]	0.4	0.4	0.4
Prevulcanization inhibitor[h]	0.1	0.1	0.1

a. Premasticated to 60 Mooney.
b. Highly crystalline *trans*-polyoctenamer (Huels).
c. *eg Dutrex 729UK* (Shell).
d. *eg Escorez 1102* (Esso).
e. *eg BLE 75* (Uniroyal).
f. *eg Cellobond J1114W* (BP Chemicals).
g. *eg Vulkacit H30* (Bayer).
h. *eg Santogard PVI* (Monsanto).

Rheological properties

	1	2	3
Mooney viscosity, 100°C	81	60	39
Mooney scorch, 120°C, min	12	13	25
Monsanto *Rheometer*, 160°C			
M_{HR}, torque units	52	59	50
M_L, torque units	12	8	5
scorch, t_{s1}, min	1.8	2.0	2.3
cure, $t_c'(95)$, min	10	11	11
cure, $t_c'(100)$, min	15	18	18
Extrusion test, 25mm extruder, 40rev/min			
barrel temperature, 65°C, die temperature, 85°C			
extrusion rate, cm/min	150	180	220

6.1 (cont)

Vulcanizate properties, unaged

Formulation	1	2	3
Cure time at 160°C, min	10	12	12
Hardness, IRHD	90	93	88
Density, Mg/m^3	1.21	1.18	1.14
Abrasion, DIN, mm^3	290	300	290
Tensile properties			
M100, MPa	5.7	6.1	4.6
M200, MPa	12.8	12.8	9.6
TS, MPa	16	14	16
EB, %	250	215	340
Tear, ISO trouser			
23°C, median, kN/m	11	4.7	23
high/low ratio	1.6	1.2	1.3
100°C, median, kN/m	14	4.9	8.9
high/low ratio	1.4	2.4	1.7
Ring fatigue life, 0–100% strain			
median, kc	99	46	66
high/low ratio	2.4	6.3	1.4
Compression set, %			
3 days at 23°C	19	29	24
1 day at 70°C	42	43	41
Adhesion to steel cords[a], kN	0.9	0.93	0.84

a. Courtauld-modified Pirelli test.

Environmental ageing data

Air-oven ageing for 14 days at 70°C			
change in M100, %	+70	+50	+44
change in TS, %	−18	−8	−23
change in EB, %	−53	−54	−50

6.2 Light-coloured compounds **40 IRHD**

SP rubbers give good extrusion properties, especially in soft mixes. Formulations 1–3 meet the requirements of BS 1155:1979.

Formulation

	1	2	3	4
SMR WF	75	50		25
PA 80[a]	25	50		
SP 20[b]			100	
PA 57[c]				75
Coated calcium carbonate[d]				40
Zinc oxide	6	6	6	5
Stearic acid	2.25	2.25	2.25	2
Paraffin wax				2
Antioxidant[e]	1	1	1	1
Sulphur	1.35	1.2	1.35	0.6
MBTS	0.8	0.8	0.8	
DPG	0.12	0.04	0.12	
MBT				0.3
TMTD				0.1

a. Superior processing rubber.
b. Superior processing rubber.
c. Superior processing rubber.
d. *eg Calofort S* (John & E Sturge).
e. *eg* Non-staining phenolic type.

Properties

	1	2	3	4
Mooney viscosity, 100°C	40	48	41	26
Cure time at 140°C, min	30	30	30	10
Hardness, IRHD	39	39	40	39
Density, Mg/m³	0.97	0.97	0.97	1.15
Tensile properties				
TS, MPa	22.5	23	24	14.5
EB, %	740	750	720	660
Compression set, %				
1 day at 70°C,	22	22	24	28

Reference: *NR Technology*, 1970, **1**, Part 1, No.5; Technical Information Sheets D114 and D115:1982.

6.3 EPDM blends, LCM vulcanization

Light-coloured formulations for vacuum extrusion

A non-staining antiozonant gives good ozone resistance with a minimum level of EPDM in the blend. Increasing the proportion of EPDM to about 40% gives good protection without antiozonant, but the tensile and set properties will be seriously impaired.

Formulation

	1	2	3
	solid rubber		sponge
SMR CV	80	80	80
Vistalon 6505[a]	20	20	20
Coated calcium carbonate[b]	30		30
Aluminium silicate		30	
Titanium dioxide	5	5	5
Zinc oxide	5	5	5
Stearic acid	1	1	1
Antioxidant[c]	2	2	2
Antiozonant[d]	5	5	5
Sulphur	1.75	1.75	1.75
MBTS	2	2	2
ZDMC	0.7	0.7	0.7
Blowing agent[e]			5
Desiccant[f]	5	5	2

a. Fast-curing EPDM (Exxon).
b. *eg Winnofil S* (ICI).
c. *eg* A 50/50 blend of *Wingstay L* (Goodyear) and *Vulkanox ZMB2* (Bayer).
d. *Antiozonant AFS 50* (Bayer).
e. *eg Genitron CR* (Fisons).
f. *eg Caloxol W5G* (John & E Sturge).

Rheological properties

	1	2	3
Mooney viscosity, 100°C	48	57	40
Mooney scorch, 120°C, min	7.5	5	8
Monsanto *Rheometer*, 200°C			
M_{HR}, torque units	20	25	25
M_L, torque units	6.5	10	4.5
scorch, t_{s1}, min	0.7	0.3	0.5
cure, $t_c'(95)$, min	1.2	0.7	1.0
cure, $t_c'(100)$, min	1.4	0.8	1.2
time to 5% reversion, min	2.2	1.0	1.9

6.3 (cont)

Vulcanizate properties, unaged
Cured in an Iddon 9m salt bath at 200°C

Formulation	1	2	3
Cure time, min	1.4	1.0	1.5
Strip thickness, mm	2	2	5
Hardness, IRHD	48	53	
Hardness, Shore 00			73
Density, Mg/m^3	1.19	1.15	0.87
Tensile properties			
M100, MPa	0.9	1.0	0.4
M300, MPa	1.8	2.7	1.0
TS, MPa	12.0	13.0	3.1
EB, %	710	650	555
Compression set, %, 1 day at 70°C			30[a]
Ozone resistance, 50 pphm, 40°C, 20% strain time to first crack, days	>14	>14	

a. 50% compression. Measured on tube 20mm diameter, 6mm wall thickness.

6.4General-purpose extrusions, LCM vulcanization 55–60 IRHD

Formulations for vacuum extrusion

These formulations illustrate some accelerator combinations designed for LCM curing at 200°C; they show how scorch time may be controlled using sulphenamides as primary accelerators and thiocarbamyl derivatives as secondary accelerators. In formulation 2, rubber-soluble TBTD as a secondary accelerator avoids unsightly dithiocarbamate bloom, but is slightly slower curing. The reversion resistance of the sulphenamide cure systems 6 and 7 is inferior to that of MBTS-accelerated systems 4 and 5. Formulation 7 is a higher modulus variant of formulation 6.

Formulation

	1	2	3	4	5	6	7
SMR 5[a]	100	100	100	100	100	100	100
N550, FEF black	50	50	50	50	50	50	50
Paraffinic oil[b]	5	5	5	5	5	5	5
Zinc oxide	5	5	5	5	5	5	5
Stearic acid	1	1	1	1	1	1	1
Antioxidant, TMQ[c]	2	2	2	2	2	2	
Antidegradant, HPPD[d]							2
Wax blend[e]	5	5	5	5	5	5	3
Sulphur	2	1	1	1	1	1	1.2
MBTS	1			2	2		
CBS		1.6	1.6			1.7	2
TMTM				0.7			
TMTD	0.5						
TBTD		1					
BiDMC			0.7		0.7		
ZDMC						0.5	0.5
Desiccant[f]	3	3	3	3	3	3	3

a. Premasticated to 60 Mooney.
b. *eg Sunpar 2280* (Sun Oil).
c. *eg Flectol H* (Monsanto).
d. *eg Santoflex 13* (Monsanto).
e. *eg Sunproof Improved* (Uniroyal).
f. *eg Caloxol W5G* (John & E Sturge).

6.4 (cont)

Rheological properties

Formulation	1	2	3	4	5	6	7
Mooney viscosity, 100°C	44	53	49	48	46	50	54
Mooney scorch, 120°C, min	10	18	16	14	6	11	6
After storage for 6 weeks at 23°C							
Mooney viscosity change	+3	+3	+2		+1	+1	
Mooney scorch change, min	−1.5	0	0		−1.5	−1	
Monsanto *Rheometer*, 200°C							
M_{HR}, torque nits	28	27	31	27	30	27.5	32.5
M_L, torque units	4.5	6	7	5	6	6	6.5
scorch, t_{s1}, min	0.5	0.7	0.5	0.55	0.36	0.5	0.4
cure, $t_c'(95)$, min	0.9	1.2	0.9	1.05	0.75	0.9	0.8
cure, $t_c'(100)$, min	1.0	1.3	1.1	1.3	1.05	1.05	1.0
time to 5% reversion, min	1.2	1.7	1.5	1.65	2.5	1.4	1.3
reversion after 6min, %	38	35	32	22	18	34	32

6.4 (cont)

Trial results Effect of cure time on physical properties of 2mm strip

LCM vulcanization using Iddon 9 m salt bath
extruder barrel temperature 50–70°C
die temperature 86°C

Formulation	1	2	3	4	5	6	7
Cure 1							
Cure time, s	26	29	25	23	20	28	25
Average bath temperature, °C	202	196	195	202	199	197	199
Hardness, micro, IRHD	64	60	63	54	60	58	62
Tensile properties							
M100, MPa	2.4	2.1	2.4	1.9	2.4	1.9	2.7
M300, MPa	13.5	12	14.5	11.0	14.0	11.3	12.5
TS, MPa	22.0	20.5	23.5	17.0	23.5	23.5	23.5
EB, %	450	440	450	420	450	495	460
Air-oven ageing for 7 days at 70°C							
change in hardness, IRHD	+6	+10	+2	+10	+3	+5	+6
change in M100, %	+90	+120	+70	+78	+50	+74	+65
change in M300, %			+40		+30	+55	+30
change in TS, %	−20	−22	−10	−19	−9	−15	−6
change in EB, %	−40	−45	−28	−35	−22	−29	−12
Ozone resistance, 50pphm, 40°C, 20% strain							
time to first crack, days	>14	14	>14	>14	>14	10	
Cure 2							
Cure time, s	34	46	32	38	30	35	36
Average bath temperature, °C	204	200	196	202	200	197	201
Hardness, micro, IRHD	60	57	62	54	60	57	62
Tensile properties							
M100, MPa	2.2	1.9	2.3	1.8	2.3	1.7	2.6
M300, MPa	12.5	11.0	14.0	11.0	14.0	10.8	12.0
TS, MPa	20.0	19.0	22.5	17.5	22.0	21.5	23.0
EB, %	435	420	445	425	435	480	460
Air-oven ageing for 7 days at 70°C							
change in hardness, IRHD	+6	+6	+2	+6	+2	+4	+4
change in M100, %	+70	+54	+45	+60	+25	+60	+40
change in M300, %	+40		+28	+33	+21	+45	+25
change in TS, %	−9	−15	−8	−13	−4	−15	−4
change in EB, %	−26	−30	−22	−26	−15	−28	−13
Ozone resistance, 50pphm, 40°C, 20% strain							
time to first crack, days	>14	>14	>14	>14	>14	>10	

6.4 (cont)

Formulation	1	2	3	4	5	6	7
Cure 3							
Cure time, s	48	58	50	48	44	51	51
Average bath temperature, °C	205	199	196	204	202	199	199
Hardness, micro, IRHD	57	58	59	54	60	57	60
Tensile properties							
M100, MPa	1.9	1.8	2.1	1.8	2.4	1.7	2.5
M300, MPa	10.6	10.5	13.5	11.0	13.5	10.3	11.3
TS, MPa	20.0	18.8	22.0	17.0	22.0	21.0	22.5
EB, %	455	430	440	420	435	480	475
Air-oven ageing for 7 days at 70°C							
change in hardness, IRHD	+5	+4	+1	+3	+2	+2	+3
change in M100, %	+50	+65	+30	+28	+16	+33	+34
change in M300, %	+40	+40	+20	+19	+13	+32	+20
change in TS, %	0	−10	−3	−10	0	−9	−2
change in EB, %	−16	−30	−15	−15	−7	−19	−10
Ozone resistance, 50pphm, 40°C, 20% strain							
time to first crack, days	>14	>14	>14	>14	>14	>10	3
Cure 4							
Cure time, s	60	93	66	65	60	70	69
Average bath temperature, °C	204	198	198	204	205	199	199
Hardness, micro, IRHD	56	55	61	56	59	56	59
Tensile properties							
M100, MPa	1.7	1.7	2.1	1.8	2.2	1.6	2.1
M300, MPa	9.7	10.5	12.5	11.0	13.0	9.3	11.0
TS, MPa	19.0	20.0	21.5	18.5	22.0	23.5	23.5
EB, %	475	430	445	435	435	525	475
Air-oven ageing for 7 days at 70°C							
change in hardness, IRHD	+5	+4	+1	+3	+1	+2	+3
change in M100, %	+40	+35	+20	+18	+15	+20	+34
change in M300, %	+35	+30	+15	+11	+11	+30	+17
change in TS, %	−6	−2	0	−7	−6	+5	+3
change in EB, %	−19	−14	−10	−14	−8	−9	−3
Ozone resistance, 50pphm, 40°C, 20% strain							
time to first crack, days	>14	>14	>14	>14	>14	>10	>10

6.5 Heat resistant extrusions, LCM vulcanization **60 IRHD**
Formulations for vacuum extrusion

These heat-resistant EV and *Novor* formulations illustrate accelerator combinations for LCM vulcanization at 200°C and the use of three different systems for protection against ozone attack: (1) dialkyl-*p*-phenylenediamine; (2) wax; and (3) a combination of wax and an alkyl-phenyl-*p*-phenylenediamine.

Formulation

	1	2	3
SMR 5[a]	100	100	100
N550, FEF black	50	50	50
Paraffinic oil[b]	5	5	5
Zinc oxide	5	5	5
Stearic acid	1	1	1
Antioxidant, TMQ[c]	1	2	1
Antioxidant, ZMBI[d]		2	1
Antiozonant, DOPPD[e]	4		
Antidegradant, HPPD[f]			2
Wax blend[g]		5	3
Sulphur	0.35	1.2	0.7
Novor 924[h]		3.2	2.8
TBBS	3	0.24	0.2
TMTD	2.2		
TMTM		1.3	0.7
DPG	0.5		
Desiccant[i]	3	5	3

a. Premasticated to 60 Mooney.
b. *eg Sunpar 2280* (Sun Oil).
c. *eg Flectol H* (Monsanto).
d. *eg Vulkanox ZMB2* (Bayer).
e. *eg UOP 88* (Universal Oil Products).
f. *eg Santoflex 13* (Monsanto).
g. *eg Sunproof Improved* (Uniroyal).
h. Urethane crosslinker (Durham Chemicals). *Novor 950* will give substantially the same results.
i. *eg Caloxol W5G* (John & E Sturge).

6.5 (cont)
Rheological properties

Formulation	1	2	3
Mooney viscosity, 100°C	55	52	62
Mooney scorch, 120°C, min	4	10	12
After 6 weeks storage at 23°C			
Mooney viscosity change,	+1	+3	+3
Mooney scorch change, min	−1	+1	+1
Monsanto *Rheometer*, 200°C			
M_{HR}, torque units	32	32	28
M_L, torque units	7	6	7
scorch, t_{s1}, min	0.4	0.5	0.6
cure, $t_c'(95)$, min	1.7	1.0	1.2
cure, $t_c'(100)$, min	2.0	1.2	1.5
time to 5% reversion, min	3.6	1.7	2.1
reversion after 6 min, %	5.5	26	20

6.5 (cont)

Trial results Effect of cure time on physical properties of 2mm strip

LCM vulcanization using Iddon 9m salt bath
extruder barrel temperature 50–70°C
die temperature 86°C

Formulation	1	2	3
Cure 1			
Cure time, s	70	41	55
Average bath temperature, °C	199	199	199
Hardness, micro, IRHD	58	67	64
Tensile properties			
M100, MPa	2.1	2.8	2.7
M300, MPa	12.0	14.7	13.4
TS, MPa	17.5	20.5	22.5
EB, %	400	405	465
Air-oven ageing for 3 days at 100°C			
change in hardness, IRHD	+10	+5	+3
change in M100, %	+100	+60	+44
change in TS, %	−11	−60	−18
change in EB, %	−32	−55	−20
Ozone resistance, 50pphm, 40°C, 20% strain			
time to first crack, days	3	>14	>14
Cure 2			
Cure time, s	129	90	109
Average bath temperature, °C	199	199	200
Hardness, micro, IRHD	60	62	63
Tensile properties			
M100, MPa	2.4	2.5	2.4
M300, MPa	13.3	13.7	12.8
TS, MPa	20.5	20	23
EB, %	430	415	475
Air-oven ageing for 3 days at 100°C			
change in hardness, IRHD	+7	+1	+3
change in M100, %	+50	+34	+27
change in M300, %	+27		0
change in TS, %	−5	−33	−30
change in EB, %	−18	−35	−22
Ozone resistance, 50pphm, 40°C, 20% strain			
time to first crack, days	3	>7	>14

6.5 (cont)

Formulation	1	2	3
Cure 3			
Cure time, s	215	160	182
Average bath temperature, °C	199	199	200
Hardness, micro, IRHD	60	60	61
Tensile properties			
M100, MPa	2.4	2.4	2.4
M300, MPa	12.8	12.9	12.6
TS, MPa	18.5	20	22
EB, %	400	430	470
Air-oven ageing for 3 days at 100°C, %			
change in hardness, IRHD	+6	+1	+1
change in M100, %	+48	+37	+25
change in M300, %	+25		0
change in TS, %	−7	−35	−25
change in EB, %	−20	−35	−17
Ozone resistance, 50pphm, 40°C, 20% strain			
time to first crack, days	3	>14	>14

6.6 Light-coloured extrusions, LCM vulcanization **45–65 IRHD**

Formulations for vacuum extrusion

PA 80 in formulations 2 and 3 reduces die swell and prevents extrusion collapse or loss of shape during cure. In factory trials a 12mm rod was successfully cured in 2min at 200°C. Part of the sulphenamide may be replaced by a thiuram to reduce accelerator levels.

Formulation

	1	2	3
SMR 5	100	75	75
PA 80[a]		25	25
Coated calcium carbonate[b]			50
Soft clay[c]			25
Zinc oxide	5	5	5
Stearic acid	1	1	1
Wax			2
Sulphur	0.33	0.26	0.26
CBS	5	4	4
Dibutylthiourea	0.5	0.5	0.5

a. Superior processing rubber.
b. *eg Calofort S* (John & E Sturge).
c. *eg Devolite* (English China Clays).

Properties

	1	2	3
Mooney viscosity, 100°C	29	35	38
Mooney scorch, 120°C, min	20	10	6.5
Cure: 10min at 153°C			
Hardness, IRHD	45	51	66
Density, Mg/m³	0.97	0.97	1.29
Tensile properties			
TS, MPa	25.5	26.5	19.3
EB, %	700	645	490

Reference: Technical Information Sheet D37:1978.

6.7 Seals, LCM vulcanization — 60–70 IRHD

Formulations for vacuum extrusion

Formulation

	1	2	3	4	5
SMR 20[a]	100	100	100	100	100
N990, MT	100				
N330, HAF		40			
N550, FEF			40	75	50
Whiting[b]		100	100		
Coated calcium carbonate[c]					110
Paraffinic oil[d]	5	5	5	20	5
Process aid[e]	4	4	2	2	4
Zinc oxide	5	5	5	5	5
Stearic acid	1	1	1	1	1
Antioxidant[f]	2.5	2.5	2.5	2.5	2.5
Wax blend[g]	7	7	7	7	7
Sulphur	1.2	1.2	1.2	1.2	1.2
MBTS	2	2	2	2	2
BiDMC	0.5	0.5	0.5	0.5	0.5
Desiccant[h]	6	6	6	6	6

a. Premasticated to 60–65 Mooney.
b. Fine ground whiting *eg Britomya Violet* (Croxton and Garry).
c. *eg Winnofil S* (ICI).
d. *eg Sunpar 2280* (Sun Oil).
e. *eg Struktol WB212* (Schill and Seilacher).
f. A blend of 2 parts phr TMQ *eg Flectol H* (Monsanto) and 0.5 parts phr diaryl-*p*-phenylenediamine *Wingstay 100* (Goodyear).
g. *eg Sunproof Improved* (Uniroyal).
h. *eg Caloxol CP2* (John & E Sturge).

Rheological properties

	1	2	3	4	5
Mooney viscosity, 100°C	39	44	43	34	56
Mooney scorch, 120°C, min	6.5	6.5	7.0	5.0	7.5
Monsanto *Rheometer*, 200°C					
M_{HR}, torque units	30.5	34.5	33	23	32
M_L, torque units	5.0	6.8	5.8	6.2	7.0
scorch, t_1, min	0.4	0.4	0.4	0.4	0.4
cure, $t_c'(95)$, min	0.8	0.8	0.8	0.8	0.7
cure, $t_c'(100)$, min	1.0	1.0	1.0	1.0	0.9
time to 5% reversion, min	1.5	1.4	1.5	1.2	1.3
reversion after 3 min, %	17	17	17	22	19

6.7 (cont)

Trial results Effect of cure time on physical properties

LCM vulcanization using Iddon 9m salt bath at 200°C
extruder barrel temperature50–70°C
die temperature 90°C

Formulation	1	2	3	4	5
(A) 2mm strip					
Cure time, s	70	65	60	70	60
Hardness, micro, IRHD	60	66	64	58	68
Density, Mg/m³	1.23	1.42	1.42	1.17	1.43
Tensile properties					
M100, MPa	2.1	2.0	2.1	2.0	2.4
M300, MPa	8.0	6.8	7.5	10.6	10.0
TS, MPa	15.5	16.5	15.5	17.5	14.0
EB, %	505	510	475	460	405
Air-oven ageing for 7 days at 70°C					
Change in hardness, IRHD	+2	+1	+2	+1	0
change in M100, %	+10	+15	+10	+12	+20
change in M300, %	+5	+24	+15	+20	+10
change in TS, %	0	−5	0	−3	−9
change in EB, %	0	−12	−5	−15	−15
Ozone resistance, 50 pphm, 40°C, 20% strain					
time to first cracks, days	>3	>3	>3	>3	
(B) 10mm diameter rod					
Cure times, s					
cure 1	65	65	65	70	65
cure 2	100	90	100	100	90
cure 3	160	160	160	170	
Compression set, 3 days at 23°C, %					
cure 1	10	15.5	13	11	14
cure 2	8	13	10	12	12.5
cure 3	8	14	11	13	
Compression set, 1 day at 70°C, %					
cure 1	33	33	39	47	33
cure 2	19	25	24	18.5	19
cure 3	14	17.5	15	18	

6.8 Sponge rubber, LCM vulcanization

Novor vulcanization system for good heat resistance

Formulation

SMR 20	100
N550, FEF black	15
Whiting	40
Process oil[a]	10
Zinc oxide	5
Stearic acid	2
Antioxidant, TMQ[b]	2
Antioxidant, ZMBI[c]	2
Novor 924[d]	2.7
Sulphur	1
MBTS	0.15
ZDMC	1.3
Blowing agent[e]	5

a. *eg Dutrex 729UK* (Shell).
b. *eg Flectol H* (Monsanto).
c. *eg Vulkanox ZMB* (Bayer).
d. Urethane crosslinker (Durham Chemicals). *Novor 950* will give substantially the same results.
e. *eg Vulcacel BN94* (ICI).

Vulcanizate properties, unaged

LCM cured using Iddon 9-m salt bath at 205°C

4mm flat strip	
Cure time: 3min	
Hardness, Shore 00	88
Density, Mg/m^3	0.89
Tensile properties	
M100, MPa	0.55
M300, MPa	2.1
TS, MPa	6.7
EB, %	520

6.9 Microwave vulcanization, black-filled — 70 IRHD

Designed to give a suitable heating rate with a blend of PA 80 and SMR CV for good extrusion properties.

Formulation

SMR CV	75
PA 80[a]	25
N330, HAF black[b]	25
N550, FEF black[b]	25
Process oil[c]	5
Zinc oxide	5
Stearic acid	1
Antioxidant[d]	2
Sulphur	0.33
MBS	4
ZDMC	0.5
Desiccant[e]	8

a. Superior processing rubber.
b. A blend of blacks gives a fast but controlled heating rate.
c. *eg* Low volatility paraffinic oil.
d. *eg p*-Phenylenediamine type.
e. *eg Caloxol W5G* (John & E Sturge).

Rheological properties

Mooney viscosity, 120°C	50	
Mooney scorch, 120°C, min	18.5	
Monsanto *Rheometer*, °C	160	200
scorch, t_{s1},min	1.3	0.45
cure, $t_c'(95)$,min	7.2	1.3
time to 5% reversion, min	>40	2.3

Vulcanizate properties, unaged

Cure: 10min at 160°C	
Hardness, IRHD	72.5
Density, Mg/m³	1.15
Tensile properties	
M300, MPa	16.3
TS, MPa	18.5
EB, %	355
Compression set, %	
1 day at 70°C	18

Reference: Technical Information sheet D79:1979.

6.10 Tubing, laboratory **45 IRHD**

SP rubber is used for easy processing. The formulation meets BS2775:1967. It is also suitable for moulding laboratory stoppers.

Formulation

SP 50[a]	100
Soft clay[b]	30
Whiting	30
Process oil[c]	15
Zinc oxide	3
Stearic acid	1.5
Phenolic Antioxidant[d]	1.5
Sulphur	2
MBTS	0.5
TMTD	0.15
Red ochre pigment	5

a. Superior processing rubber.
b. *eg Devolite* (English China Clays).
c. Naphthenic oil, *eg Circosol 380* (Sun Oil).
d. *eg Permanax WSP* (Vulnax).

Vulcanizate properties, unaged

Cure: 15min at 153°C	
Hardness, IRHD	46
Density, Mg/m³	1.22
Tensile properties	
M100, MPa	1.1
M300, MPa	2.2
TS, MPa	14.5
EB, %	750
Compression set, %	
1 day at 70°C	27
Tension set, 10min at 100% extension, 23°C, %	3

Environmental ageing data

Air-oven ageing for 7 days at 70°C	
change in hardness, IRHD	+3
change in M100, %	+15
change in TS, %	−1
change in EB, %	−9

Reference: Technical Information Sheet D35:1978.

6.11 Transparent tubing **35–45 IRHD**

Superior processing rubbers prevent extrudate collapse in tubing containing low filler levels. Formulations 2 and 3 meet the USA Food and Drugs Administration (FDA) requirements; formulation 4 meets the requirements of the West German Bundesgesundheitsamt (BGA); formulation 5 is heat resistant. Formulations 1 and 5 contain a rubber-soluble activator, which may be replaced by stearic acid. A UV absorber will reduce light crazing.

Formulation

	1	2	3	4	5
SP 20[a]	100	100		100	
SP 40[b]			100		100
Zinc Oxide, active[c]	0.8	0.8	0.8	0.8	0.8
Stearic acid		0.5	0.5	0.5	
Zinc 2-ethylhexanoate[d]	0.6				0.6
Antioxidant[e]	0.5	0.5	0.5		
Antioxidant[f]				0.5	0.5
Antioxidant, ZMBI[g]					0.5
Sulphur	2.2	2.2	0.8	2.2	
MBT	0.6	0.8			
MBTS					1
DTDM[h]			0.8		0.6
ZDBC		0.1	0.2	0.3	
TBTD	0.2				0.7
UV absorber[i]			as required		

a. Superior processing rubber.
b. Superior processing rubber.
c. *eg Zinkoxyd aktiv* (Bayer).
d. *eg Zinc Octoate* (Tenneco).
e. *eg Wingstay L* (Goodyear).
f. *eg Vulkanox TSP* (Bayer).
g. *eg Vulkanox ZMB* (Bayer).
h. *eg Sulfasan R* (Monsanto).
i. *eg Tinuvin P* (Ciba–Geigy).

Rheological properties

	1	2	3	4	5
Mooney viscosity, 100°C	57	48	45	41	47
Mooney scorch, 120°C, min	7	5	12	6	12
Monsanto *Rheometer*, 140°C					
M_{HR}, torque units	19	18	20	16	21
M_L, torque units	7.5	7	6	5.5	6
scorch, t_{s1}, min	3.5	2	5	3	7.5
cure, $t_c'(95)$, min	11	7	11	9	24
cure, $t_c'(100)$, min	16	10	14	15	60
time to 5% reversion, min	30	15	25	22	*ca* 90

6.11 (cont)

Vulcanizate properties, unaged

Formulation	1	2	3	4	5
Cure time at 140°C, min	15	10	15	15	40
Hardness, IRHD	36	36	39	35	39
Density, Mg/m^3	0.94	0.94	0.94	0.94	0.94
MR100, MPa	0.68	0.65	0.75	0.60	0.75
Resilience, Lupke, %	83	82	86	79	84
Tensile properties					
M100, MPa	0.7	0.7	0.7	0.6	0.8
M300, MPa	1.5	1.4	1.7	1.3	1.8
TS, MPa	24	23	29	22.5	25
EB, %	910	910	825	880	700
Tear, ISO trouser					
23°C, median, kN/m	7.4	7.7	6.7	6.9	8.9
high/low ratio	1.6	1.6	1.5	1.4	1.1
100°C, median, kN/m	2.5	3.1	2.5	3.2	1.6
high/low ratio	1.4	2	1.7	1.1	1.4
Ring fatigue life, 0–100% strain					
median, kc	115	110	89	140	90
high/low ratio	1.4	1.7	1.3	1.7	1.9
Compression set, %					
3 days at 23°C	9	8	7	10	6
1 day at 70°C	28	34	33	32	17
1 day at 100°C	53	61	55	50	40

6.11 (cont)

Environmental ageing data

Formulation	1	2	3	4	5
Air-oven ageing for 7 days at 70°C					
change in hardness, IRHD	+5	+5	0	+3	+2
change in M100, %	+10	+5	+7	+5	0
change in M300, %	+25	+25	+20	+15	+10
change in TS, %	0	+5	+3	+30	−14
change in EB, %	−18	−15	−10	−4	−3
Air-oven ageing for 3 days at 100°C					
change in M100, %					−4
change in M300, %					+10
change in TS, %					−18
change in EB, %					−9
Volume swell in water					
3 days at 100°C, %	4.0	5.1	7.6	5.6	3.8

Section 7 Footwear

7.1 Shoe soles, sports or casual
7.2 Shoe soles
7.3 Heavy-duty boot soles
7.4 Shoe soles, resin and skim rubber
7.5 Shoe soles, transparent

7.1 Sports or casual shoe soles **60–65 IRHD**
High-quality formulations for injection moulding

Formulation similar to 1 and 3 have been successfully injection moulded on a 12–station *MAS 802* machine and tested in SATRA wear trials. Formulations 2 and 4 are faster curing and will give vulcanizates of lighter colour.

Formulation

	1	2	3	4
SMR L	100	100	90	90
High-styrene resin[a]			20	20
Light oil[b]	10	10	10	10
Aluminium silicate[c]	35	35	30	30
Coated calcium carbonate[d]	80	80	70	70
Zinc oxide	5	5	5	5
Titanium dioxide	10	10	10	10
Stearic acid	1	1	1	1
Antioxidant[e]	0.7	0.7	0.7	0.7
Paraffin wax	1	1	1	1
Sulphur	1.3	1.3	1.3	1.3
CBS	2.2		2.2	
MBTS		2.4		2.4
Hexamine[f]		0.5		0.5
TMTM		0.1		
TMTD			0.5	0.3

a. *eg Polysar SS250*, 50% styrene masterbatch (Polysar).
b. *eg Fina Process Oil 2059* (Petrofina).
c. *eg Silteg AS7* (Degussa).
d. *eg Winnofil S* (ICI).
e. *eg Wingstay L* (Goodyear).
f. *eg Vulkacit H30* (Bayer).

Rheological properties

	1	2	3	4
Mooney viscosity, 100°C	59	58	60	46
Mooney scorch, 120°C, min	24	11	14	11
Monsanto *Rheometer*, 160°C				
M_{HR}, torque units	34	29	31	28
M_L, torque units	7.5	7	7	5.5
scorch, t_{s1}, min	2.5	1.8	2.2	1.8
cure, $t_c'(95)$, min	4.0	3.3	4.0	3.0
cure, $t_c'(100)$, min	4.5	4.0	5.0	3.7
time to 5% reversion, min	11.5	6.2	13	9.5

For further information on injection moulding of soles see *NR Technology*, 1971, **2**, Part 1, No 1.

7.1 (cont)

Vulcanizate properties, unaged

Injection moulded using *REP B43K* machine

extruder jacket temperature	90°C
injection chamber temperature	100°C
compound injection temperature	130–135°C

Formulation	1	2	3	4
Cure time at 160°C, min	3.5	3.0	3.5	3.0
Hardness, IRHD	60	57	67	64
Density, Mg/m^3	1.36	1.39	1.34	1.34
Resilience, Lupke, %	70	69	65	65
Abrasion, DIN, mm^3	360		380	
Tensile properties, radial[a]				
M100, MPa	1.7	1.3	1.8	1.5
M300, MPa	5.2	4.2	5.4	5.0
TS, MPa	16.5	16.5	14	15
EB, %	540	585	500	535
Tensile properties, tangential[a]				
M100, MPa	1.9	1.4	1.9	1.6
M300, MPa	5.9	4.9	5.9	5.6
TS, MPa	19	18.5	16	18.5
EB, %	555	590	510	570
Tear, ISO trouser, radial[a]				
23°C, median, kN/m	19.5	22	17	18
high/low ratio	1.3	1.3	1.4	1.4
100°C, median, kN/m	10	13	7.1	8.2
high/low ratio	1.2	1.3	1.7	1.5
Tear, ISO trouser, tangential[a]				
23°C, median, kN/m	22	24	14	21
high/low ratio	1.4	1.2	1.5	1.5
Ring fatigue life, 0–100% strain				
median, kc	22	24	14	21
high/low ratio	1.4	1.2	1.5	1.5
Compression set, %				
3 days at 23°C	11	12	17	17
1 day at 70°C	53	37	42	41

a. Measured along radial and tangential flow lines on a sheet produced in a centre-gated mould.

7.1 (cont)

Environmental ageing data

Formulation	1	2	3	4
Air-oven ageing for 7 days at 70°C				
change in hardness, IRHD	+3	+1	+5	−1
change in M100, %	0	+20	+30	+15
change in M300, %	+20	+45	+30	+15
change in TS, %	0	0	−3	0
change in EB, %	−6	−5	−10	−4
Air-oven ageing for 14 days at 70°C				
change in hardness, IRHD	+3	−2	+6	−1
change in M100, %	+14	+16	+40	+13
change in M300, %	+33	+30	+38	+10
change in TS, %	−2	−7	−12	−9
change in EB, %	−9	−6	−15	−3
Air-oven ageing for 1 day at 100°C				
change in hardness, IRHD	+2	−2	+2	−1
change in M100, %	−2	−6	+30	0
change in M300, %	+20	+11	+33	0
change in TS, %	−11	−14	−8	−4
change in EB, %	−9	−5	−12	−2

7.2 Shoe soles **55–75 IRHD**

Lower-quality formulations for injection moulding

Lower rubber hydrocarbon content than in Section 7.1; fast-curing, easy-processing formulations for fast injection moulding.

Formulation

	1	2
Nominal hardness	55	75
SMR GP	70	90
High-styrene resin[a]		20
Light oil[b]	30	10
Aluminium silicate[c]	30	
Hard clay[d]		75
Coated calcium carbonate[e]	70	
Whiting[f]		80
Zinc oxide	5	5
Titanium dioxide	10	5
Stearic acid	2	2
Antioxidant[g]	0.7	0.5
Antioxidant[h]		0.5
Paraffin wax	1	1
Sulphur	1.2	2.5
MBTS	2.4	1.3
TMTM	0.2	0.5

a. eg *Polysar SS250*, 50% styrene masterbatch (Polysar).
b. eg *Fina Process Oil 2059* (Petrofina).
c. eg *Silteg AS7* (Degussa).
d. eg *Hexafil*, a secondary clay (English China Clays).
e. eg *Winnofil S* (ICI).
f. eg *Britomya Violet* (Croxton and Garry).
g. eg *Wingstay L* (Goodyear).
h. eg *Polygard* (Uniroyal).

Rheological properties

	1	2
Mooney viscosity, 100°C	39	50
Mooney scorch, 120°C, min	8	11
Monsanto *Rheometer*, 160°C		
M_{HR}, torque units	25	35
M_L, torque units	5	6.5
scorch, t_s, min	1.5	1.5
cure, $t_c'(95)$, min	2.6	3.3
cure, $t_c'(100)$, min	3.1	4.5
time to 5% reversion, min	4.2	12.5

7.2 (cont)

Vulcanizate properties, unaged

Injection moulded using *REP B43K* machine

extruder jacket temperature	85°C
injection chamber temperature	95°C
compound injection temperature	135°C

Formulation	1	2
Cure time at 160°C, min	3.0	4.0
Hardness, IRHD	53	75
Density, Mg/m^3	1.39	1.50
Resilience, Lupke, %	70	60
Tensile properties		
M100, MPa	1.3	3.3
M300, MPa	4.0	6.9
TS, MPa	10.5	11.5
EB, %	500	455
Tear, ISO trouser		
23°C, median, kN/m	18.1	
high/low ratio	1.2	
100°C, median, kN/m	11	
high/low ratio	1.3	
Compression set, %		
3 days at 23°C	11	14
1 day at 70°C	35	49

7.2 (cont)

Environmental ageing data

Formulation	1	2
Air-oven ageing for 7 days at 70°C		
change in hardness, IRHD	−1	
change in M100, %	+4	+40
change in M300, %	+10	+6
change in TS, %	−4	−18
change in EB, %	0	−20
Air-oven ageing for 14 days at 70°C		
change in hardness, IRHD	−2	
change in M100, %	+2	
change in M300, %	+11	
change in TS, %	−22	
change in EB, %	−10	
Air-oven ageing for 1 day at 100°C		
change in hardness, IRHD	−1	
change in M100, %	−17	
change in M300, %	−6	
change in TS, %	−14	
change in EB, %	0	

7.3 Heavy-duty boot soles **80–90 IRHD**

High-quality formulations for injection moulding

Similar formulations have been successfully injection-compression moulded on a 10-station *Desma 905* machine. The formulations meet physical property requirements of ISO 2023 for lined industrial rubber footwear.

Formulation

	1	2
SMR CV	100	100
High-styrene resin[a]		20
N326, HAF-LS black	80	75
Mineral rubber[b]	5	5
Zinc oxide	5	5
Stearic acid	2	2
Antioxidant[c]	1	1
Sulphur	2.0	2.5
MBS	1.5	1.0
TMTM	0.1	
TMTD		0.3

a. *eg Polysar SS250*, 50% styrene masterbatch (Polysar).
b. *eg MRX* (Anchor).
c. *eg Flectol H* (Monsanto).

Rheological properties

	1	2
Mooney viscosity, 100°C	48	64
Mooney scorch, 120°C, min	30	11.5
Monsanto *Rheometer*, 160°C		
M_{HR}, torque units	24	25
M_L, torque units	2.5	6
scorch, t_{s1}, min	3.3	2.1
cure, $t_c'(95)$, min	6.2	5.0

7.3 (cont)

Vulcanizate properties, unaged

Injection moulded using *REP B43K* machine

extruder jacket temperature	80°C
injection chamber temperature	95°C
compound injection temperature	130°C

Formulation	1	2
Cure time at 160°C, min	6	4
Hardness, IRHD	82	88
Hardness, Shore A	76	80
Hardness, Shore D	25	28
Density, Mg/m^3	1.19	1.17
Abrasion, DIN, mm^3	247	240
Tensile properties, radial[a]		
M100, MPa	4.2	4.5
M300, MPa	20	17
TS, MPa	21	20
EB, %	315	350
Tensile properties, tangential[a]		
M100, MPa	5.3	5.1
M300, MPa	23	19
TS, MPa	23.5	22
EB, %	305	350
Tear, ISO trouser, radial[a]		
23°C, median, kN/m	20	18
high/low ratio	2	1.7
100°C, median, kN/m	25	16
high/low ratio	1.5	1.8
Tear, ISO trouser, tangential[a]		
23°C, median, kN/m	15	13
high/low ratio	1.5	1.8
Ring fatigue life, 0–100% strain		
median, kc	68	62
high/low ratio	3.1	2.2
Compression set, %		
3 days at 23°C	12	21
1 day at 70°C	32	31

Environmental ageing data

Air-oven ageing for 7 days at 70°C,		
change in M100, %	+30	+18
change in TS, %	0	−8
change in EB, %	−24	−22

a. Measured along radial and tangential flow lines on a sheet produced in a centre-gated mould.

7.4 Shoe soles, resin and skim rubber formulations — 90 IRHD

For injection moulding: extended mixing times may be required in order to reduce the mix viscosity.

Formulation

	1	2	3
SMR GP	45		
Skim rubber[a]		45	100
High-styrene resin[b]	55	55	
Aluminium silicate[c]	60	60	50
Zinc oxide	5	5	5
Stearic acid	2	2	2
Antioxidant[d]	0.5	0.5	0.5
Antioxidant[e]	0.5	0.5	0.5
Sulphur	2.3	2	1.3
CBS	0.8	0.8	0.8
TMTD	0.1	0.1	0.1

a. *Dunlocrumb S(P20)* (Dunlop Estates).
b. *eg Polysar SS250*, 50% styrene masterbatch (Polysar).
c. *eg Silteg AS7* (Degussa).
d. *eg Wingstay L* (Goodyear).
e. *eg Polygard* (Uniroyal).

Rheological properties

	1	2	3
Mooney viscosity, 100°C	96	110	92
Mooney scorch, 120°C, min	24	18	15
Monsanto *Rheometer*, 160°C			
M_{HR}, torque units	38	37	35
M_L, torque units	10	10	10
scorch, t_{s1}, min	2.7	2.1	1.6
cure, $t_c'(95)$, min	6.2	6.2	4.6
cure, $t_c'(100)$, min	10	10	7.5
time to 5% reversion, min	>30	>30	18

7.4 (cont)

Vulcanizate properties, unaged

Injection moulded using *REP B43K* machine

extruder jacket temperature	90°C
injection chamber temperature	95°C
compound injection temperature	130–135°C

Formulation	1	2	3
Cure time at 160°C, min	5	4	4
Hardness, IRHD	92	93	89
Density, Mg/m^3	1.24	1.25	1.2
Resilience, Lupke, %	43	58	40
Abrasion, DIN, mm^3	worn away	490	400
Tensile properties, radial[a]			
M100, MPa	5.0	4.7	2.2
M300, MPa	9.2	8.2	6.6
TS, MPa	10.5	9.5	14.5
EB, %	350	355	495
Tensile properties, tangential[a]			
M100, MPa	5.6	5.6	2.5
M300, MPa	10.5	10.0	7.7
TS, MPa	11.5	10.5	16.0
EB, %	345	335	515
Tear, ISO trouser radial[a]			
23°C, median, kN/m	8.6	10	24
high/low ratio	1.3	1.3	1.2
100°C median, kN/m	7.6	11	13
high/low ratio	1.7	1.4	1.4
Tear, ISO trouser tangential[a]			
23°C, median, kN/m	7.2	8.7	32
high/low ratio	1.1	1.2	1.2
Ring fatigue life, 0–100% strain			
median, kc	22	23	40
high/low ratio	7.1	2.8	1.4
Compression set, %			
3 days at 23°C	35	40	21

a. Measured along radial and tangential flow lines on a sheet produced in a centre-gated mould.

7.4 (cont)

Environmental ageing data

Formulation	1	2	3
Air-oven ageing for 7 days at 70°C			
change in hardness, IRHD	−2	−3	+2
change in M100, %	+13	+26	+23
change in M300, %	+7		+31
change in TS, %	0	−2	−5
change in EB, %	0	−30	−9

7.5 Transparent shoe soles — 60–70 IRHD

Precipitated silica is generally used for abrasion-resistant transparent shoe soles. Magnesium silicate may be used to improve processing and ease of flow in moulding. Low levels of a light-coloured oil aid transparency.

Formulation

	1	2	3
Pale crepe[a]	100	100	100
Precipitated silica[b]	40	40	25
Magnesium carbonate[c]			30
Light oil[d]		10	5
Basic zinc carbonate[e]	0.8	0.8	0.8
Stearic acid	0.5		0.5
Zinc 2-ethylhexanoate[f]		0.8	
Diethylene glycol	1	1	1
Antioxidant[g]	0.5	0.5	0.5
Sulphur	3.5	2.5	2.5
TBTD	0.4	0.4	0.4
Hexamine[h]	0.5	0.5	0.4

a. Premasticated to 60 Mooney.
b. *eg Ultrasil VN3* (Degussa).
c. *eg* Light calcined magnesium carbonate.
d. *eg Fina Process Oil 2059* (Petrofina).
e. *eg Zinc Oxide Transparent* (Bayer).
f. *eg Zinc Octoate* (Tenneco), added to improve transparency.
g. *eg Permanax WSL* (Vulnax Int).
h. *eg Vulkacit H30* (Bayer).

Properties

	1	2	3
Mooney viscosity, 100°C	80	68	53
Mooney scorch, 120°C, min	12	5	5
Monsanto *Rheometer*, 160°C			
scorch, t_{s1}, min	1.7	1.5	1.3
cure, $t_c'(95)$, min	3.0	2.7	2.3
Cure: 6min at 160°C			
Hardness, IRHD	69	62	62
Tensile properties			
M100, MPa	1.9	1.4	1.9
M300, MPa	5.4	4.2	5.0
TS, MPa	24.5	22	21
EB, %	660	685	620
Compression set, %			
1 day at 70°C	53	48	59

Section 8 Hose

8.1 Automotive hose lining and cover
8.2 Covers, coloured
8.3 Covers, high-quality
8.4 Linings, general-purpose
8.5 Linings, grit blast
8.6 Linings, heat-resistant

For tubing see: Extrusions (Section 6)

8.1 Automotive hose lining and cover **70 IRHD**

The material property requirements of several motor manufacturers are met in applications where resistance to hydrocarbon oils is not required.

Formulation

	1	2
	Lining	Cover
SMR 20	100	100
N762, SRF-LM-NS black	65	90
Whiting	100	
Coated calcium carbonate[a]		100
Process oil[b]	20	30
Factice[c]		10
Zinc oxide	5	5
Stearic acid	2	2
Antioxidant, TMQ[d]	2	
Antidegradant, HPPD[e]		2
Wax blend[f]		3
DTDM	0.75	0.8
TMTD	1.5	2
MBTS	1.8	2

a. *eg Winnofil S* (ICI).
b. *eg Dutrex 729UK* (Shell).
c. *eg Whitbro 844* (Anchor).
d. *eg Flectol H* (Monsanto).
e. *eg Santoflex 13* (Monsanto).
f. *eg Sunproof Improved* (Uniroyal).

Rheological properties

Mooney viscosity, 100°C	45	50
Mooney scorch, 120°C, min	13	9
Monsanto *Rheometer*, 140°C		
M_{HR}, torque units	37.5	40
M_L, torque units	6.5	5
scorch, t_{s1}, min	6.8	4.7
cure, $t_c'(95)$, min	33	40
cure, $t_c'(100)$, min	60	60

Reference: Technical Information Sheet D120:1982.

8.1 (cont)

Vulcanizate properties, unaged

Formulation	1	2
	Lining	Cover
Cure time at 140°C, min	40	25
Hardness, IRHD	72	73
Density, Mg/m^3	1.41	1.37
MR100, MPa	1.83	2.88
Resilience, Lupke, %	53	51
Tensile properties		
M100, MPa	2.4	3.1
M300, MPa	9.2	
TS, MPa	13.0	10.2
EB, %	440	295
Tear, ISO trouser		
23°C, median, kN/m	25	6.9
high/low ratio	1.5	2.5
100°C, median, kN/m	20	1.7
high/low ratio	2.7	2.8
Ring fatigue life, 0–100% strain		
median, kc	23	14
high/low ratio	1.6	2.9
Compression set, %		
1 day at −26°C	36	43
1 day at 0°C	19	23
3 days at 23°C	18	15
1 day at 70°C	14	23
1 day at 100°C	33	50

8.1 (cont)

Environmental ageing data

Formulation	1	2
	Lining	Cover
Air-oven ageing for 3 days at 70°C		
change in hardness, IRHD	0	+5
change in M100, %	+10	+20
change in M300, %	+5	
change in TS, %	−5	−5
change in EB, %	−5	−15
Air-oven ageing for 7 days at 70°C		
change in hardness, IRHD	0	+8
change in M100, %	+30	+35
change in M300, %	+15	
change in TS, %	−5	−5
change in EB, %	−15	−20
Ozone resistance, 50pphm, 40°C, 20% strain		
time to first crack, days		7

8.2 Light-coloured hose covers — 50–70 IRHD

A wide range of filler loadings for hose covers is illustrated. The formulations meet the material requirements of many national and international standards.

Formulation

	1	2	3	4	5	6	7
SMR L	100	100	100	100	100	100	100
Whiting[a]	50	100	150			50	50
Soft clay[b]				50	100	50	100
Factice[c]	10			10			
Zinc oxide	5	5	5	5	5	5	5
Stearic acid	2	2	2	2	2	2	2
Antioxidant[d]	2	2	3	2	2	2	2
Titanium dioxide	5	5	5	5	5	5	5
Wax blend[e]	4	4	4	4	4	4	4
Sulphur	3	3	3	3	3	3	3
MBTS	1	1	1	1	1	1	1
TMTD	0.1	0.1	0.1	0.2	0.2	0.2	0.2
Pigment				as required			

a. *eg Snowcal 2ML* (Blue Circle Industries).
b. *eg Devolite* (English China Clays).
c. *eg Whitbro 844* (Anchor).
d. *eg Antioxidant 2246* (Cyanamid).
e. *eg Sunproof Improved* (Uniroyal).

Rheological properties

	1	2	3	4	5	6	7
Mooney viscosity, 100°C	42	40	40	35	38	32	37
Mooney scorch, 120°C, min	27	24	27	22	23	27	26
Monsanto *Rheometer*, 140°C							
M_{HR}, torque units	29	33.5	34.5	27.5	36	33.5	35.5
M_L, torque units	7.5	5.5	5.5	5.5	5.5	4	3
scorch, t_{s1}, min	8.5	11	12	6	7	10	8.3
cure, $t_c'(95)$, min	18	21	22	16	16	19	16
cure, $t_c'(100)$, min	25	27	30	20	22	25	22

Reference: Technical Information Sheet: D118:1982.

8.2 (cont)

Vulcanizate properties, unaged

Formulation	1	2	3	4	5	6	7
Cure time at 140°C, min	20	25	25	20	20	25	20
Hardness, IRHD	51	59	63	55	69	62	72
Density, Mg/m^3	1.21	1.37	1.48	1.20	1.39	1.38	1.50
MR100, MPa	0.87	1.02	1.05	1.47	2.35	1.52	1.97
Resilience, Lupke, %	80	75	73	80	76	77	67
Tensile properties							
M100, MPa	0.9	1.1	1.2	1.6	2.8	1.6	2.3
M300, MPa	1.93	1.9	2.0	3.3	5.3	3.2	4.2
TS, MPa	18	14	12	21	16	13	10
EB, %	710	660	650	655	560	560	535
Tear, ISO trouser							
23°C, median, kN/m	7	5.7	5.1	2.5	4	4.2	4.5
high/low ratio	1.3	1.8	1.3	1.4	1.2	1.7	1.1
100°C, median, kN/m	3	4	5	2	2.2	2.1	2
high/low ratio	1.4	1.5	1.3	1.3	1.4	1.5	1.6
Ring fatigue life, 0–100% strain							
median, kc	56	24	14	65	8	16	5.8
high/low ratio	1.9	1.6	1.7	2.5	5.1	1.4	1.4
Compression set, %							
1 day at −26°C	24	21	25	22	24	24	34
3 days at 23°C	7	8	9	6	8	8	10
1 day at 70°C	33	26	31	30	29	25	34
1 day at 100°C	62	48	54	60	54	48	61

8.2 (cont)

Environmental ageing data

Formulation	1	2	3	4	5	6	7
Air-oven ageing for 3 days at 70°C							
change in hardness, IRHD	+2	+3	+4	+2	+2	0	+2
change in M100, %	+30	+20	+30	+20	+20	+30	+20
change in M300, %	+40	+25	+20	+20	+10	+20	+15
change in TS, %	−5	−10	−5	−10	−10	0	−5
change in EB, %	−10	−10	−10	−10	−5	−5	−10
Air-oven ageing for 7 days at 70°C							
change in hardness, IRHD	+4	+3	+4	+4	+4	+3	+5
change in M100, %	+35	+35	+30	+30	+25	+25	+30
change in M300, %	+60	+30	+30	+30	+10	+20	+20
change in TS, %	−10	−10	−5	−10	−10	−5	−5
change in EB, %	−20	−10	−10	−10	−10	−10	−10
Volume swell in water							
3 days at 100°C, %	6.2	4.2	4.4	6.5	8.0	7.9	10.3
Low-temperature storage at −26°C							
time to 5 point IRHD rise, days	>28	>28	>28	>28	>28	>28	>28
Ozone resistance, 50pphm, 40°C, 20% strain							
time to first crack, days	>7	>7	>7	>7	>7	>7	>7

8.3 High-quality hose covers — 70 IRHD

General-purpose and heat-resistant formulations

High-quality formulations which meet the physical property requirements of a wide range of national and international standards.

Formulation

	1	2
	General-purpose	Heat-resistant
SMR 20	100	100
N550, FEF black	60	60
Process oil[a]	5	5
Zinc oxide	5	5
Stearic acid	2	2
Antidegradant, HPPD[b]	2	2
Wax blend[c]	2	2
Sulphur	2.5	1.2
TBBS	0.6	1
DTDM[d]		1

a. *eg Dutrex 729UK* (Shell).
b. *eg Santoflex 13* (Monsanto).
c. *eg Sunproof Improved* (Uniroyal).
d. *eg Sulfasan R* (Monsanto).

Rheological properties

	1	2
Mooney viscosity, 100°C	66	68
Mooney scorch, 120°C, min	12	23
Monsanto *Rheometer*, 140°C		
M_{hR}, torque units	42	43
M_L, torque units	10.5	10
scorch, t_{s1}, min	6.2	10.5
cure, $t_c'(95)$, min	25	24
cure, $t_c'(100)$, min	40	45
time to 5% reversion, min	*ca* 65	>70

Reference: Technical Information Sheet D117:1982.

8.3 (cont)

Vulcanizate properties, unaged

Formulation	1	2
	General-purpose	Heat-resistant
Cure: 45min at 140°C		
Hardness, IRHD	69	70
Density, Mg/m^3	1.14	1.14
MR100, MPa	3.28	3.88
Resilience, Lupke, %	64	64
Tensile properties		
M100, MPa	3.1	3.8
M300, MPa	16	17
TS, MPa	22	22
EB, %	400	410
Tear, ISO trouser		
23°C, median, kN/m	13	13
high/low ratio	1.5	1.9
100°C, median, kN/m	9.3	8.0
high/low ratio	1.6	1.4
Ring fatigue life, 0–100% strain		
median, kc	123	73
high/low ratio	2.2	1.6
Compression set, %		
1 day at −26°C	25	40
3 days at 23°C	8	8
1 day at 70°C	23	16
1 day at 100°C	49	44

8.3 (cont)

Environmental ageing data

Formulation	1	2
	General-purpose	Heat-resistant
Air-oven ageing for 7 days at 70°C		
change in hardness, IRHD	+3	+3
change in M100, %	+40	+45
change in M300, %	+10	+10
change in TS, %	−10	0
change in EB, %	−10	−10
Air-oven ageing for 3 days at 100°C		
change in hardness, IRHD	+2	+2
change in M100, %	+50	+45
change in TS, %	−45	−20
change in EB, %	−50	−25
Air-oven ageing for 7 days at 100°C		
change in hardness, IRHD		+2
change in M100, %		+45
change in TS, %		−40
change in EB, %		−30
Ozone resistance, 50pphm, 40°C, 20% strain		
time to first crack, days	>21	>21

8.4 General-purpose hose linings **65–70 IRHD**

A wide range of ingredients may be used. Vulcanizate quality decreases from Formulation 1 to 4. Wax may be added to improve the surface finish.

Formulation

	1	2	3	4
SMR 20	100	100	100	100
N550, FEF black	20		50	80
N330, HAF black		10		
Hard clay[a]	60	50		
Whiting		50	100	150
Reclaim[b]				100
Process oil[c]	5	5	5	30
Factice[d]	5	5	10	
Mineral rubber[e]			20	
Zinc oxide	5	5	5	5
Stearic acid	2	2	2	2
Antioxidant, TMQ[f]	2	2	2	3
Antioxidant, IPPD[g]				2
Sulphur	2.5	2.5	3	4
CBS	0.6	0.6		
MBTS			1	1.2
DPG			0.1	

a. *eg Stockalite* (English China Clays).
b. *eg Grade 411* reclaim (Rubber Regenerating).
c. *eg* High viscosity aromatic oil, *Dutrex729UK* (Shell).
d. *eg Whitbro 844* (Anchor).
e. *eg* Mineral rubber *MRX* (Rubber Regenerating).
f. *eg Flectol H* (Monsanto).
g. *eg Permanax IPPD* (Vulnax Int).

Rheological properties

	1	2	3	4
Mooney viscosity, 100°C	51	57	49	35
Mooney scorch, 120°C, min	31	34	18	21
Monsanto *Rheometer*, 140°C				
M_{HR}, torque units	33.5	36	40.5	21.5
M_L, torque units	9.5	10.5	9	5
scorch, t_{s1}, min	11.5	13	6	7.2
cure, $t_c'(95)$, min	31	33	24	31
cure, $t_c'(100)$, min	45	45	35	45

Reference: Technical Information Sheet D104:1982.

8.4 (cont)

Vulcanizate properties, unaged

Formulation	1	2	3	4
Cure time at 140°C, min	35	35	30	30
Hardness, IRHD	65	65	71	69
Density, Mg/m^3	1.26	1.37	1.39	1.42
MR100, MPa	2.15	1.73	1.60	1.38
Resilience, Lupke, %	72	72	47	33
Tensile properties				
M100, MPa	2.5	2.0	2.1	2.0
M300, MPa	8.3	5.8	5.6	5.3
TS, MPa	20	16	10	7.3
EB, %	515	515	490	400
Tear, ISO trouser				
23°C, median, kN/m	4.5	4.3	3	2
high/low ratio	1.3	1.4	1.4	2.3
100°C, median, kN/m	6.2	8	1.9	1.8
high/low ratio	3.6	1.5	1.2	1.4
Ring fatigue life, 0–100% strain				
median, kc	26	14	17	24
high/low ratio	2.1	2	1.4	1.6
Compression set, %				
1 day at −26°C	18	22	26	47
1 day at 0°C	6	7	9	23
3 days at 23°C	8	7	10	15
1 day at 70°C	48	48	37	49

8.4 (cont)

Environmental ageing data

Formulation	1	2	3	4
Air-oven ageing for 3 days at 70°C				
change in hardness, IRHD	+2	+4	+4	+4
change in M100, %	+35	+35	+15	+40
change in M300, %	+25	+25	+10	+30
change in TS, %	0	−10	−10	+10
change in EB, %	−10	−10	−10	−10
Air-oven ageing for 7 days at 70°C				
change in hardness, IRHD	+3	+4	+5	+7
change in M100, %	+40	+35	+40	+60
change in M300, %	+30	+25	+30	+35
change in TS, %	0	−10	−5	0
change in EB, %	−10	−10	−15	−20
Air-oven ageing for 3 days at 100°C				
change in hardness, IRHD	−3	−3	+3	+6
change in M100, %	+40	+30	+40	+60
change in M300, %	+15	+15		
change in TS, %	−30	−30	−40	−25
change in EB, %	−20	−20	−40	−40

8.5 Grit blast hose linings

40–65 IRHD

Unfilled natural rubber gives excellent resistance to abrasion and tearing in grit blast hose liners. The carbon black-filled formulation reduces the possibility of build-up of static electricity. The formulations meet a number of national and international standards.

Formulation

	1	2	3
SMR 20	100		100
SP 20[a]		100	
N660, GPF black			15
N220, ISAF black			30
Factice[b]	25		
Process oil[c]			10
Zinc oxide	5	5	5
Stearic acid	2	2	2
Antioxidant, TMQ[d]	2	2	2
Sulphur	3	3	2.5
CBS	0.6	0.4	0.6

a. Superior processing rubber.
b. *eg Whitbro 844* (Anchor).
c. *eg Dutrex 729UK* (Shell).
d. *eg Flectol H* (Monsanto).

Rheological properties

Mooney viscosity, 100°C	25	44	50
Mooney scorch, 120°C, min	18	19	28
Monsanto *Rheometer*, 140°C			
M_{HR}, torque units	22	24.5	35
M_L, torque units	6	8	7
scorch, t_{s1}, min	7.2	7.2	11
cure, $t_c'(95)$, min	27	28	29
cure, $t_c'(100)$, min	45	45	40

Reference: Technical Information Sheet D105:1982.

8.5 (cont)

Vulcanizate properties, unaged

Formulation	1	2	3
Cure: 30min at 140°C			
Hardness, IRHD	42	45	67
Density, Mg/m^3	0.99	0.97	1.13
MR100, MPa	0.76	0.81	2.90
Resilience, Lupke, %	81	79	62
Tensile properties			
M100, MPa	0.7	0.8	1.7
M300, MPa	2.4	2.0	9.1
TS, MPa	23	24	24
EB, %	740	745	575
Tear, ISO trouser			
23°C, median, kN/m	5.8	8.3	28
high/low ratio	1.6	2	1.2
100°C, median, kN/m	3.2	3.9	17
high/low ratio	2	2.4	1.5
Ring fatigue life, 0–100% strain			
median, kc	122	190	100
high/low ratio	2.1	2.7	1.6
Compression set, %			
1 day at −26°C	23	11	17
3 days at 23°C	4	4	8
1 day at 70°C	58	38	35

8.5 (cont)

Environmental ageing data

Formulation	1	2	3
Air-oven ageing for 3 days at 70°C			
change in hardness, IRHD	+4	+3	+3
change in M100, %	+25	+15	+45
change in M300, %	+35	+25	+35
change in TS, %	0	+10	0
change in EB, %	−10	−10	−5
Air-oven ageing for 7 days at 70°C			
change in hardness, IRHD	+5	+6	+4
change in M100, %	+30	+15	+60
change in M300, %	+45	+25	+45
change in TS, %	−10	+5	0
change in EB, %	−15	−10	−15
Volume swell in water			
3 days at 100°C, %	13.2	6.2	

8.6 Heat-resistant hose linings **60–70 IRHD**

Designed for heat resistance and may be suitable for low pressure steam. The use of carbon black and several inorganic fillers as well as different heat-resistant cure systems are illustrated.

Formulation

	1	2	3	4	5	6
SMR 10	50	50	50	50	50	50
SBR 1500	50	50	50	50	50	50
N330, HAF black	10	20				
N550, FEF black			40	50	50	50
Hard clay[a]	50	50	20			
Whiting	50					
Process oil[b]	5	5	5	5	5	5
Reclaim	10	10	10			
Zinc oxide	10	10	10	10	10	10
Stearic acid	2	2	2	2	2	2
Antioxidant, TMQ[c]	2	2	2	2	2	2
Antioxidant, MBI[d]	2	2	2	2	2	2
Sulphur	0.25	0.25	0.25	0.25		
TBBS	2.1	2.1	2.1	2.1		
TMTD	1	1	1	1		3
MBD[e]					1.5	
CdEDC[f]					1.5	
Tellurium[g]						0.5

a. *eg Stockalite* (English China Clays).
b. *eg Dutrex 729UK* (Shell).
c. *eg Flectol H* (Monsanto).
d. *eg Vulkanox MB* (Bayer).
e. *eg Morfax* (Vanderbilt).
f. *eg Ethyl Cadmate* (Vanderbilt).
g. *eg Telloy* (Vanderbilt).

Rheological properties

	1	2	3	4	5	6
Mooney viscosity, 100°C	56	52	51	64	66	63
Mooney scorch, 120°C, min	37	32	35	29	13	11
Monsanto *Rheometer*, 140°C						
M_{HR}, torque units	35.5	32	33	40	35.5	37
M_L, torque units	11	11	10	11	11.5	11
scorch, t_{s1}, min	13	12	13	11	6	4.5
cure, $t_c'(95)$, min	45	40	40	45	40	40
cure, $t_c'(100)$, min	80	60	70	>60	>60	60

Reference: Technical Information Sheet D119:1982.

8.6 (cont)

Vulcanizate properties, unaged

Formulation	1	2	3	4	5	6
Cure time at 140°C, min	45	45	45	60	60	60
Hardness, IRHD	65	65	62	70	69	70
Density, Mg/m^3	1.40	1.27	1.20	1.17	1.17	1.17
MR100, MPa	1.54	1.83	1.69	2.54	2.06	2.37
Resilience, Lupke, %	60	58	58	59	59	60
Abrasion, DIN, mm^3	419	349	334	230	240	283
Tensile properties						
M100, MPa	1.9	2.1	1.9	2.7	2.2	2.8
M300, MPa	4.6	6.2	7.6	12	10	11
TS, MPa	11	18	17	18	17	16
EB, %	535	580	535	450	500	420
Tear, ISO trouser						
23°C, median, kN/m	5.9	8.1	9.5	9.2	10	6
100°C,median, kN/m	2	9.5	14	2.7	10	8
Ring fatigue life, 0–100% strain						
median, kc	25	71	73	46	66	68
high/low ratio	1.4	2.4	1.7	1.8	1.7	1.6
Compression set, %						
1 day at −26°C	40	49	41	47	65	71
3 days at 23°C	21	24	21	14	14	15
1 day at 70°C	31	30	22	15	16	14
1 day at 100°C	48	45	37	20	22	22
1 day at 125°C	57	57	41	28	33	33

8.6 (cont)

Environmental ageing data

Formulation	1	2	3	4	5	6
Air-oven ageing for 7 days at 70°C						
change in hardness, IRHD	+1	0	0	0	−1	0
change in M100, %	+25	+20	+25	+30	+5	+35
change in M300, %	+15	+15	+15	+20	+10	0
change in TS, %	+5	+5	+5	−10	0	+15
change in EB, %	−5	−5	−5	−5	−5	+10
Air-oven ageing for 3 days at 100°C						
change in hardness, IRHD	0	−2	0	0	−1	−1
change in M100, %	+10	+6	+15	+25	+10	+10
change in M300, %	0	+5	+5	+20	+10	+6
change in TS, %	−10	0	−5	+10	+5	+3
change in EB, %	−5	−5	−5	−5	0	−5
Air-oven ageing for 3 days at 125°C						
change in hardness, IRHD	+4	+3	+3	−2	−3	−1
change in M100, %	+20	+20	+25	+20	+25	+5
change in TS, %	−40	−60	−40	−20	−15	−5
change in EB, %	−30	−15	−30	−20	−20	−15
After steam-pan ageing for 2 days at 150°C						
change in hardness, IRHD	−14	−14	−12	−7	−7	−8
change in M100, %	−50	−50	−40	−25	−10	−30
change in TS, %	−25	−25	−20	−10	−5	−5
change in EB, %	+20	+10	+10	0	−5	0
Volume swell in water 3 days at 100°C, %	7.3	6.8	6.4	12.1	8.0	8.8

Section 9 Mouldings, hardness classified

9.1 Mouldings, 20–25 IRHD
9.2 Mouldings, 30 IRHD
9.3 Mouldings, 40–80 IRHD
9.4 Mouldings, 90–95 IRHD
9.5 Mouldings, 70–90 IRHD, reversion-resistant
9.6 Mouldings, 40–60 IRHD, meeting BS 1154 (Y series)
9.7 Mouldings, 40–80 IRHD, meeting BS 1154 (Z series)
9.8 Mouldings, 80–95 IRHD, light-coloured

Notes on Sections 9.9–14

9.9 Mouldings, 30–40 Shore A, meeting ASTM D2000
9.10 Mouldings, 50 Shore A, meeting ASTM D2000
9.11 Mouldings, 60 Shore A, meeting ASTM D2000
9.12 Mouldings, 70 Shore A, meeting ASTM D2000
9.13 Mouldings, 80 Shore A, meeting ASTM D2000
9.14 Mouldings, 90 Shore A, meeting ASTM D2000
9.15 Injection mouldings, 65 IRHD, silica-filled
9.16 Injection mouldings, 40–80 IRHD, soluble EV
9.17 Injection mouldings, 95 IRHD

See also: Engineering applications, Section 5
Mouldings, classified by application, Section 10.

9.1 Mouldings **20–25 IRHD**

The substantial amount of oil needed to reduce hardness to this level is conveniently added using OENR or PA 57. The latter increases mix viscosity. Carbon black may added as a pigment. The lightly-crosslinked formulation 1 is not recommended for use at low temperature.

Formulation

	1	2	3	4
Nominal hardness	20	20	25	25
OENR 75/25N[a]	100		100	50
PA 57[b]		80		50
Process oil[c]		20		
Zinc oxide	3	3	3	3
Stearic acid	1	1	1	1
Antioxidant[d]	1	1	1	1
Sulphur	1	0.5	1.5	1
CBS	0.2	0.1	0.3	0.2

a. Oil-extended natural rubber, 25% naphthenic oil.
b. Superior processing rubber.
c. *eg Fina Process Oil 2059* (Petrofina).
d. *eg* Amine or non-staining phenolic.

Properties

	1	2	3	4
Mooney viscosity, 100°C	11	17	11	17
Cure: 40min at 140°C				
Hardness, IRHD	17.5	18	24.5	24.5
Density, Mg/m³	0.94	0.94	0.94	0.94
MR100, MPa	0.22	0.25	0.32	0.33
Resilience, Dunlop, %	74	79	81	84
Tensile properties				
M100, MPa	0.25	0.25	0.4	0.4
M300, MPa	0.5	0.6	0.8	0.8
TS, MPa	10.9	4.8	15.8	13.8
EB, %	1050	725	850	850
Compression set, %				
3 days at 23°C	1	7	4	7
1 day at 70°C	54	49	36	39
Tear, ISO trouser				
23°C, median, kN/m	4.3	1.9	4.8	5.6

9.1 (cont)

Environmental ageing data[a]

Formulation	1	2	3	4
Air-oven ageing for 7 days at 70°C				
change in hardness, IRHD	+3	+3	+2	
change in M300, %	+13	+11	+12	
change in TS, %	+27	+6	−9	
change in EB, %	−11	−4	−6	
Low-temperature storage at −26°C				
time to				
5 point IRHD rise, days	2	>28	17	25
10 point IRHD rise, days	2	>28	22	>28

a. Using *Flectol H* (Monsanto) as antioxidant.

9.2 Mouldings

30 IRHD

The substantial amount of oil needed to reduce hardness to this level is conveniently added using OENR or PA 57. The latter increases mix viscosity. Carbon black may added as a pigment.

Formulation

	1	2	3
SMR CV	50		
PA 57[a]	50	50	
OENR 75/25N[b]		50	100
Zinc oxide	3	3	3
Stearic acid	1	1	1
Antioxidant, TMQ[c]	1	1	1
Sulphur	1	1.5	2
CBS	0.2	0.3	0.4

a. Superior processing rubber, 29% oil.
b. Oil extended natural rubber, 25% naphthenic oil.
c. *eg Flectol H* (Monsanto).

Properties

Mooney viscosity, 100°C	28	17	11
Cure: 40min at 140°C			
Hardness, IRHD	30	29	30
Density Mg/m³	0.94	0.94	0.94
MR100, MPa	0.41	0.44	0.43
Resilience, Dunlop, %	81	89	92
Tensile properties			
M100, MPa	0.45	0.45	0.5
M300, MPa	1.0	1.15	1.15
TS, MPa	19.5	16.5	17.0
EB, %	905	785	775
Compression set, %			
3 days at 23°C	9	6	4
1 day at 70°C	36	29	33
Tear, ISO trouser			
23°C, median, kN/m	8.7	5.1	6
Low-temperature storage at −26°C time, days to			
5 point IRHD rise, days	12	>28	>28
10 point IRHD rise, days	16	>28	>28

9.3 Mouldings **40–80 IRHD**

Suitable for good quality mouldings not requiring heat resistance for use at low temperatures. The protective system may be changed to meet particular requirements.

Formulation

	1	2	3	4	5	6	7
Nominal hardness	40	45	50	60	70	80	80
SMR GP	100	100	100	100	100	100	100
N660, GPF black	5	20	35	60	70	100	80
Light oil[a]	10	10	10	10	10	10	10
High-styrene resin[b]							15
Zinc oxide	5	5	5	5	5	5	5
Stearic acid	2	2	2	2	2	2	2
Antidegradant, IPPD[c]	2	2	2	2	2	2	2
Wax blend[d]	2	2	2	2	5	5	5
Sulphur	2.8	2.8	2.8	2.8	2.8	2.8	3.0
CBS	0.6	0.6	0.6	0.6	0.6	0.6	0.8
TMTD							0.1

a. *eg Fina Process Oil 2059* (Petrofina).
b. *eg Pliolite S6H*, 86% styrene (Goodyear).
c. *eg Permanax IPPD* (Vulnax).
d. *eg Sunproof Improved* (Uniroyal).

Rheological properties

	1	2	3	4	5	6	7
Mooney viscosity, 100°C	27	27	33	38	56	95	64
Mooney scorch, 120°C, min	36	30	29	29	16	7	17
Monsanto *Rheometer*, 150°C							
M_{HR}, torque units	20	22.5	27.5	35	22	29	25
M_L, torque units	3.5	3.5	4.2	5	6	8.5	5.5
scorch, t_{s1}, min	5	4.5	4.8	5	3.8	2.3	4.0
cure, $t_c'(95)$, min	15	13.5	14	15	13.5	11	10
cure, $t_c'(100)$, min	20	19	20	21	20	18	13
time to 5% reversion, min	28	29	30	31	32	20	20

Reference: Technical Information Sheet D43:1978.

9.3 (cont)

Vulcanizate properties, unaged

Formulation	1	2	3	4	5	6	7
Cure: 15min at 150°C							
Hardness, IRHD	41	46	52	62	68	81	80
Hardness, Shore A					65	79	78
Hardness, Shore D					20	28	27
Density, Mg/m³	0.97	1.03	1.07	1.13	1.14	1.21	1.18
MR100, MPa	0.77	0.93	1.36	2.00	3.09	5.19	4.30
Resilience, Lupke, %	85	80	79	74	65	51	53
Abrasion, DIN, mm³					215	234	250
Tensile properties							
M100, MPa	0.65	0.9	1.3	2.1	3.3	6.0	5.4
M300, MPa	1.9	3.5	6.8	11	15		17
TS, MPa	24	23	23	20	20	16	18
EB, %	740	670	590	480	400	240	325
Tear, ISO trouser							
23°C, median, kN/m	6.3	4.6	11	18.6	19	8.3	9.4
high/low ratio	1.5		1.4	1.2	1.3	3.5	6
100°C, median, kN/m	3	4.6	5	6	8	6.6	5.1
high/low ratio	2	2.2	1.8	5	2	1.3	1.5
Ring fatigue life, 0–100% strain							
median, kc	330	120	100	130	103	77	64
high/low ratio	3.5	1.6	1.4	1.2	2.6	1.5	1.8
Compression set, %							
1 day at −26°C	10	13	13	14	21	37	33
3 days at 23°C	4	7	5	5	6	7	15
1 day at 70°C	36	36	41	42	39	41	27
1 day at 100°C	50	51	52	55			

9.3 (cont)
Environmental ageing data

Formulation	1	2	3	4	5	6	7
Air-oven ageing for 3 days at 70°C							
change in hardness, IRHD	+2	+2	+2	+3	+4	+3	+2
change in M100, %	+20	+20	+20	+40	+18	+25	+21
change in M300, %	+30	+30	+20	+20	+11		
change in TS, %	0	0	0	0	−2	−6	−5
change in EB, %	−10	−5	−5	−10	−10	−17	−4
Air-oven ageing for 7 days at 70°C							
change in hardness, IRHD	+4	+5	+5	+6	+6	+6	+4
change in M100, %	+30	+20	+30	+50	+26	+24	−4
change in M300, %	+50	+40	+40	+20	+13		
change in TS, %	0	0	−5	0	−9	−2	−6
change in EB, %	−10	−10	−10	−15	−17	−4	−3
Volume swell in water							
3 days at 100°C, %	3.6	2.5	2.2	3.6	2.5	2.2	
Low-temperature storage at −26°C							
time to 5 point IRHD rise, days	>28	>28	>28	>28	>28	>28	>28
Ozone resistance, 50pphm, 40°C, 20% strain							
time to first crack, days	>10	>10	>10	>10	>5	>5	>5

9.4 Mouldings **90–95 IRHD**

Various resins are used to give high hardness.

Formulation

	1	2	3	4	5
SMR GP	100	100	85	100	100
N330, HAF black	110	80	80	80	80
Light oil[a]	10	10	10	10	10
Process aid[b]	5				
High-styrene resin[c]		15			
Heveaplus MG49[d]			30		
Phenol-formaldehyde resin[e]				20	30
Zinc oxide	5	5	5	5	5
Stearic acid	2	2	2	2	2
Antidegradant, IPPD[f]	2	2	2	2	
Wax blend[g]	3	3	3	3	3
Sulphur	2.8	3	2.8	2.8	2.8
TBBS	0.6	0.8	0.6	0.6	0.6
TMTD		0.1		0.1	0.1
Prevulcanization inhibitor[h]	0.4				

a. *eg Fina Process Oil 2059* (Petrofina).
b. *eg Struktol A60* (Schill and Seilacher).
c. *eg Pliolite S6H*, 86% styrene (Goodyear).
d. Natural rubber/polymethylmethacrylate graft copolymer.
e. *eg Cellobond J1113H* (BP Chemicals).
f. *eg Permanax IPPD* (Vulnax).
g. *eg Sunproof Improved* (Uniroyal).
h. *eg Santogard PVI* (Monsanto).

Rheological properties

	1	2	3	4	5
Mooney viscosity, 100°C	136	104	80	107	121
Mooney scorch, 120°C, min	8	12	17	7	6
Monsanto *Rheometer*, 150°C					
M_{HR}, torque units	56	39.5	38	47	56
M_L, torque units	19	8.5	10	13	14
scorch, t_{s1}, min	4.2	4.5	2.7	2.1	1.5
cure, $t_c'(95)$, min	15	14	13	15	19
cure, $t_c'(100)$, min	23	20	20	27	35
time to 5% reversion, min	35	40	33	55	>60

Reference: Technical Information Sheet D116:1982.

9.4 (cont)

Vulcanizate properties, unaged

Formulation	1	2	3	4	5
Cure time at 150°C, min	20	15	15	20	20
Hardness, IRHD	89	88	92	90	>95
Hardness, Shore A	87	84	89	86	92
Hardness, Shore D	36	31	36	31	40
Density, Mg/m^3	1.19	1.28	1.20	1.19	1.18
MR100, MPa		3.85	4.61	3.71	3.29
Abrasion, DIN, mm^3	280	230	280	300	320
Tensile properties					
M100, MPa	8.7	5.1	6.3	4.8	6.1
TS, MPa	15.5	19.0	17.0	16.5	15.0
EB, %	170	330	290	315	285
Tear, ISO trouser					
23°C, median, kN/m	16	21	23	32	9.7
high/low ratio	2.4	1.7	1.7	3.6	2.5
100°C, median, kN/m	3.9	25	21	16.4	26
high/low ratio	2.6	1.9	1.4	1.4	1.7
Ring fatigue life, 0–100% strain					
median, kc	72	290	340	120	200
high/low ratio	2.5	1.8	1.4	1.7	1.8
Compression set, %					
3 days at 23°C	14	25	21	19	32
1 day at 70°C	42	45	63	48	55

9.4 (cont)

Environmental ageing data

Formulation	1	2	3	4	5
Air-oven ageing for 3 days at 70°C					
change in hardness, IRHD	+2	+2	+3	+1	
change in M100, %	+20	+15	+30	+25	+60
change in TS, %	−5	−5	−2	0	0
change in EB, %	−20	−25	−20	−10	−10
Air-oven ageing for 7 days at 70°C					
change in hardness, IRHD	+4	+3	+2	+5	
change in M100, %	+30	+25	+40	+35	+25
change in TS, %	−10	−5	−5	−10	−20
change in EB, %	−25	−25	−35	−25	−40
Air-oven ageing for 3 days at 100°C					
change in hardness, IRHD	+4	+3	+2	+2	
change in M100, %		+40	+20	+35	+40
change in TS, %	−40	−40	−45	−25	−30
change in EB, %	−40	−55	−60	−40	−55
Ozone resistance, 50pphm, 40°C, 20% strain					
time to first crack, days	>7	>7	>7	>7	>7

9.5 Reversion-resistant mouldings **70–90 IRHD**

Semi-EV systems also give improved ageing resistance; see Section 9.7 for formulations of 40–80 IRHD.

Formulation

	1	2	3	4	5
Nominal hardness	70	80	90	90	90
SMR GP	100	100	100	100	100
N660, GPF black	80	100			
N330, HAF black			110	80	80
Light oil[a]	10	10	10	10	10
Process aid[b]			3	3	3
Zinc oxide	5	5	5	5	5
Stearic acid	2	2	1	1	1
Antidegradant, IPPD[c]	2	2	3	3	3
Wax blend[d]	2	3	5	5	5
Phenol-formaldehyde resin[e]				20	30
Sulphur	1.2	1.2	1.2	1.2	1.2
TBBS	2	2	2	2	2
TMTD	0.1	0.1	0.1	0.1	0.1
Prevulcanization inhibitor[f]		0.2	0.4	0.1	0.1

a. *eg Fina Process Oil 2059* (Petrofina).
b. *eg Struktol A60* (Schill and Seilacher).
c. *eg Permanax IPPD* (Vulnax).
d. *eg Sunproof Improved* (Uniroyal).
e. *eg Cellobond J1115H* (BP Chemicals).
f. *eg Santogard PVI* (Monsanto).

Rheological properties

	1	2	3	4	5
Mooney viscosity, 100°C	74	92	110	90	95
Mooney scorch, 120°C, min	16	15	14	12	12
Monsanto *Rheometer*, 150°C					
M_{HR}, torque units	41	49	58	56	58
M_L, torque units	9	12	21	15	16
scorch, t_{s1}, min	4.5	4.5	4.0	1.8	1.4
cure, $t_c'(95)$, min	8.5	9.2	8.2	7	7
cure, $t_c'(100)$, min	20	25	15	15	15
time to 5% reversion, min	>30	>30	>30	>30	30

9.5 (cont)

Vulcanizate properties, unaged

Formulation	1	2	3	4	5
Cure: 10min at 150°C					
Hardness, IRHD	69	77	87	90	92
Hardness, Shore A			88	90	92
Hardness, Shore D			35	30	35
Density, Mg/m^3	1.17	1.21	1.21	1.16	1.16
MR100, MPa	3.8	4.9			
Resilience, Lupke, %	63	57	36		
Abrasion, DIN, mm^3	226	236	245	295	310
Tensile properties					
M100, MPa	4.0	5.5	5.5	4.3	4.7
M300, MPa	16.5	17		13	12.6
TS, MPa	20.0	18.5	15.0	17.0	15.0
EB, %	375	310	210	400	350
Tear, ISO trouser					
23°C, median, kN/m	19.3	23	19	36	25
high/low ratio	2.2	3.2	1.9	1.4	2
100°C, median, kN/m	11	9.2	12	28	31
high/low ratio	1.6	2.9	1.8	1.3	1.4
Ring fatigue life, 0–100% strain					
median, kc	59	37	100	84	60
high/low ratio	1.5	3	1.2	1.8	2.2
Compression set, %					
3 days at 23°C	9	9	10	20	19
1 day at 70°C	24	30	26	36	41
Cure: 25min at 150°C					
Compression set, %					
3 days at 23°C	8	9	12	19	24
1 day at 70°C	16	16	21	35	40
1 day at 100°C	38	38	40	48	44

9.5 (cont)

Environmental ageing data

Formulation	1	2	3	4	5
Cure: 10min at 150°C					
Air-oven ageing for 7 days at 70°C					
change in hardness, IRHD	+4	+5	+4	+3	+2
change in M100, %	+25	+40	+35	+35	+16
change in TS, %	−5	−5	0	0	0
change in EB, %	−10	−23	−15	−20	−15
Air-oven ageing for 14 days at 70°C					
change in M100, %	+20	+37			
change in TS, %	−13	−11			
change in EB, %	−25	−30			
Air-oven ageing for 3 days at 100°C					
change in hardness, IRHD	+8	+5	+5	+5	+2
change in M100, %	+100	+75	+40	+40	+30
change in TS, %	−10	−15	−22	−16	−23
change in EB, %	−40	−40	−37	−40	−40
Ozone resistance, 50pphm, 40°C, 20% strain					
time to first crack days	4	4	>10	>10	>10
Cure: 25min at 150°C					
Air-oven ageing for 7 days at 70°C					
change in M100, %	+10	+25	+20	+50	+20
change in TS, %	−3	−10	−8	0	0
change in EB, %	−10	−20	−15	−28	−20

9.6 Mouldings meeting BS 1154(Y series) 40–60 IRHD

BS 1154 for high-quality natural rubber moulding or sheeting compounds is based primarily on the needs of British Government departments. The Y series may be reinforced with zinc oxide only; carbon black and mineral fillers are not permitted.

Formulation

	1	2	2
Grade	Y40	Y50	Y50
SMR L	100	100	100
Zinc oxide	5	100	200
Process oil[a]	5		
Stearic acid	2	2	2
Antioxidant[b]	2	2	2
Wax blend[c]	2	2	2
Sulphur	2	2	2
MBTS	1.5	1.5	1.5
TMTD	0.1	0.1	0.1

a. *eg Sunpar 2280* (Sun Oil).
b. *eg Antioxidant 2246* (Cyanamid).
c. *eg Sunproof Improved* (Uniroyal).

Rheological properties

Mooney viscosity, 100°C	43	44	47
Mooney scorch, 120°C, min	34	17	12
Monsanto *Rheometer*, 150°C			
M_{HR}, torque units	17.5	23.5	28.5
M_L, torque units	5	6	6
scorch, t_{s1}, min	6.5	5.3	4.0
cure, $t_c'(95)$, min	10.4	10	8
cure, $t_c'(100)$, min	12	13	10
time to 5% reversion, min	30	25	16

Reference: Technical Information Sheet D109:1982.

9.6 (cont)

Vulcanizate properties, unaged

Formulation	1	2	3
Grade	Y40	Y50	Y60
Cure time at 150°C, min	15	20	20
Hardness, IRHD	38	48	57
Density, Mg/m^3	0.97	1.50	2.00
MR100, MPa	0.66	0.94	1.32
Resilience, Lupke, %	87	77	71
Tensile properties			
M100, MPa	0.7	1.1	1.6
M300, MPa	1.6	2.7	3.7
TS, MPa	26.5	26.5	20
EB, %	800	720	635
Tear, ISO trouser			
23°C, median, kN/m	9.1	9.7	19
high/low ratio	1.5	1.1	1.3
100°C, median, kN/m	4.1	8.4	9.5
high/low ratio	1.3	1.8	1.4
Ring fatigue life, 0–100% strain			
median, kc	145	68	63
high/low ratio	2.5	1.4	2.7
Compression set, %			
1 day at −26°C	14	17	22
3 days at 23°C	12	13	16
1 day at 70°C	18	19	24

9.6 (cont)

Environmental ageing data

Formulation	1	2	3
Grade	Y40	Y50	Y60
Air-oven ageing for 7 days at 70°C			
change in hardness, IRHD	+5	+4	+3
change in M100, %	+22	+16	+17
change in M300, %	+44	+17	+6
change in TS, %	+3	−6	0
change in EB, %	−17	−11	−7
Air-oven ageing for 3 days at 100°C			
change in hardness, IRHD	+5	+4	+4
change in M100, %		+40	+30
change in TS, %		−60	−15
change in EB, %		−40	−17
Volume swell in water 3 days at 100°C, %	5.1	5.5	3.9
Low-temperature storage at −26°C time to			
5 point IRHD rise, days	21	14	7
10 point IRHD rise, days	>28	>28	28

9.7 Mouldings meeting BS 1154 (Z series) — 40–80 IRHD

BS 1154 for high quality natural rubber or sheeting compounds is based primarily on the needs of British Government Departments. The Z series may contain black and no other filler apart from zinc oxide.

Formulation

	1	2	3	4	5
Grade	Z40	Z50	Z60	Z70	Z80
SMR 10	100	100	100	100	100
N660, GPF black	1	20	40	65	85
Process oil[a]	5	5	5	5	5
Zinc oxide	5	5	5	5	5
Stearic acid	2	2	2	2	2
Antioxidant, TMQ[b]	2	2	2	2	2
Sulphur	2	2	2	2	2
CBS	0.6	0.8	0.8	0.8	0.8
TMTD	0.2	0.2	0.2	0.2	0.1

a. *eg Dutrex 729UK* (Shell).
b. *eg Flectol H* (Monsanto).

Rheological properties

Mooney viscosity, 100°C	36	35	37	48	61
Mooney scorch, 120°C, min	23	21	18	15	14
Monsanto *Rheometer*, 150°C					
M_{HR}, torque units	22	28	33	43.5	51
M_L, torque units	4.5	4	4.5	5.5	8
scorch, t_{s1}, min	3.8	4.0	3.1	2.5	2.5
cure, $t_c'(95)$, min	6.2	6.3	5.5	4.8	5.7
cure, $t_c'(100)$, min	9	10	7.5	7	9
time to 5% reversion, min	25	25	19	20	19

Reference: Technical Information Sheet D102:1982.

9.7 (cont)

Vulcanizate properties, unaged

Formulation	1	2	3	4	5
Grade	Z40	Z50	Z60	Z70	Z80
Cure: 10min at 150°C					
Hardness, IRHD	42	50	59	70	80
Density, Mg/m³	0.97	1.04	1.10	1.14	1.21
MR100, MPa	0.82	0.16	1.83	3.08	4.73
Resilience, Lupke, %	86	81	76	66	55
Abrasion, DIN, mm³			235	240	240
Tensile properties					
M100, MPa	0.79	1.1	1.7	3.9	5.3
M300, MPa	2.2	5.3	9.4	16	
TS, MPa	24.5	25	24	20	16
EB, %	680	600	540	375	235
Tear, ISO trouser					
23°C, median, kN/m	9	6.2	9.4	3.6	3.6
high/low ratio	1.5	1.3	1.2	1.1	1.1
100°C, median, kN/m	3	4.8	11	12	5.1
high/low ratio	1.8	2	1.7	1.8	2.5
Ring fatigue life, 0–100% strain					
median, kc	95	59	46	25	29
high/low ratio	1.8	1.4	2.6	1.9	1.9
Compression set, %					
1 day at −26°C	15	17	18	26	33
1 day at 0°C	6	8	9	9	9
3 days at 23°C	3	4	5	5	5
1 day at 70°C	27	19	20	18	19
1 day at 100°C	45	44	43	43	47

9.7 (cont)

Environmental ageing data

Formulation	1	2	3	4	5
Grade	Z40	Z50	Z60	Z70	Z80
Air-oven ageing for 7 days at 70°C					
change in hardness, IRHD	+5	+4	+4	+3	+5
change in M100, %	+10	+10	+20	+5	+20
change in M300, %	+20	+10	+15	+10	
change in TS, %	−5	0	−5	0	+10
change in EB, %	−10	0	−5	−10	−5
Air-oven ageing for 3 days at 100°C					
change in hardness, IRHD	+3	+3	+4	+3	+3
change in M100, %	+35	+20	+20	+20	+20
change in TS, %	−30	−40	−25	−20	−45
change in EB, %	−20	−25	−25	−30	−50
Low-temperature storage at −26°C time to 5 point IRHD rise, days	>28	>28	>28	>28	>28

9.8 Light-coloured mouldings

80–100 IRHD

High-styrene resin and inorganic fillers give high hardness without increase in mix viscosity. The semi-EV system gives improved resistance to compression set and ageing.

Formulation

	1	2	3	4	5	6	7	8	9
Nominal hardness	80	80	90	80	90	95	100	100	100
SMR L	100	100	100	100	100	100	100	100	100
High-styrene resin[a]	50	50	50	50	50	75	75	75	100
Coated calcium carbonate[b]	100								
Precipitated silica[c]		20							
Fine talc[d]			50						
Calcined clay[e]				50	100	50	75	100	50
Zinc oxide	5	5	5	5	5	5	5	5	5
Stearic acid	1	1	1	1	1	1	1	1	1
Triethanolamine		2							
Antioxidant[f]	2	2	2	2	2	2	2	2	2
Wax	2	2	2	2	2	2	2	2	2
Sulphur	1	1	1	1	1	1	1	1	1
CBS	2	2	2	2	2	2	2	2	2
TMTD	0.5	0.5	0.5	0.5	0.5	0.5	0.5	0.5	0.5

a. *eg Pliolite S6H*, 86% styrene (Goodyear).
b. *eg Winnofil S* (ICI).
c. *eg Hi-Sil 233* (PPG).
d. *eg Extra Steamic OOS* (Talcs de Luzenac).
e. *eg Pole Star 200R* (English China Clays).
f. *eg* Phenolic type.

Rheological properties

	1	2	3	4	5	6	7	8	9
Mooney viscosity, 100°C	41	40	31	40	46	42	43	47	42
Mooney scorch, 120°C, min	>60	28	>60	>60	54	>60	>60	>60	>60
Monsanto *Rheometer*, 150°C									
M_{HR}, torque units	21	17	16	18.5	25	17	19	21	15
M_L, torque units	5	4	4	4	5	4	4.5	4.5	4.5
scorch, t_{s1}, min	12	5.2	13	12	8.3	10	10	10	12
cure, $t_c'(95)$, min	16	9	21	18	14	18	18	17	22
cure, $t_c'(100)$, min	25	18	30	25	23	30	30	30	30

Reference: Technical Information Sheet 103:1982.

9.8 (cont)

Vulcanizate properties, unaged

Formulation	1	2	3	4	5	6	7	8	9
Cure: 30min at 150°C									
Hardness, IRHD	79	79	87	84	91	97	98	98	99
Hardness, Shore A	80	78	86	85	90	94	96	97	98
Hardness, Shore D	28	30	30	30	35	44	45	48	50
Density, Mg/m^3	1.28	1.04	1.15	1.14	1.29	1.14	1.20	1.26	1.13
Tensile properties									
M100, MPa	3.2	5.6	5.7	4.4	6.3	7.8	7.5	8.1	9.5
M300, MPa	8.9	12.0	12.0	11.0	11.5	12.5	12.0	12.0	13.0
TS, MPa	13.0	19.5	16.5	16.0	13.0	15.0	13.0	12.5	14.0
EB, %	405	450	395	410	395	380	345	300	355
Compression set, %									
1 day at 70°C	30	37	36	31	22	21	16	18	26
Volume swell in water									
3 days at 100°C, %	6.4	14	4.5	3.6	5.0	4.9	6.8	5.4	5.7

Environmental ageing data

	6	7	8	9
Air-oven ageing for 7 days at 70°C,				
change in M100, %	+4	0	0	−10
change in TS, %	−3	0	−2	+3
change in EB, %	0	−4	−4	+2

Notes on Sections 9.9 to 9.14

The formulations meet several grade requirements for AA materials in ASTM D2000, the classification system for rubbers in automotive applications. Each formulation has a line call-out code which consists of:

- ⋆ the prefix letter M, denoting SI units
- ⋆ grade number
- ⋆ the material designation AA, which signifies that heat resistance is tested at 70°C and that there is no oil resistance requirement
- ⋆ a three-digit number, the first digit indicating the hardness range, the others the tensile strength. Thus 717 indicates hardness of 70±5 Shore A and tensile strength of 17MPa minimum.
- ⋆ one or more combinations of suffix letters and numbers representing the supplementary requirements appropriate to the grade number. Thus A13 indicates the additional ageing requirement of 70h at 70°C, and B13 a maximum 25% compression set requirement after 22h at 70°C.

For complete information consult ASTM D2000.

The formulations given will require adjustment to meet particular ageing or ozone resistance requirements.

9.9 Mouldings meeting ASTM D2000, AA materials — 30–40 Shore A

In these soft formulations, SP/PA rubbers raise mix viscosity and improve overall processing. The mixes may also be suitable for extrusion.

Formulation

	1	2	3	4	5	6	7	8	9
Nominal hardness	30	30	30	40	40	40	40	40	40
ASTM D2000 classification	M4AA 307 A13	M4AA 310 A13	M4AA 314 A13	M4AA 407 A13 B13	M4AA 410 A13 B13	M4AA 410 A13 B13	M4AA 414 A13 B13	M4AA 414 A13	M4AA 417 A13 B13
RSS1	50	50	50	50				50	
SP RSS[a]					100	100	100		100
PA 80[a]	50	50	50	50				50	
N330, HAF black	1	1	1	1	1	1	1	1	1
Whiting	75	50		125	100	75	50	25	25
Process oil[b]	30	20	5	40	30	20	10	10	5
Zinc oxide	5	5	5	5	5	5	5	5	5
Stearic acid	1	1	1	1	1	1	1	1	1
Antioxidant, TMQ[c]	1	1	1		1	1	1	1	1
Sulphur	2	2	2	1.2	1.5	1.5	1.5	2	1.5
MBT	1	1	1					1	
MBTS				1.2	1.5	1.5	1.5		1.5
TMTM				0.12	0.15	0.15	0.15		0.15

a. Superior processing rubber.
b. *eg Dutrex 729UK* (Shell).
c. *eg Flectol H* (Monsanto).

Properties

	1	2	3	4	5	6	7	8	9
Mooney viscosity, 100°C	39	43	50	30	45	53	60	46	53
Mooney scorch, 120°C, min	7	6	5	22	29	27	26	5	28
Cure temperature, °C	140	140	140	140	150	150	150	140	150
Cure time, min	30	30	30	25	20	20	20	30	20
Hardness, IRHD	38	39	37	42	44	46	47	40	44
Hardness, Shore A	34	35	35	40	39	42	42	36	40
Tensile properties									
TS, MPa	10.0	13.0	19.5	8.3	11.0	14.0	17.5	17.5	21.0
EB, %	705	740	775	625	680	715	660	765	685
Compression set, % 1 day at 70°C	39	34	26	22	12	11	11	30	11

9.9 (cont)

Environmental ageing data

Formulation	1	2	3	4	5	6	7	8	9
Air-oven ageing for 3 days at 70°C									
change in hardness, Shore A	+7	+6	+2	+3	+2	+2	+2	+4	+2
change in TS, %	+16	+14	+8	−1	+4	−1	−2	+6	+4
change in EB, %	−5	−5	−5	−7	−4	−9	0	−5	−4
Air-oven ageing for 7 days at 70°C									
change in hardness, Shore A	+8	+6	+3	+3	+2	+2	+2	+5	+1
change in TS, %	+20	+3	+12	−7	−3	0	−2	+7	0
change in EB, %	−8	−12	−6	−9	−9	−12	−3	−10	−4

9.10 Mouldings meeting ASTM D2000, AA materials — 50 Shore A

SP rubbers improve processing. The mixes may also be suitable for extrusion.

Formulation

	1	2	3	4	5	6
ASTM D2000 classification	M2AA 503 A13	M2AA 507 A13	M4AA 510 A13	M4AA 510 A13	M4AA 514 A13 B13	M4AA 521 A13 B13
SP RSS[a]	100	100	100	100		
RSS1					100	100
N330, HAF black	2	2	2	2	2	15
Whiting	130	105	85	60	60	40
Soft clay[b]	60	50	35	25	25	
Process oil[c]	40	30	20	10	5	5
Brown factice	10					
Zinc oxide	5	5	5	5	10	10
Stearic acid	1	1	1	1	1	1
Antioxidant, TMQ[d]					1	1
Sulphur	1.5	1.5	1.5	1.5	1.5	1.5
MBTS	1	1	1	1	1	1
TMTM	0.2	0.2	0.2	0.2	0.2	0.2

a. Superior processing rubber.
b. *eg Devolite* (English China Clays).
c. *eg Dutrex 729UK* (Shell).
d. *eg Flectol H* (Monsanto).

Properties

	1	2	3	4	5	6
Mooney viscosity, 100°C	33	43	49	51	48	49
Mooney scorch, 120°C, min	18	23	21	19	23	15
Cure time at 140°C, min	15	15	15	15	30	30
Hardness, Shore A	50	53	52	53	54	51
Hardness, IRHD	52	52	55	55	57	55
Tensile properties						
TS, MPa	6.5	8.5	11.0	14.0	17.5	22.5
EB, %	550	560	575	595	580	570
Compression set, %						
1 day at 70°C	32	25	24	23	20	14

9.10 (cont)

Environmental ageing data

Formulations	1	2	3	4	5	6
Air-oven ageing for 3 days at 70°C						
change in hardness, Shore A	+5	+4	+5	+4	+2	+1
change in TS, %	−1	+7	−9	−5	−12	−8
change in EB, %	−4	−4	−6	−6	−3	−4
Air-oven ageing for 7 days at 70°C						
change in hardness, Shore A	+8	+8	+6	+6	+2	+1
change in TS, %	−9	0	−10	−12	−26	−16
change in EB, %	−7	−7	−4	−13	−9	−7

9.11 Mouldings meeting ASTM D2000, AA materials **60 Shore A**

SP rubbers improve processing and shaping. The mixes may also be suitable for extrusion.

Formulation

	1	2	3	4	5	6	7	8	9	10
ASTM D2000 classification	M2AA 603 A13	M2AA 603 A13	M2AA 606 A13	M2AA 607 A13	M2AA 608 A13	M2AA 608 A13	M4AA 614 A13	M4AA 617 A13	M4AA 617 A13	M4AA 624 A13
RSS1	100		100	100			100	100	100	100
SP RSS[a]		100			100	100				
N330, HAF black	2	2	2	2	2	2	10	15	20	25
Whiting	150	130	125	100	90	75	50	25	25	
Soft clay[b]	150	60	125	100	40	35	50	25		
Process oil[c]	50	30	40	30	20	15	20	10	5	5
Brown factice		10								
Zinc oxide	5	5	5	5	5	5	5	10	10	10
Stearic acid	1	1	1	1	1	1	1	1	1	1
Antioxidant, TMQ[d]	1		1	1			1	1	1	1
Sulphur	3	1.5	3	3	1.5	1.5	3	3	3	3
MBTS	1	1	1	1	1	1	1	1	1	1
DPG	0.2		0.2	0.2			0.2	0.2	0.2	0.2
TMTM		0.2			0.2	0.2				

a. Superior processing rubber.
b. *eg Devolite* (English China Clays).
c. *eg Dutrex 729UK* (Shell).
d. *eg Flectol H* (Monsanto).

Properties

	1	2	3	4	5	6	7	8	9	10
Mooney viscosity, 100°C	37	50	39	45	51	55	45	49	55	55
Mooney scorch, 120°C, min	19	14	21	18	18	16	10	8	7	7
Cure time at 140°C, min	30	20	30	30	20	20	20	20	20	20
Hardness, Shore A	56	57	57	60	57	56	56	57	57	56
Hardness, IRHD	59	60	60	63	60	59	59	61	61	60
Tensile properties										
TS, MPa	5.2	6.2	7.2	8.1	9.7	10.5	15.0	19.0	21.5	29.0
EB, %	370	525	460	475	550	550	570	530	510	575
Compression set, % 1 day at 70°C	43	29	32	29	22	19	36	31	28	28

9.11 (cont)

Environmental ageing data

	1	2	3	4	5	6	7	8	9	10
Air-oven ageing for 3 days at 70°C,										
change in hardness,										
Shore A	+8	+5	+8	+5	+4	+4	+4	+5	+4	+4
change in TS, %	−2	−8	0	+1	−6	+1	+4	−2	−8	−5
change in EB, %	+7	−7	0	−4	−9	−6	−6	−9	−4	−1
Air-oven ageing for 7 days at 70°C										
change in hardness,										
Shore A	+7	+5	+8	+5	+4	+4	+3	+3	+3	+2
change in TS, %	−2	−11	−12	0	−10	−13	−1	−6	−7	−10
change in EB, %	−12	−12	−1	−5	−9	−10	−11	−11	−12	−18

9.12 Mouldings meeting ASTM D2000, AA materials — 70 Shore A

Formulation

	1	2	3	4	5	6	7	8	9	10
ASTM D4000 classification	M2AA 703 A13	M2AA 703 A13	M2AA 703 A13	M2AA 706 A13	M2AA 706 A13	M2AA 707 A13	M2AA 710 A13	M2AA 714 A13	M2AA 717 A13 B13	M2AA 721 A13 B13
RSS1	100	100	100	100	100	100	100	100	100	100
N330, HAF black	20	30	25	40	30	35	40	45	60	50
Whiting	300	300	250	200	200	150	100	50	10	
Process oil[a]	30	30	25	20	20	15	10	5	10	2
Zinc oxide	5	5	5	5	5	5	5	5	5	5
Stearic acid	1	2	1	2	1	1	1	1	2	2
Sulphur	3	2.5	3	2.5	3	3	3	3	2.5	2.5
MBTS	1.5		1.5		1.5	1.5	1.5	1.5		
CBS		1		1					1	1
DPG	0.1		0.1		0.1	0.1	0.1	0.1		

a. *eg Dutrex 729UK* (Shell).

Properties

	1	2	3	4	5	6	7	8	9	10
Mooney viscosity, 100°C	48	49	48	46	52	54	60	69	81	74
Mooney scorch, 120°C, min	10	23	11	22	10	9	7	7	16	17
Cure: 30min at 140°C										
Hardness, Shore A	70	70	71	74	71	71	72	70	75	72
Hardness, IRHD	73	73	73	77	72	73	74	72	79	76
Tensile properties										
TS, MPa	4.7	5.0	5.5	6.7	7.2	8.4	11.0	16.0	20.5	24.5
EB, %	405	400	390	330	390	365	345	365	340	350
Compression set, % 1 day at 70°C	34	44	28	41	25	26	23	25	21	19

Environmental ageing data

	1	2	3	4	5	6	7	8	9	10
Air-oven ageing for 3 days at 70°C										
change in hardness, Shore A	+5	+3	+4	+4	+4	+4	+2	+2	+2	+2
change in TS, %	−4	−4	−2	−6	−11	−3	−4	−7	−7	−9
change in EB, %	−14	−7	−10	−5	−12	−7	−7	−11	−24	−21
Air-oven ageing for 7 days at 70°C										
change in hardness, Shore A	+4	+4	+4	+3	+4	+3	+2	+2	+2	+1
change in TS, %	0	−27	+4	−26	0	+1	+1	−9	−13	−17
change in EB, %	−19	−14	−20	−15	−14	−12	−14	−19	−18	−23

9.13 Mouldings meeting ASTM D2000, AA materials — 80 Shore A

Formulation

	1	2	3	4	5	6
ASTM D2000 classification	M2AA 803 A13	M2AA 807 A13	M2AA 807 A13	M2AA 810 A13	M2AA 817 A13	M2AA 817 A13
RSS1	100	100	100	100	100	100
N330, HAF black	40	45	50	55	60	60
Whiting	300	150	100	50	25	10
Process oil[a]	30	10	10	5	5	10
Zinc oxide	5	5	5	5	5	5
Stearic acid	2	2	2	2	2	2
Sulphur	2.5	2.5	2.5	2.5	2.5	2.5
CBS	1	1	1	1	1	1

a. *eg Dutrex 729UK* (Shell).

Properties

	1	2	3	4	5	6
Mooney viscosity, 100°C	57	74	68	81	91	81
Mooney scorch, 120°C, min	23	18	17	14	13	16
Cure: 30min at 140°C						
Hardness, Shore A	78	80	77	78	78	75
Hardness, IRHD	79	83	79	80	80	79
Tensile properties						
TS, MPa	4.8	9.3	10.3	13.5	18.0	20.5
EB, %	320	270	280	240	255	340
Compression set, % 1 day at 70°C	30	25	32	29	24	21

Environmental ageing data

	1	2	3	4	5	6
Air-oven ageing for 3 days at 70°C						
change in hardness, Shore A	+3	+2	+3	+1	+2	+2
change in TS, %	−6	−6	−2	−18	−18	−9
change in EB, %	−19	−11	−11	−12	−14	−21
Air-oven ageing for 7 days at 70°C						
change in hardness, Shore A	+4	+2	+3	+1	+2	+2
change in TS, %	−16	−13	−14	−26	−24	−13
change in EB, %	−17	−15	−18	−23	−23	−18

9.14 Mouldings meeting ASTM D2000, AA materials — 90 Shore A

Formulation

	1	2	3
ASTM D2000 classification	M2AA 903 A13	M2AA 907 A13	M2AA 910 A13
RSS1	70	70	70
High-styrene resin[a]	30	30	30
N330, HAF black	35	45	55
Whiting	250	150	50
Process oil[b]	20	10	5
Zinc oxide	5	5	5
Stearic acid	2	2	2
Sulphur	2.5	2.5	2.5
CBS	1	1	1

a. *eg Polysar SS250*, 50% styrene masterbatch (Polysar).
b. *eg Dutrex 729UK* (Shell).

Properties

	1	2	3
Mooney viscosity, 100°C	63	67	69
Mooney scorch, 120°C, min	36	32	28
Cure: 30min at 140°C			
Hardness, Shore A	89	90	90
Hardness, IRHD	92	92	92
Tensile properties			
TS, MPa	5.4	8.2	13.5
EB, %	290	245	225
Compression set, %			
1 day at 70°C	40	31	29

Environmental ageing data

	1	2	3
Air-oven ageing for 3 days at 70°C			
change in hardness, Shore A	+2	+2	+1
change in TS, %	−9	−12	−12
change in EB, %	−19	−26	−24
Air-oven ageing for 7 days at 70°C			
change in hardness, Shore A	+2	+2	+1
change in TS, %	−16	−10	−13
change in EB, %	−38	−26	−29

9.15 Silica-filled injection moulding formulations **60–70 IRHD**

Many vulcanization systems may be used for injection moulding silica-filled formulations. Precipitated silica gives very high tear strength but compression set is generally higher than obtained with carbon black-filled vulcanizates.

Formulation

	1	2	3	4	5
SMR CV	100	100	100	100	100
Precipitated silica[a]	40	40	40	40	40
Process aid[b]	4	4	4	2	4
Triethanolamine		1			
Diethylene glycol	2		2		
Silane coupling agent[c]				2	2.4
Titanium dioxide	5	5	5	5	5
Zinc oxide	5	5	5	5	5
Stearic acid	2	2	2	2	2
Antioxidant[d]	1	1	1		
Antioxidant[e]				1	1
Wax blend[f]	5	5	5	5	5
Sulphur	3	2.5	2	2	
MBTS	1	1			
MBS			1.2	1.2	
TMTM	0.3				
DOTG		0.8			
ZDBC			0.5	0.5	
DDTS[g]					3.0

a. *eg Ultrasil VN3* (Degussa).
b. *eg Struktol WB16* (Schill & Seilacher).
c. *eg Si 69* (Degussa).
d. *eg Wingstay L* (Goodyear).
e. *eg Vulkanox KSM* (Bayer).
f. *eg Sunproof Improved* (Uniroyal).
g. *eg Vulkacit J* (Bayer).

Rheological properties

	1	2	3	4	5
Mooney viscosity, 100°C	62	52	63	67	70
Mooney scorch, 120°C, min	9	11	14	23	17
Monsanto *Rheometer*, 180°C					
M_{HR}, torque units	33	34	32	32.5	30
M_L, torque units	10	6.5	9	10.5	10
scorch, t_{s1}, min	0.9	0.4	1.2	1.5	1.3
cure, $t_c'(95)$, min	1.8	2.5	2.0	2.5	3.7
cure, $t_c'(100)$, min	3.0	3.3	2.4	3.0	5.0
time to 5% reversion, min	4.5	5.1	3.9	6	10

9.15 (cont)

Vulcanizate properties, unaged

Injection moulded using *REP B43K* machine

extruder jacket temperature	80°C
injection chamber temperature	100°C
compound injection temperature	115–125°C

Formulation	1	2	3	4	5
Cure time at 180°C, min	1.0	1.5	1.25	1.5	4
Hardness, IRHD	70	69	71	70	60
Density, Mg/m^3	1.13	1.14	1.13	1.14	1.12
Resilience, Lupke[a], %	64	64	60	63	64
Abrasion, DIN, mm^3	280	278	234	242	303
Tensile properties, radial[b]					
M100, MPa	1.4	1.7	1.4	1.8	1.2
M300, MPa	3.3	4.6	3.5	6.2	4.7
TS, MPa	23	24.5	23.5	23.5	21.5
EB, %	725	650	700	640	645
Tensile properties, tangential[b]					
M100, MPa	1.6	1.9	1.6	2.1	1.3
M300, MPa	3.8	5.0	3.9	6.4	5.4
TS, MPa	25	25.5	26	24.5	20.5
EB, %	735	645	715	640	600
Tear, ISO trouser, radial[b]					
23°C, median, kN/m	34	29	40	25	29
high/low ratio	1.1	1.2	1.2	1.7	1.1
100°C, median, kN/m	15	17	13	16	>30[c]
high/low ratio	1.2	1.2	1.3	1.4	
Tear, ISO trouser, tangential[b]					
23°C, median, kN/m	24	26	29	37	26
high/low ratio	1.7	1.2	1.3	1.3	1.1
Ring fatigue life, 0–100% strain					
median, kc	115	74	63	114	64
high/low ratio	1.8	1.4	4.1	1.3	1.4
Compression set, %					
3 days at 23°C	20	21	29	18	18
1 day at 70°C	38	46	47	40	31

a. Lupke resilience test pieces cured 2min longer.
b. Measured along radial and tangential flow lines on a sheet produced in a centre-gated mould.
c. Sample slipped out of grips.

9.15 (cont)

Environmental ageing data

Formulation	1	2	3	4	5
Air-oven ageing for 7 days at 70°C					
change in hardness, IRHD	+4	+3	+5	+3	
change in M100, %	+37	+18	+45	+32	
change in M300, %	+70	+24	+75	+45	
change in TS, %	0	−10	−10	−15	
change in EB, %	−10	−6	−17	−18	
Air-oven ageing for 14 days at 70°C					
change in hardness, IRHD					
change in M100, %	+40	+18	+48	+24	−20
change in M300, %	+80	+35	+100	+38	−35
change in TS, %	−11	−15	−21	−30	−75
change in EB, %	−16	−11	−23	−25	−35
Volume swell in water					
3 days at 100°C, %	12	15	11	10	12
Ozone resistance, 50pphm, 40°C, 20% strain					
time to first crack, days	3	3	2	2	

9.16 Soluble EV formulations for injection moulding — 40–80 IRHD

Soluble EV systems give low compression set and good heat resistance.

Formulation

	1	2	3	4	5
Nominal hardness	40	50	60	70	80
SMR CV	100	100	100	100	100
N762, SRF-LM-NS black		30	60	100	120
Zinc oxide	5	5	5	5	5
Zinc 2-ethylhexanoate[a]	1	1	1	1	1
Antioxidant	1	1	1	1	1
Sulphur	0.7	0.7	0.7	0.7	0.7
MBS	1.7	1.7	1.7	1.7	1.7
TBTD	0.7	0.7	0.7	0.7	0.7

a. *eg Zinc Octoate* (Tenneco).

Rheological properties

	1	2	3	4	5
Mooney viscosity, 135°C	34	41	46	53	109
Moooney scorch, 135°C, min	12	7.5	6.5	5.8	6.1
Monsanto *Rheometer*					
test temperature, °C	190	190	180	180	180
scorch, t_{s1}, min	0.75	0.5	1.0	0.75	1.0
cure, $t_c'(95)$, min	1.85	1.6	2.35	1.85	2.6
time to 5% reversion, min	5.0	4.0	8.65	6.75	7.0

Vulcanizate properties, unaged

Injection moulded using *REP B43K* machine.

	1	2	3	4	5
Cure temperature, °C	190	190	180	180	180
Cure time, min	0.75	0.75	1.5	1.0	1.25
Hardness, IRHD	39	52	60	72	82
Density, Mg/m^3	0.97	1.07	1.16	1.25	1.28
MR100, MPa	0.64	1.08	1.69	4.04	5.14
Resilience, Dunlop, %	88	82	71	59	46
Tensile properties, radial[a]					
M300, MPa	1.4	5.4	10.3		
TS, MPa	17.5	23.5	18.5	16.5	14.5
EB, %	715	590	475	290	235

a. Measured along radial flow lines on a sheet produced in a centre-gated mould.

Reference: Technical Information Sheet D24:1977.

9.17 Hard, flexible injection mouldings **90 IRHD**

Blends of natural rubber and natural rubber/polymethyl methacrylate graft copolymers filled with carbon black and short fibres give materials that may be suitable for automative body components such as sight shields and bumpers.

Formulation

	1	2	3
SMR CV	70	70	70
Heveaplus MG49[a]	30	30	30
N326, HAF-LS black	70	50	50
Glass fibre[b]		25	
Cellulose fibre[c]			24
Bonding agent[d]			2.5
Zinc oxide	5	5	5
Stearic acid	2	2	2
Antioxidant[e]	1	1	1
Sulphur	2.5	2.5	2.5
CBS	0.5	0.5	0.5
Prevulcanization inhibitor[f]	1	0.6	0.6

a. Polymethyl methacrylate graft copolymer.
b. *eg Rubber Impregnated Chopped Strand* (Owens-Corning Fibreglass).
c. *eg Santoweb D* (Monsanto).
d. *eg Resimene 3520* (Monsanto).
e. *eg* Non-staining phenolic type if the component is to be painted.
f. *eg Santogard PVI* (Monsanto).

Rheological properties

	1	2	3
Mooney viscosity, 135°C	69	48	45
Mooney scorch, 135°C	14	23.5	19.5
Monsanto *Rheometer*, 180°C			
M_{HR}, torque units	43	50	47
M_L, torque units	9.5	10	9.5
scorch, t_{s1}, min	0.8	1.0	1.3
cure, $t_c'(95)$, min	4.3	3.9	5.0

Reference: Technical Information Sheet D95:1981.

9.17 (cont)

Vulcanizate properties, unaged

Injection moulded using *REP 43K* machine
extruder jacket temperature 110°C
injection chamber temperature 110°C

Formulation	1	2	3
Cure time at 180°C, min	2.5	2.5	4
Hardness, IRHD	90	89	91
Density, Mg/m^3	1.21	1.23	1.19
Resilience, Dunlop, %	38	43	44
Tensile properties,[a]			
TS, MPa	17.5	15.5	10.8
EB, %	280	290	230
Flexural modulus, MPa[a]	100	180	275

a. Measured along radial flow lines on a sheet produced in a centre-gated mould.

Section 10 Mouldings, classified by application

10.1 Food contact applications meeting BGA regulations
10.2 Milk liners
10.3 Hot water bottles, injection-moulded
10.4 Heating pad, *Novor* cured
10.5 Heat- and ozone-resistant blends
10.6 Heat-resistant rollers

For laboratory stoppers see: Tubing, laboratory (Section 6.10)

10.1 Food contact applications meeting BGA regulations **50 IRHD**

Recommendations of the German Bundesgesundheitsamt (BGA) for rubbers in long term contact with food are met. Applications include linings for storage tanks or bins. Formulations 1 and 2 give almost tasteless and odourless vulcanizates; formulations 3 and 4 give vulcanizates with improved heat resistance but with a distinct odour associated with zinc dithiocarbamate.

Formulation

	1	2	3	4
SMR L	100	100	100	100
Coated calcium carbonate[a]	60	50	70	60
Zinc oxide	5	5	5	5
Stearic acid	2	2	2	2
Antioxidant[b]	1	1	1	1
Sulphur (insoluble)	3	2.5		
TMTM	0.3	0.2		
ortho-Tolylbiguanide[c]		0.5		
TMTD			3	
DPTT[d]				3
Titanium dioxide		5		

a. *eg Winnofil S* (ICI).
b. *eg Permanax WSP* (Vulnax).
c. *eg Vulkacit 1000* (Bayer).
d. *eg Robac P25* (Robinson Brothers).

Rheological properties

	1	2	3	4
Mooney viscosity, 100°C	31	41	38	33
Mooney scorch, 120°C, min	15	9	11	9
Monsanto *Rheometer*, 160°C				
M_{HR}, torque units	24	27	24	23.5
M_L, torque units	4.5	5.5	5	4
scorch, t_{s1}, min	2.0	1.7	1.6	1.3
cure, $t_c'(95)$, min	5.1	6.5	13	2.8
cure, $t_c'(100)$, min	6.0	10	30	3.5
time to 5% reversion, min	7.7	15		9

Reference: Technical Information Sheet D107:1982. See also *NR Technology*, 1982, **13**, 21.

10.1 (cont)

Vulcanizate properties, unaged

Formulation	1	2	3	4
Cure time at 160°C, min	5	8	20	4
Hardness, IRHD	50	53	50	53
Density, Mg/m^3	1.24	1.22	1.27	1.19
MR100, MPa	0.805	1.01	0.80	0.85
Resilience, Lupke, %	73	79	71	76
Tensile properties				
M100, MPa	0.85	1.0	0.85	0.9
M300, MPa	1.8	2.8	2.2	2.0
TS, MPa	21	24	23	26
EB, %	795	710	725	750
Tear, ISO trouser				
23°C, median, kN/m	9.5	10	26	14.5
high/low ratio	1.9	1.6	1.4	1.3
100°C, median, kN/m	9.2	8.7	15	12
high/low ratio	1.6	1.6	1.7	1.6
Ring fatigue life, 0–100% strain				
median, kc	97	73	39	61
high/low ratio	1.4	1.3	1.2	1.5
Compression set, %				
1 day at −26°C	23	17	92	24
1 day at 0°C	8	6	8	8
3 days at 23°C	10	6	7	12
1 day at 70°C	27	26	12	20
1 day at 100°C	43	47	18	33

10.1 (cont)

Environmental ageing data

Formulation	1	2	3	4
Air-oven ageing for 3 days at 70°C				
change in hardness, IRHD	0	0	−2	−2
change in M100, %	+20	+20	0	+10
change in M300, %	+25	+10	+5	+10
change in TS, %	−20	−5	0	−10
change in EB, %	−15	−5	0	−10
Air-oven ageing for 7 days at 70°C				
change in hardness, IRHD	0	−1	−3	−3
change in M100, %	+25	+15	0	+15
change in M300, %	+30	+15	+5	+20
change in TS, %	−30	−15	−5	−20
change in EB, %	−30	−10	0	−15
Volume swell in water				
3 days at 100°C, %	4.4	3.1	2.3	2.4
BGA solvent extraction tests[a] 10 days at 40°C, amount extracted, mg/100cm²				
10% alcohol	27	13	22	16
water	45	3	4	3

a. BGA Category 1 limits are 50mg/100cm² in either solvent. Values were obtained from 2mm thick sheets.

10.2 Milk liners **50 IRHD**

Requirements of USA Food and Drugs Administration, Section 21 part 177.2600, for rubbers in contact with food are met. After minor modifications to plasticizer and antioxidant, the formulations should also meet German Bundesgesundheitsamt (BGA) requirements.

Formulation

	1	2	3
SMR CV	65	50	35
Acrylonitrile-isoprene copolymer[a]	35	50	
NBR[b]			35
SBR 1502			30
N330, HAF black	15	15	10
Plasticizer[c]	5	5	5
Zinc oxide	5	5	5
Stearic acid	2	2	2
Antioxidant[d]	1.5	1.5	1.5
Wax blend[e]	2	2	2
Sulphur	2.25	2.25	1.8
MBTS	0.45	0.45	0.45
TMTM	0.1	0.1	0.45

a. 33% acrylonitrile, *eg Krynac 833* (Polysar).
b. 38% acrylonitrile, *eg Breon 1041* (BP Chemicals).
c. *eg* Dioctyl phthalate.
d. *eg Permanax IPPD* (Vulnax).
e. *eg Sunproof Improved* (Uniroyal).

Rheological properties

	1	2	3
Mooney viscosity, 100°C	35	32	35
Mooney scorch, 120°C, min	19	20	18
Monsanto *Rheometer*, 160°C			
M_{HR}, torque units	28	28	30
M_L, torque units	5.5	5	5
scorch, t_{s1}, min	1.7	2.1	1.9
cure, $t_c'(95)$, min	4.0	4.7	6.5
cure, $t_c'(100)$, min	5.7	6.5	*ca* 20
time to 5% reversion, min	12	13	>30

10.2 (cont)

Vulcanizate properties, unaged

Formulation	1	2	3
Cure: 6min at 160°C			
Hardness, IRHD	51	51	52
Density, Mg/m^3	1.05	1.06	1.04
MR100, MPa	1.01	1.05	1.06
Resilience, Lupke, %	50	42	61
Tensile properties			
M100, MPa	1.0	1.1	1.0
M300, MPa	3.9	4.2	3.4
TS, MPa	21	22.5	14.5
EB, %	640	635	530
Ring fatigue life, 0–100% strain			
median, kc	135	88	83
high/low ratio	2.8	1.9	1.8
Compression set, %			
1 day at 70°C	31	36	22

Environmental ageing data

Air-oven ageing for 3 days at 100°C			
change in hardness, IRHD	+4	+5	+9
change in M100, %	+40	+30	+50
change in M300, %	+70	+60	+100
change in TS, %	−15	−20	−38
change in EB, %	−25	−25	−40
Volume swell, 1 day at 100°C			
butter oil, %	76	51	48
ASTM No 1 oil, %	53	30	31
ASTM No 3 oil, %	155	110	120

10.3 Injection-moulded hot water bottles **40–50 IRHD**

Injection-moulded test sheets cured at 180°C meet the physical property requirements of BS 1970:1961 (TS 13.7 MPa; EB 500% min; tension set 20% max). Natural rubber is eminently suited for this application because of its high tear strength at high temperatures.

Formulation

	1	2
SMR CV	100	
Pale crepe		100
Coated calcium carbonate[a]	60	40
Hard clay[b]		40
Precipitated whiting[c]	30	
Light oil[d]		1
Titanium dioxide	5	2
Zinc oxide	5	5
Stearic acid	1	0.5
Antioxidant[e]	1	1
Antioxidant[f]	1	1
Sulphur		2
DTDM	1	
TMTD	1.2	
TBTD	1.5	
MBTS	1.0	0.6
TMTM		0.2

a. *eg Winnofil S* (ICI).
b. *eg Stockalite* (English China Clays).
c. *eg Britomya Violet* (Croxton and Garry).
d. *eg Fina Process Oil 2059* (Petrofina).
e. *eg Permanax CNS* (Vulnax).
f. *eg Polygard* (Uniroyal).

Rheological properties

	1	2
Mooney viscosity, 100°C	59	51
Mooney scorch, 120°C, min	11	20
Monsanto *Rheometer*, 180°C		
M_{HR}, torque units	29	20
M_L, torque units	6.4	5
scorch, t_{s1}, min	1.1	1.1
cure, $t_c'(95)$, min	3.4	2.4
time to 5% reversion, min	>12	3.5

10.3 (cont)

Vulcanizate properties, unaged

Injection moulded using *REP 843K* machine

extruder jacket temperature	85°C
injection chamber temperature	95°C
compound injection temperature	125°C

Formulation	1	2
Cure time at 180°C, min	3.0	2.0
Hardness, IRHD	53	42
Density, Mg/m^3	1.34	1.31
Resilience, Lupke, %	77	67
Tensile properties, radial[a]		
M100, MPa	1.3	0.8
M300, MPa	3.8	2.4
TS, MPa	18.0	17.0
EB, %	590	745
Tensile properties, tangential[a]		
M100, MPa	1.3	1.1
M300, MPa	3.7	3.2
TS, MPa	19.5	17.5
EB, %	605	700
Tear, ISO trouser, radial[a]		
23°C, median, kN/m	14	5.1
high/low ratio	1.1	1.8
100°C, median, kN/m	6.4	12
high/low ratio	1.6	1.2
Tear, ISO trouser, tangential[a]		
23°C, median, kN/m	4.4	3.5
high/low ratio	1.8	1.2
Compression set		
3 days at 23°C, %	10	14
1 day at 70°C, %	17	32
Tension set		
10 min at 350% extension, %	9.1	10.1

a. Measured along radial and tangential flow lines on a sheet produced in a centre-gated mould.

10.3 (cont)

Environmental ageing data

Formulation	1	2
Air-oven ageing for 7 days at 70°C[a]		
change in hardness, IRHD	+3	+4
change in M100, %	+30	−22
change in M300, %	+23	−18
change in TS, %	−10	−5
TS, MPa	16	15.5
change in EB, %	−16	−6
EB, %	495	700
After ageing for 7 days at 70°C in water[b]		
change in M100, %	+9	+27
change in M300, %	−13	−14
change in TS, %	−13	−11
TS, MPa	15.6	14.5
change in EB, %	+10	−4
EB, %	545	720
Volume swell in water		
7 days at 70°C, %	3.0	2.8

a. BS 1970 limits: TS 10.3 MPa, EB 425% min.
b. BS 1970 limits: TS 10.3 MPa, EB 425% min.

10.4 *Novor*-vulcanized heating pad **60 IRHD**

Designed for on-site vulcanization units for repairing *eg* off-the-road tyres or conveyor belts.

Formulation

SMR L	100
N762, SRF-LM-NS black	50
Process oil[a]	5
Antioxidant, TMQ[b]	2
Antioxidant, ZMBI[c]	2
Novor 924[d]	6.7
ZDMC	2
Desiccant[e]	3

a. *eg Dutrex 729UK* (Shell).
b. *eg Flectol H* (Monsanto).
c. *eg Vulkanox ZMB* (Bayer).
d. Urethane crosslinker (Durham Chemicals). *Novor 950* will give substantially the same results.
e. *eg Caloxol W5G* (John & E Sturge).

Rheological properties

Mooney viscosity, 100°C	
Mooney scorch, 120°C, min	17
Monsanto *Rheometer*, 160°C	
M_{HR}, torque units	33
M_L, torque units	5.5
scorch, t_{s1}, min	1.8
cure, $t_c'(95)$, min	35
cure, $t_c'(100)$, min	65

Further information on *Novor* vulcanization may be obtained from NR Technical Bulletin *Vulcanization with urethane reagents* and *NR Technology* 1983, **14**, 17.

10.4 (cont)

Vulcanizate properties, unaged

Cure: 35min at 160°C	
Hardness, IRHD	56
MR100, MPa	1.42
Resilience, Lupke, %	71
Tensile properties	
M100, MPa	1.6
M300, MPa	8.8
TS, MPa	19.8
EB, %	505
Tear, ISO trouser	
23°C, median, kN/m	7.2
high/low ratio	1.3
100°C, median, kN/m	11.2
high/low ratio	2.8
Ring fatigue life, 0–100% strain	
median, kc	41
Compression set, %	
3 days at 23°C	7
1 day at 70°C	14
1 day at 100°C	24
1 day at 125°C	39

Environmental ageing data

Air-oven ageing for 7 days at 100°C	
change in hardness, IRHD	+1
change in M100, %	+11
change in M300, %	+5
change in TS, %	−23
change in EB, %	−25
ring fatigue life, kc	89

10.5 Heat- and ozone-resistant blends **70–80 IRHD**

Blends of natural rubber with EPDM and EVA

A delayed-action peroxide/coagent cure system and high levels of antioxidant give good high temperature performance. Zinc oxide and stearic acid aid mould release. Addition of EVA lowers resilience and increases compression set.

Formulation

	1	2	3	4	5
SMR CV50	100	75	75	50	50
EPDM[a]		25		50	
EVA[b]			25		50
N330, HAF black	50	50	50	50	50
Zinc oxide	3	3	3	3	3
Stearic acid	1	1	1	1	1
Acrylic monomer coagent[c]	6	6	6	6	6
Antioxidant, TMQ[d]	1.5	1.5	1.5	1.5	1.5
ZMBI[e]	1.5	1.5	1.5	1.5	1.5
ZDMC	1.5	1.5	1.5	1.5	1.5
Dicumyl peroxide[f]	1.5	1.5	1.5	1.5	1.5

a. *eg Vistalon 6505* (Exxon).
b. *eg Levapren 450* (Bayer).
c. *eg ATM 16* (Ancomer) or *Saret 500* (Sartomer).
d. *eg Flectol H* (Monsanto).
e. *eg Vulkanox ZMB2* (Bayer).
f. *eg Dicup R* (Hercules).

Rheological properties

	1	2	3	4	5
Mooney viscosity, 100°C	60	71	58	78	37
Mooney scorch, 120°C, min	12	19	15	17	17
Monsanto *Rheometer*, 160°C					
M_{HR}, torque units	30	35	27.5	33.5	20
M_L, torque units	7	8	7.5	8.5	4.5
scorch, t_{s1}, min	2.0	2.1	2.0	2.1	2.5
cure, $t_c'(95)$, min	30	30	25	28	30
cure, $t_c'(100)$, min	45	50	45	50	60

10.5 (cont)

Vulcanizate properties, unaged

Formulation	1	2	3	4	5
Cure: 30min at 160°C					
Hardness, IRHD	72	73	76	80	80
Density, Mg/m^3	1.13	1.13	1.14	1.15	1.13
MR100, MPa	2.33	2.40	1.98	1.85	1.47
Resilience, Lupke, %	55	53	42	53	34
Abrasion, DIN, mm^3	240	240	325	worn away	
Tensile properties					
M100, MPa	2.5	2.6	2.9	2.1	2.2
M300, MPa	17.5	15.1	12.5	8.7	6.4
TS, MPa	25.0	21.0	18.0	17.0	11.4
EB, %	395	390	440	510	510
Tear, ISO trouser					
23°C, median, kN/m	18	20	22	9.1	28
high/low ratio	1.8	1.2	2	1.1	1.3
100°C, median, kN/m	7.5	9.5	14	15	7.1
high/low ratio	1.9	1.3	1.4	1.2	1.5
Ring fatigue life, 0–100% strain					
median, kc	122	174	98	290	195
high/low ratio	2.2	2.2	1.6	2.3	10
Compression set, %					
1 day at 70°C	22	26	30	36	50
1 day at 100°C	27	27	39	37	50
1 day at 125°C	50	49	70	57	76

10.5 (cont)

Environmental ageing data

Formulation	1	2	3	4	5
Air-oven ageing for 7 days at 100°C					
change in hardness, IRHD	+1	+2	0	+1	0
change in M100, %	+8	+18	+10	+40	+30
change in M300, %	−8	+3	0	+30	+35
change in TS, %	−20	−8	−12	−2	0
change in EB, %	−10	−4	−12	−18	−15
Air-oven ageing for 14 days at 100°C					
change in hardness, IRHD	+1	+4	+2	+2	+3
change in M100, %	+10	+30	+16	+50	+50
change in M300, %	−11	+3	−2	+50	+45
change in TS, %	−27	−12	−18	−5	0
change in EB, %	−14	−8	−12	−25	−20
Air-oven ageing for 3 days at 125°C					
change in hardness, IRHD	−3	−1	−1	+2	+2
change in M100, %	−1	−22	−2	+45	+30
change in M300, %	−20	−27	−12	+20	+24
change in TS, %	−43	−17	−32	−20	−10
change in EB, %	−14	−4	−18	−25	−13
Ozone resistance, 50pphm, 40°C, 20% strain					
time to first crack, days	<1	>7	>7	>7	>7

10.6 *Novor*-vulcanized, heat-resistant rollers — 40–90 IRHD

Novor cure systems give vulcanizates with good resistance to high-temperature ageing, suitable for arduous conditions.

Formulation

	1	2	3
Nominal hardness	40	50	90
SMR L	100	100	100
N660, GPF black	5		
N762, SRF-LM-NS black		30	
N220, ISAF black			60
Process oil[a]		4	10
Sulphonated oil blend[b]			2
Zinc oxide	5	5	5
Stearic acid	1		1
Zinc 2-ethylhexanoate[c]		2	
Antioxidant, TMQ[d]	2	2	2
Antioxidant, ZMBI[e]	2	2	2
Paraffin wax[f]	1.5		
Sulphur	0.25	0.4	0.7
Novor 924[g]	2.7	4.2	7.5
MBS		0.1	
CBS	0.05		
TBBS			0.14
TMTM	1.3		1.6
TBTD		1.5	
Desiccant[h]	3		

a. *eg Dutrex 729UK* (Shell).
b. *eg Ancoplas ER* (Anchor).
c. *eg Zinc Octoate* (Tenneco).
d. *eg Flectol H* (Monsanto).
e. *eg Vulkanox ZMB2* (Bayer).
f. Process aid.
g. Urethane crosslinker (Durham Chemicals). *Novor 950* will give substantially the same results.
h. *eg Caloxol W5G* (John & E Sturge).

Further information on *Novor* vulcanization may be obtained from NR Technical Bulletin *Vulcanization with urethane reagents* and *NR Technology*, 1983, **14**, 17.

10.6 (cont)

Rheological properties

Mooney viscosity, 100°C			72
Mooney scorch, 120°C, min	24	16	12
Monsanto *Rheometer*			
test temperature, °C	160	160	150
M_{HR}, torque units	18.5	26	50
M_L, torque units	4.5	5	8
scorch, t_{s1}, min	2.7	2	2.5
cure, $t_c'(95)$, min	10.5	8	13
cure, $t_c'(100)$, min	18	15	35

Vulcanizate properties, unaged

Formulation	1	2	3
Cure time, min	18	17	30
Cure temperature	160	160	150
Hardness, IRHD	38	49	88
Density, Mg/m^3	0.98	1.07	1.14
MR100, MPa	0.65	1.14	2.93
Resilience, Lupke, %	83	80	
Tensile properties			
M100, MPa	0.65	1.2	3.7
M300, MPa	1.9	5.8	15.3
TS, MPa	23.5	24.5	19.5
EB, %	740	605	370
Tear, ISO trouser			
23°C, median, kN/m	11.4	14.3	19.2
high/low ratio	3.4	1.8	1.7
100°C, median, kN/m	4.3	6.4	11.8
high/low ratio	1.4	2.4	1.1
Ring fatigue life, 0–100% strain			
median, kc	96	59	105
Compression set, %			
3 days at 23°C	8	7	24
1 day at 70°C	15	18	31
1 day at 100°C	26	28	49
1 day at 125°C	36	43	

10.6 (cont)

Environmental ageing data

Formulation	1	2	3
Air-oven ageing for 3 days at 100°C			
change in hardness, IRHD	+3	+2	+2
change in M100, %	+15	−12	+16
change in M300, %	+25	−2	
change in TS, %	−22	−23	−20
change in EB, %	−24	−6	−35
Air-oven ageing for 7 days at 100°C			
change in hardness, IRHD	+1	+2	0
change in M100, %	+3	+36	+25
change in M300, %	+20	+39	
change in TS, %	−37	−36	−25
change in EB, %	−15	−25	−25
ring fatigue life, median, kc	198	106	

Section 11 Printing and Stationery

11.1 Erasers
11.2 Stereo rubbers
11.3 Stationers' bands

11.1 Erasers

Generally either cured in simple clamped moulds in a steam pan or extruded and steam cured. Moulded erasers may be either individually moulded or cut to size from sheet; the cured erasers are generally tumbled with an abrasive to produce a roughend surface.

Formulation

	Ink	Pencil	
SMR L	100	100	100
White factice[a]	50	100	400
Magnesia[b]	30	30	30
Lithopone	20	100	
Barytes		80	
Whiting		150	300
Pumice	150		50
Titanium dioxide	5	10	
Light oil[c]		30	100
Zinc oxide	10	10	10
Stearic acid	2	2	2
Sulphur	6	8	7
MBTS	1	1	1.5
DPG	1.5	2	2.5
Pigment		as required	

a. *eg White factice* (Anchor).
b. *eg Maglite D* (Merck).
c. *eg Fina Process Oil 2059* (Petrofina).

Properties

Mooney scorch, 120°C, min	3	8	60
Cure: 30min at 150°C in steam			
Hardness, IRHD	67	40	30
Density, Mg/m³	1.5	1.7	1.6

Reference: *NR Technology*, 1983, **14**, 41.

11.2 Stereo rubbers **20–60 IRHD**

For printing a wide range of articles from paperback books to plastic bottles and bag labels.

Formulation

	1	2	3	4	5	6
Nominal hardness	20	30	40	50	55	60
SMR CV		20	100	100	100	100
PA 57[a]	100	80				
Factice[b]			10	10		
Barytes	30	30	40	40	40	40
Soft clay[c]				20	40	50
Light oil[d]	30	30	12	5	2	2
Zinc oxide	3	3	5	5	5	5
Antioxidant, TMQ[e]	1	1	1	1	1	1
Sulphur	0.5	1	1.5	1.5	1.5	1.5
CBS			1.5	1.5	1.5	1.5
ZDEC			0.2	0.2	0.2	0.2
MBTS		1				
TMTD	0.3	0.2				

a. Superior processing rubber.
b. *eg Whitbro 844* (Anchor).
c. *eg Devolite* (English China Clays).
d. *eg Fina Process Oil 2059* (Petrofina).
e. *eg Flectol H* (Monsanto).

Rheological properties

	1	2	3	4	5	6
Mooney viscosity, 100°C	19	19	33	32	33	39
Mooney scorch, 120°C, min	12	21	18	18	25	27
Monsanto *Rheometer*, 150°C						
M_{HR}, torque units	9	13.5	22.5	27.5	27.5	30.5
M_L, torque units	5.5	5	6.5	6.5	4	5.5
scorch, t_{s1}, min	2.2	4	4.2	4	3.7	3.6
cure, $t_c'(95)$, min	6.5	7.5	7	6	8.2	7.9
cure, $t_c'(100)$, min	7.5	10	11	10	9	10

Reference: Technical Information Sheet D39:1978

11.2 (cont)

Vulcanizate properties, unaged

Formulation	1	2	3	4	5	6
Nominal hardness	20	30	40	50	55	60
Cure time at 150°C, min	8	7	10	10	8	8
Hardness, IRHD	22	30	40	48	54	58
Density, Mg/m^3	1.09	1.06	1.17	1.27	1.35	1.4
MR100, MPa	0.26	0.39	0.64	0.88	1.27	1.32
Resilience, Lupke, %	78	84	87	86	80	83
Tensile properties						
M100, MPa	0.28	0.38	0.65	1.0	1.5	1.8
M300, MPa	0.64	1.0	1.7	2.4	3.4	4.0
TS, MPa	3.0	7.5	13	18	21	20
EB, %	630	640	720	665	630	600
Tear, ISO trouser						
23°C, median, kN/m	0.8	2	5.2	5.2	2.9	3.2
100°C,median, kN/m	0.3	0.7	1.9	2.3	5.3	6
Ring fatigue life, 0–100% strain						
median, kc		85	115	60	30	25
high/low ratio		3.6	1.2	1.2	1.5	1.5
Compression set, %						
1 day at −26°C	15	6	10	12	23	25
3 days at 23°C	8	3	4	3	6	7
1 day at 70°C	50	24	33	32	41	42
1 day at 100°C	63	57	62	61	60	59

11.2 (cont)

Environmental ageing data

Formulation	1	2	3	4	5	6
Air-oven ageing for 3 days at 70°C						
change in hardness, IRHD	+5	+4	+4	+4	+4	+3
change in M100, %	+30	+25	+20	+15	+20	+20
change in M300, %	+30	+30	+25	+10	+20	+10
change in TS, %	+30	+10	−5	−5	0	−5
change in EB, %	−5	−5	−10	−10	−5	−5
Air-oven ageing for 7 days at 70°C						
change in hardness, IRHD	+7	+7	+10	+7	+6	+5
change in M100, %	+30	+30	+30	+25	+30	+20
change in M300, %	+35	+35	+35	+30	+20	+20
change in TS, %	+50	+10	−10	−10	0	0
change in EB, %	−5	−10	−15	−10	−10	−5

11.3 Stationers' bands

40 IRHD

Bands produced by extrusion from formulation 1 will possess a somewhat rough surface appearance; those from formulation 2 will have a smooth surface on extrusion.

Formulation

	1	2
SMR L	100	
SP 20[a]		100
Active zinc oxide[b]	1	1
Stearic acid	1	1
Antioxidant[c]	1	1
Sulphur	2	2
MBTS	1	1
TMTM	0.1	0.05

a. Superior processing rubber.
b. *eg Zinkoxyd aktiv* (Bayer).
c. *eg Antioxidant 2246* (Cyanamid).

Rheological properties

Mooney viscosity, 100°C	34	37
Mooney scorch, 120°C, min	36	21
Monsanto *Rheometer*, 150°C		
M_{HR}, torque units	20	19
M_L, torque units	4.5	4.5
scorch, t_{s1}, min	6.2	4.8
cure, $t_c'(95)$, min	9.2	8.6
cure, $t_c'(100)$, min	11	11
time to 5% reversion, min	14	15

Reference: Technical Information Sheet D108:1982

11.3 (cont)

Vulcanizate properties, unaged

Formulation	1	2
Cure: 10min at 150°C		
Hardness, IRHD	38	38
Density, Mg/m^3	0.94	0.94
MR100, MPa	0.57	0.58
Resilience, Lupke, %	79	79
Tensile properties		
M100, MPa	0.3	0.50
M300, MPa	1.2	1.3
TS, MPa	23	23
EB, %	860	840
Tear, ISO trouser		
23°C, median, kN/m	11	9
high/low ratio	1.2	1.3
100°C, median, kN/m	3	4
high/low ratio	2.6	2
Ring fatigue life, 0–100% strain		
median, kc	190	175
high/low ratio	1.9	1.9
Compression set, %		
1 day at −26°C	20	22
3 days at 23°C	5	6
1 day at 70°C	30	35
1 day at 100°C	54	62

11.3 (cont)

Environmental ageing data

Formulation	1	2
Air-oven ageing for 3 days at 70°C		
change in hardness, IRHD	+4	+6
change in M100, %	+50	+60
change in M300, %	−25	+60
change in TS, %	+15	+25
change in EB, %	−10	−10
Air-oven ageing for 7 days at 70°C		
change in hardness, IRHD	0	+1
change in M100, %	+40	+50
change in M300, %	+30	+50
change in TS, %	+20	+25
change in EB, %	−10	−10
Air-oven ageing for 3 days at 100°C		
change in hardness, IRHD	+1	0
change in M100, %	+40	+45
change in TS, %	−25	−20
change in EB, %	−25	−25

Section 12 Seals and gaskets

12.1 Brake seals
12.2 Pipe sealing rings, water and drainage
12.3 Non-black seals
12.4 Washing machine seals

12.1 Brake seals

65–70 IRHD

Natural rubber is used for brake seals operating at low to moderate temperatures. The heat-resistant formulations given here contain low levels of thiurams for a fast cure rate without serious accelerator bloom. Formulation 2 contains ZMBI, which improves air ageing at high temperatures but increases compression set. The sulphenamide level is marginally increased to offset this effect.

Formulation

	1	2
SMR CV50	100	100
N326, HAF-LS black	50	50
Zinc oxide	5	5
Stearic acid	1	1
Antioxidant, TMQ[a]	1	1
Antioxidant[b]	1	1
ZMBI[c]		1
Sulphur	0.5	0.5
CBS	1	1.5
DTDM	1	1
TETD	0.3	0.3

a. *eg Flectol H* (Monsanto).
b. *eg Permanax BL* (Vulnax).
c. *eg Vulkanox ZMB2* (Bayer).

Rheological properties

	1	2
Mooney viscosity, 100°C	63	65
Mooney scorch, 120°C, min	25	19
Monsanto *Rheometer*, 160°C		
M_{HR}, torque units	32	33.5
M_L, torque units	7.5	7.5
scorch, t_{s1}, min	3.0	2.7
cure, $t_c'(95)$, min	5.9	6.2
cure, $t_c'(100)$, min	10	10
time to 5% reversion, min	35	30

12.1 (cont)

Vulcanizate properties, unaged

Formulation	1	2
Cure: 12min at 160°C		
Hardness, IRHD	63	68
Density, Mg/m^3	1.13	1.13
MR100, MPa	1.78	1.78
Resilience, Lupke, %	57	55
Abrasion, DIN, mm^3	193	204
Tensile properties		
M100, MPa	1.9	1.9
M300, MPa	10.5	9.5
TS, MPa	27	26
EB, %	540	590
Tear, ISO trouser		
23°C, median, kN/m	38	37
high/low ratio	1.3	2.1
100°C, median, kN/m	17	23
high/low ratio	1.3	1.6
Ring fatigue life, 0–100% strain		
median, kc	74	82
high/low ratio	1.2	1.8
Compression set, %		
3 days at 23°C	13	21
1 day at 70°C	18	24
1 day at 100°C	41	47

12.1 (cont)

Environmental ageing data

Formulation	1	2
Air-oven ageing for 14 days at 70°C		
change in hardness, IRHD	+3	+2
change in M100, %	+21	+24
change in M300, %	+24	+28
change in TS, %	−10	−8
change in EB, %	−12	−13
Air-oven ageing for 3 days at 100°C		
change in hardness, IRHD	+3	+1
change in M100, %	+8	+26
change in M300, %	+8	+22
change in TS, %	−20	−12
change in EB, %	−13	−6
After ageing for 7 days at 70°C in brake fluid[a],		
change in hardness, IRHD	−8	−7
change in M100, %	+2	−4
change in M300, %	+7	+7
change in TS, %	−6	−12
change in EB, %	−7	−13
Volume swell in brake fluid[a]		
7 days at 70°C, %	4.8	4.9

a. Society of Automotive Engineers Standard J1703 (RM1 fluid).

12.2 Pipe sealing rings

40–90 IRHD

Water and drainage

Physical property requirements of BS 2494:1976 are met.

Formulation

	1	2	3	4	5	6
Nominal hardness	40	50	60	70	80	90
SMR CV	100	100	100	100	100	100
N550, FEF black	5	25	50	65	75	80
Whiting				30	60	120
Phenol formaldehyde resin[a]						10
Zinc oxide	3	3	3	3	3	3
Zinc 2-ethylhexanoate[b]	1	1	1	1	1	1
Chlorinated wax[c]	5	5	5	5	5	5
Antiozonant, DHPPD[d]	3	3	3	3	3	3
Sulphur	0.5	0.5	0.5	0.5	0.5	0.5
MBS	2.0	2.0	2.0	2.0	2.0	2.0
TBTD	1.4	1.4	0.7	0.7	0.7	0.7

a. *eg Cellobond J113H* (BP Chemicals).
b. *eg Zinc Octoate* (Tenneco).
c. *eg Cereclor 42* (42% chlorine) (ICI).
d. *eg Santoflex 77* (Monsanto).

Rheological properties

Mooney viscosity, 100°C	38	39	52	68	95	120
Mooney scorch, 120°C, min	20	18	15	15	10	14
Monsanto *Rheometer*, 150°C						
M_{HR}, torque units	21.5	27	34	44.5	50	54
M_L, torque units	3	7	8.5	12	16	27
scorch, t_{s1}, min	5	4.3	4	3.8	2.5	4.1
cure, $t_c'(95)$, min	11	11	10	8.5	8.2	14
cure, $t_c'(100)$, min	25	25	20	25	25	25

12.2 (cont)

Vulcanizate properties, unaged

Formulation	1	2	3	4	5	6
Cure: 22min at 150°C						
Hardness, IRHD	39	49	60	72	81	91
Density, Mg/m^3	0.97	1.05	1.11	1.25	1.36	1.50
MR100, MPa	0.675	1.13	1.96	3.01	4.27	3.95
Resilience, Lupke, %	82	79	66	61	50	42
DIN abrasion, mm^3			220	320	279	>500
Tensile properties						
M100, MPa	0.66	1.1	1.9	3.6	4.8	5.2
M300, MPa	1.9	5.5	11	15		
TS, MPa	23	27	24	17	14	11
EB, %	700	630	520	340	250	235
Tear, ISO trouser						
23°C, median, kN/m	7	8.4	12	17	3.1	8
high/low ratio	1.8	1.4	3.4	12	1.3	2.5
100°C, median, kN/m	3.5	4	4	5.3	2.2	2.4
high/low ratio	1.9	2.1	3.5	2.5	2.1	1.3
Ring fatigue life, 0–100% strain						
median, kc	180	67	47	10.2	3.7	1.9
high/low ratio	4.9	1.5	1.7	1.4	3.5	1.4
Compression set, %						
1 day at 0°C	5	5	7	8	19	24
3 days at 23°C	3	4	5	5	5	9
1 day at 70°C	16	17	18	18	15	23
1 day at 100°C	35	37	38	35	31	44
1 day at 125°C	42	45	48	46	45	63

12.2 (cont)

Environmental ageing data

Formulation	1	2	3	4	5	6
Air-oven ageing for 7 days at 70°C						
change in hardness, IRHD	+4	+2	+2	+1	+1	0
change in M100, %	+10	+20	+20	+10	+20	+20
change in M300, %	+20	+20	+10	+20	+20	+10
change in TS, %	0	−10	−15	0	−10	−15
change in EB, %	−5	−10	−15	−5	−10	−15
Air-oven ageing for 3 days at 100°C						
change in hardness, IRHD	+6	+8	+6	+3	+6	+1
change in M100, %	+15	+10	+15	+15	+25	+15
change in TS, %	−5	−15	−20	−5	−15	−20
change in EB, %	−15	−15	−15	−15	−15	−30
Volume swell in water						
7 days at 70°C, %	4.0	5.3	5.1	4.0	3.8	4.0
Low-temperature storage at −26°C						
time to						
5 point IRHD rise, days	3	5	3	2	2	3
10 point IRHD rise, days	10	10	5	3	3	
Ozone resistance, 50pphm, 40°C, 20% strain						
time to first crack, days	>18	>18	8	4	3	3

12.3 Non-black seals — 60–80 IRHD

A silane coupling agent gives improved resistance to compression set.

Formulation

	1	2	3
Nominal hardness	60	70	80
SMR CV	100	100	100
Precipitated silica[a]	25	40	50
Silane coupling agent[b]	3	3	3
Polyethylene glycol[c]	1	1	1
Zinc oxide	5	5	5
Zinc 2-ethylhexanoate[d]	2	2	2
Chlorinated wax[e]	3	3	3
Antiozonant, DHPPD[f]	3	3	3
Sulphur	0.5	0.5	0.5
MBS	2	2	2
TBTD	2.5	2.5	2.5

a. *eg Ultrasil VN3* (Degussa).
b. *eg Si 69* (Degussa).
c. *eg PEG 4000* (Shell).
d. *eg Zinc Octoate* (Tenneco).
e. *eg Cereclor 42* (42% chlorine) (ICI).
f. *eg Santoflex 77* (Monsanto).

Rheological properties

	1	2	3
Mooney viscosity, 100°C	45	51	55
Mooney scorch, 120°C, min	13	14	19
Monsanto *Rheometer*, 160°C			
M_{HR}, torque units	20	22.5	27.5
M_L, torque units	4	5	4.5
scorch, t_{s1}, min	2.2	2.3	2.3
cure, $t_c'(95)$, min	22	22	23
cure, $t_c'(100)$, min	45	45	45

12.3 (cont)

Vulcanizate properties, unaged

Formulation	1	2	3
Cure: 15min at 160°C[a]			
Hardness, IRHD	61	68	79
Density, Mg/m^3	1.08	1.12	1.16
MR100, MPa	1.66	2.04	2.9
Resilience, Lupke, %	88	82	71
Tensile properties			
M100, MPa	1.8	2.4	3.8
M300, MPa	9.4	12	16
TS, MPa	26	26	25
EB, %	490	470	430
Tear, ISO trouser			
23°C, median, kN/m	3.1	2.3	6.3
100°C,median, kN/m	1.4	3.0	2.3
Ring fatigue life, 0–100% strain			
median, kc	55	52	62
high/low ratio	1.9	1.6	1.1
Compression set[a], %			
1 day at −26°C	10	8	12
1 day at 0°C	4	5	6
3 days at 23°C	5	6	9
1 day at 70°C	22	23	24
1 day at 100°C	36	33	41
1 day at 125°C	45	45	53

a. A longer cure would further reduce compression set.

12.3 (cont)

Environmental ageing data

Formulation	1	2	3
Air-oven ageing for 3 days at 70°C			
change in hardness, IRHD	+4	+3	+3
change in M100, %	+15	+20	+10
change in M300, %	+10	+15	+15
change in TS, %	−15	−5	−5
change in EB, %	−10	−10	−10
Air-oven ageing for 7 days at 70°C			
change in hardness, IRHD	+5	+5	+4
change in M100, %	+50	+70	+50
change in M300, %	+60	+50	+40
change in TS, %	−10	−5	−5
change in EB, %	−20	−20	−25
Air-oven ageing for 3 days at 100°C			
change in hardness, IRHD	+6	+7	+7
change in M100, %	+55	+75	+50
change in TS, %	−40	−35	−40
change in EB, %	−35	−45	−50
Volume swell in water			
3 days at 70°C, %	2.9	3.8	3.8
Low-temperature storage at −26°C			
time to			
5 point IRHD rise, days	>28	>28	>28
Low temperature storage at 0°C for 3 days			
change in hardness, IRHD	+1	+1	+2
Ozone resistance 50pphm, 40°C, 20% strain			
time to first crack, days	3	3	3

12.4 Detergent-resistant washing machine seals **45 IRHD**

High levels of antioxidants resistant to leaching are required. These vulcanizates would also pass the physical property requirements of BS 1154, W40 grade if the level of zinc oxide were increased to 5 parts phr.

Formulation

	1	2
SMR 10	100	100
Coated calcium carbonate[a]	20	20
Titanium dioxide	10	10
Zinc oxide	4	4
Stearic acid	2	2
Antioxidant, TMQ[b]	1	1
Antioxidant[c]	6	2.5
Antioxidant[d]		1
Sulphur	1	1
MBS	1.2	1.2
TMTD	0.3	0.3

a. *eg Winnofil S* (ICI).
b. *eg Flectol H* (Monsanto).
c. *Perkanox P15/60* (Akzo Chemie).
d. *Wingstay L* (Goodyear).

Rheological properties

	1		2	
Mooney viscosity, 100°C	28		26	
Mooney scorch, 120°C, min	24		26	
Monsanto *Rheometer*				
test temperature°C	160	180	160	180
M_{HR}, torque units	21.5	20	21	19.2
M_L, torque units	2.5	2.5	2	2
scorch, t_{s1}, min	2.7	1.4	2.7	1.3
cure, $t_c'(95)$, min	5.8	2.7	6.0	2.6
cure, $t_c'(100)$, min	10	3.5	15	4.0
time to 5% reversion, min	>30	>6	>30	>6

12.4 (cont)

Vulcanizate properties, unaged

Formulation	1	2
Cure: 8min at 160°C		
Hardness, IRHD	45	44
Density, Mg/m^3	1.13	1.11
MR100, MPa	0.87	0.85
Resilience, Lupke, %	83	80
Abrasion, DIN, mm^3	305	280
Tensile properties		
M100, MPa	0.9	0.9
M300, MPa	2.7	2.4
TS, MPa	24	26.5
EB, %	655	695
Tear, ISO trouser		
23°C, median, kN/m	6.6	7.5
high/low ratio	1.2	1.2
100°C, median, kN/m	8.1	5.1
high/low ratio	1.3	1.3
Ring fatigue life, 0−100% strain		
median, kc	68	67
high/low ratio	2.9	1.7
Compression set, %		
1 day at −26°C	18	20
3 days at 23°C	8	9
1 day at 70°C	20	20
1 day at 100°C	39	40

12.4 (cont)

Environmental ageing data

Formulation	1	2
Air-oven ageing for 7 days at 70°C		
change in hardness, IRHD	+3	+3
change in M100, %	+14	+16
change in M300, %	+19	+24
change in TS, %	−2	−8
change in EB, %	−6	−13
Air-oven ageing for 3 days at 100°C		
change in hardness, IRHD	+5	+5
change in M100, %	0	0
change in M300, %	+10	+27
change in TS, %	−18	−2
change in EB, %	−8	−15
After ageing for 4 days at 100°C in 0.5% detergent solution[a],		
change in M300, %	−41	−45
change in TS, %	−20	−24
change in EB, %	+4	+10
Volume swell in water		
3 days at 100°C, %	6.1	6.8
Resistance to immersion in 2% detergent solution[a]		
50 days at 90°C	no surface deterioration, stickiness or disintegration	

a. Aqueous *Ariel* (Proctor and Gamble).

Section 13 Tyres and associated components

13.1 Fork-lift truck tyres
13.2 Solid tyres, *Novor* cured
13.3 Truck retreads
13.4 Winter passenger tyre retreads
13.5 Cushion gum for precured treads
13.6 White sidewalls
13.7 Curing bags, *Novor* cured
13.8 Inner tubes

For tyre beads see: Extrusions, hard compounds (Section 6.1)

13.1 Fork-lift truck tyres — 65–70 IRHD

Factory trials have shown that natural rubber fork-lift truck tyres possess extremely good abrasion resistance and low rolling resistance. Oil-extended formulation 2 is suitable for less demanding applications. Microwave pre-heating may be used to shorten cure time and reduce backrinding if this is a problem.

Formulation

	1	2
SMR 20	100	100
N550, FEF black	60	80
Light oil[a]	5	25
Zinc oxide	5	5
Stearic acid	2	2
Antidegradant, HPPD[b]	1.5	1.5
Sulphur	2.5	2.5
TBBS	0.5	0.75

a. *eg Fina Process Oil 2059* (Petrofina).
b. *eg Santoflex 13* (Monsanto).

Rheological properties

	1	2
Mooney viscosity, 100°C	69	63
Mooney scorch, 120°C, min	18	16
Monsanto *Rheometer*, 150°C		
M_{HR}, torque units	43	37
M_L, torque units	9	8
scorch, t_{s1}, min	3.4	3.8
cure, $t_c'(95)$, min	14.2	13
cure, $t_c'(100)$, min	21	19
time to 5% reversion, min	32.5	29

Reference: Technical Information Sheets D30:1976 and D121:1983.

13.1 (cont)

Vulcanizate properties, unaged

Formulation	1	1	2	2
Cure time at 150°C, min	15	30	15	30
Hardness, IRHD	67	65	70	65
Density, Mg/m^3	1.15	1.15	1.16	1.16
MR100, MPa	2.59	2.52	3.00	2.59
Resilience, Lupke, %	66	60	60	58
Tensile properties				
M100, MPa	2.7	3.4	3.1	2.7
M300, MPa	15	14	15	13
TS, MPa	21	19	18	17
EB, %	425	395	380	370
Tear, ISO trouser				
23°C, median, kN/m	13	13	11	14
high/low ratio	2.3	2	1.4	3.3
100°C, median, kN/m	15	15	21	17
high/low ratio	1.2	2	2.3	2.4
Ring fatigue life, 0–100% strain				
median, kc	166	164	170	100
high/low ratio	1.2	1.2	2	1.8
Compression set, %				
1 day at −26°C	19	18	22	21
3 days at 23°C	7	7	7	7
1 day at 70°C	44	30	40	29
1 day at 100°C	71	57	65	52
Goodrich *Flexometer*				
Static stress 1MPa (24lb), stroke 5.71mm (0.225in), start 100°C				
temperature rise after 2h, °C	25	20	39	30

13.1 (cont)

Environmental ageing data

Formulation	1A	1B	2A	2B
Air-oven ageing for 3 days at 70°C				
change in hardness, IRHD	+1	+3	+6	+6
change in M100, %	+25	+35	+35	+20
change in M300, %	+15	+10	+15	+15
change in TS, %	−5	+5	0	0
change in EB, %	−15	−5	−10	−15
Air-oven ageing for 7 days at 70°C				
change in hardness, IRHD	+7	+5	+7	+7
change in M100, %	+25	+32	+25	+30
change in M300, %	+15	+10	+15	+15
change in TS, %	−10	−5	−5	−5
change in EB, %	−15	−15	−20	−15
Air-oven ageing for 3 days at 100°C				
change in hardness, IRHD	+6	+7	+7	+8
change in M100, %	+65	+90	+50	+75
change in TS, %	−35	−20	−30	−25
change in EB, %	−45	−45	−40	−45
Volume swell in water 3 days at 100°C, %	8.3	7.9	7.9	6.8

13.2 *Novor*-vulcanized solid tyres **70–90 IRHD**

The *Novor* system gives vulcanizates with good resistance to high temperature ageing and suitable for arduous conditions.

Formulation

	1	2
Nominal hardness	70	90
SMR L	100	100
N550, FEF black	40	
N220, ISAF black		60
Process oil[a]	4	10
Sulphonated oil blend[b]		2
Zinc oxide	4	5
Stearic acid	3	1
Antioxidant, TMQ[c]	2	2
Antioxidant, ZMBI[d]	2	2
Sulphur	1	0.7
Novor 924[e]	7.3	7.5
CBS	0.2	
TBBS		0.14
TMTM	1.9	1.6
Desiccant[f]	3	

a. *eg Dutrex 729UK* (Shell).
b. *eg Ancoplas ER* (Anchor).
c. *eg Flectol H* (Monsanto).
d. *eg Vulkanox ZMB2* (Bayer).
e. Urethane crosslinker (Durham Chemicals). *Novor 950* will give substantially the same results.
f. *eg Caloxol W5G* (John & E Sturge).

Rheological properties

	1	2
Mooney viscosity, 100°C	53	72
Mooney scorch, 120°C, min	13	12
Monsanto *Rheometer*, °C	160	150
M_{HR}, torque units	42	50
M_L, torque units	5	8
scorch, t_{s1}, min	1.5	2.5
cure, $t_c'(95)$, min	8.5	13
cure, $t_c'(100)$, min	30	35

Reference: Technical Information Sheet D129:1983. Further information on *Novor* vulcanization may be obtained from Technical Bulletin *Vulcanization with urethane reagents* and *NR Technology*, 1983, **14**, 17.

13.2 (cont)

Vulcanizate properties, unaged

Formulation	1	2
Cure time, min	30	30
Cure temperature, °C	160	150
Hardness, IRHD	71	88
Density, Mg/m^3	1.10	1.14
MR100, MPa	2.76	2.93
Resilience, Lupke, %	71	
Abrasion, Akron, mm^3/500rev	63	33
Tensile properties		
M100, MPa	3.0	3.7
M300, MPa	13.4	15.3
TS, MPa	17.6	19.4
EB, %	385	370
Tear, ISO trouser		
23°C, median, kN/m	3.3	19.2
high/low ratio	1.3	1.7
100°C, median, kN/m	3.6	11.8
high/low ratio	2.6	1.1
Ring fatigue life, 0–100% strain		
median, kc	33	105
high/low ratio	2.1	1.3
Compression set, %		
3 days at 23°C	13	24
1 day at 70°C	19	31
1 day at 100°C	27	49

13.2 (cont)

Environmental ageing data

Formulation	1	2
Air-oven ageing for 3 days at 100°C		
change in hardness, IRHD	+1	+2
change in M100, %	+11	+16
change in TS, %	−28	−20
change in EB, %	−35	−35
Air-oven ageing for 7 days at 100°C		
change in hardness, IRHD	0	0
change in M100, %	+30	+25
change in TS, %	−48	−25
change in EB, %	−48	−25
Volume swell in water		
3 days at 100°C, %	5.3	4.7

13.3 Truck tyre retreads

65 IRHD

Light and heavy duty

Oil-extended natural rubber gives a good balance of wear resistance, grip and resistance to groove cracking in light duty retreads. Low oil levels give lowest heat generation and best resistance to wear in heavy duty retreads.

Formulation

	1	2
	Light duty	Heavy duty
OENR 75/25A[a]	107	
SMR 20[b]		80
Low-*cis* polybutadiene[c]	20	20
N220, ISAF black	70	
N375, HAF black[d]		45
Process oil[e]		5
Zinc oxide	5	5
Stearic acid	2	2
Antidegradant[f]	2	2
Wax blend[g]	1	1
Sulphur	1.5	1.5
TBBS	1.5	1.5

a. Oil-extended natural rubber, 25% aromatic oil.
b. Premasticated to 60 Mooney.
c. *Intene 50* (Enichem).
d. *eg Vulcan J* (Cabot Carbon).
e. *eg Dutrex 729UK* (Shell).
f. *eg Santoflex 13* (Monsanto).
g. *eg Sunproof Improved* (Uniroyal).

Rheological properties

Mooney viscosity, 100°C	70	65
Mooney scorch, 120°C, min	26	24
Monsanto *Rheometer*		
test temperature, °C	140	150
M_{HR}, torque units	35	40
M_L, torque units	10	8
scorch, t_{s1}, min	10.6	4.6
cure, $t_c'(95)$, min	20	10.4
cure, $t_c'(100)$, min	35	25
time to 5% reversion, min	>60	>60

13.3 (cont)

Vulcanizate properties, unaged

Formulation	1	1	2	2
Cure time, min	20	90	15	35
Cure temperature, °C	140	140	150	150
Hardness, IRHD	65	67	66	66
Density, Mg/m^3	1.14	1.14	1.10	1.10
MR100, MPa	1.67	1.78	2.16	2.08
Resilience, Lupke, %	41	40	63	61
Abrasion, DIN, mm^3	200	195	161	158
Abrasion, Akron, mm^3/500rev	12	18	18	20
Tensile properties				
M100, MPa	2.0	2.2	2.6	2.5
M300, MPa	9.7	10.7	13	13
TS, MPa	20	20.5	26	24.5
EB, %	525	495	505	455
Tear, ISO trouser 23°C, median, kN/m	33	16	10.5	9.5
Ring fatigue life, 0–100% strain				
median, kc	270	185	150	86
high/low ratio	2.2	2	1.5	2.2
Compression set, %				
1 day at −26°C	21	21	13	14
3 days at 23°C	11	12	8	8
1 day at 70°C	45	25	33	24
1 day at 100°C	70	41	53	44
Goodrich *Flexometer*				
Static stress 1MPa (24lb), stroke 5.71mm (0.225in), start 100°C				
temperature rise after 2h			42	40
time to failure, min	65	60		

13.3 (cont)

Environmental ageing data

Formulation	1	1	2	2
Air-oven ageing for 3 days at 70°C				
change in hardness, IRHD	+6	+2	+4	+4
change in M100, %	−4	−4	+8	+8
change in M300, %	+12	+3	+12	+7
change in TS, %	0	−2	−2	−4
change in EB, %	−9	−3	−10	−4
Air-oven ageing for 7 days at 70°C				
change in hardness, IRHD	+5	+3	+5	+4
change in M100, %	+25	+4	+20	+18
change in M300, %	+20	+10	+20	+15
change in TS, %	−3	−3	−15	−9
change in EB, %	−8	−5	−20	−11
Air-oven ageing for 3 days at 100°C				
change in hardness, IRHD	+8	+4	+8	+6
change in M100, %	+50	+8	+34	+34
change in TS, %	−20	−25	−25	−20
change in EB, %	−30	−20	−35	−25
Volume swell in water				
3 days at 100°C, %	3.2		2.2	

13.4 Winter passenger tyre retreads **60–70 IRHD**

Oil-extended formulations designed for good grip and wear resistance and for satisfactory extrusion in Barwell, Orbitread or conventional cold feed extruders. Tested for grip in temperate and cold winter conditions.

Formulation

	1	2	3
SMR[a]	80	80	80
High-*cis* polybutadiene[b]	20	20	20
N220, ISAF black	70	42	28
Precipitated silica[c]		28	42
Process oil[d]	15	15	15
Zinc oxide	6	6	6
Stearic acid	2.5	2.5	2.5
Antioxidant, IPPD[e]	2.5	2.5	2.5
Silane coupling agent[f]		3.8	5.6
Sulphur	1.5	1.5	1.5
CBS	1.5	1.5	1.5

a. Premasticated.
b. *eg Europene Cis* (Enichem).
c. *eg Ultrasil VN3* (Degussa).
d. *eg Dutrex 729UK* (Shell).
e. *eg Permanax IPPD* (Vulnax).
f. *eg Si 69* (Degussa).

Rheological properties

	1	2	3
Mooney viscosity, 100°C	55	51	45
Mooney scorch, 120°C, min	17	12	15
Monsanto *Rheometer*, 165°C			
M_{HR}, torque units	35.5	32	30
M_L, torque units	7	7	6
scorch, t_{s1}, min	1.8	1.5	2.0
cure, $t_c'(95)$, min	4.0	4.5	5.5
cure, $t_c'(100)$, min	5.5	6.5	7.8
time to 5% reversion, min	10	12	14

13.4 (cont)

Vulcanizate properties, unaged

Formulation	1	2	3
Cure: 15min at 165°C			
Hardness, IRHD	70	62	60
MR100, MPa	1.59	1.33	1.25
Resilience, Lupke, %	44	51	59
Abrasion, Akron, mm^3/500rev	16	14	15
Tensile properties			
M100, MPa	1.8	1.5	1.4
M300, MPa	10.3	8.2	7.6
TS, MPa	20	21	21
EB, %	520	570	610
Tear, ISO trouser			
23°C, median, kN/m	23	19	18
Ring fatigue life, 0–100% strain			
median, kc	314	405	758
Compression set, %			
1 day at 70°C	30	29	29

Environmental ageing data

Air-oven ageing for 14 days at 70°C,			
change in M100, %	+15	+55	+50
change in M300, %	+29	+54	+58
change in TS, %	−13	−4	0
change in EB, %	−29	−22	−20

13.5 Cushion gum for pre-cured tread **70 IRHD**

For retread process curing at 140°C.

Formulation

SMR CV	100
N660, GPF black	60
Pine tar	4
Cobalt naphthenate[a]	2
Zinc oxide	5
Stearic acid	2
Antioxidant, TMQ[b]	2
Sulphur, insoluble	2.5
ZMBT	1
DPG	0.5

a. *eg Manobond CN10* (Manchem).
b. *eg Flectol H* (Monsanto).

Rheological properties

Mooney viscosity, 100°C	59
Mooney scorch, 120°C, min	4
Monsanto *Rheometer*, 140°C	
M_{HR}, torque units	38
M_L, torque units	8.5
scorch, t_{s1}, min	2.0
cure, $t_c'(95)$, min	12
cure, $t_c'(100)$, min	20
time to 5% reversion, min	>60

Reference: Technical Information Sheet D113:1982

13.5 (cont)

Vulcanizate properties, unaged

Cure: 12min at 140°C	
Hardness, IRHD	71
Density, Mg/m^3	1.15
MR100, MPa	2.05
Resilience, Lupke, %	66
Tensile properties	
M100, MPa	2.3
M300, MPa	11
TS, MPa	21
EB, %	505
Tear, ISO trouser	
23°C, median, kN/m	14
high/low ratio	1.6
100°C, median, kN/m	19
high/low ratio	1.6
Ring fatigue life, 0−100% strain	
median, kc	60
high/low ratio	1.7
Compression set, %	
1 day at −26°C	34
3 days at 23°C	11
1 day at 70°C	35

Environmental ageing data

Air-oven ageing for 3 days at 70°C	
change in hardness, IRHD	+2
change in M100, %	+15
change in M300, %	+10
change in TS, %	−10
change in EB, %	−10
Air-oven ageing for 7 days at 70°C	
change in hardness, IRHD	+4
change in M100, %	+20
change in M300, %	+20
change in TS, %	−10
change in EB, %	−15
Air-oven ageing for 3 days at 100°C	
change in hardness, IRHD	+2
change in M100, %	+50
change in TS, %	−25
change in EB, %	−45

13.6 White sidewalls **40–50 IRHD**

A wide variety of formulations is currently in use for white sidewalls. For halobutyl blends, zinc oxide should be added towards the end of the mixing cycle and the dump temperature should not exceed 140°C.

Formulation

	1	2	3	4
SMR L	85	50	60	50
SBR 1502	15			25
Bromobutyl[a]			20	
Chlorobutyl[b]		50		
EPDM[c]			20	25
Semi-reinforcing silica[d]	30			15
Reinforcing silica[e]		30		
Talc[f]			20	
Hard clay[g]			30	
Titanium dioxide	20	30	35	35
Light oil[h]		8		5
Tackifying resin[i]			5	
Zinc oxide	10	5	3	20
Stearic acid	1	2	2	2
Triethanolamine		3		
Antioxidant[j]	2	2	2	2
Wax blend[k]	5	3		3
Sulphur	3.2	1.5	1	2
MBS	0.9			
DOTG		2.5		
TBBS			1.25	
TMTD			0.2	
ZDMC				0.45
Ultramarine blue	0.2	0.2	0.2	0.2

a. eg *Bromobutyl X2* (Polysar).
b. eg *Exxon Chlorobutyl HT1066* (Exxon).
c. eg *Vistalon 6505* (Exxon).
d. eg *Silene D* (Pittsburg Plate Glass).
e. eg *Ultrasil VN3* (Degussa).
f. eg *Extra Steamic OOS* (Talc de Luzanac).
g. eg *Stockalite* (English China Clays).
h. eg *Fina Process Oil 2059* (Petrofina).
i. eg *Piccolyte S105* (Hercules Powder).
j. eg *Permanax WSP* (Vulnax).
k. eg *Sunproof Improved* (Uniroyal).

Reference : Technical Information Sheet D 123:1983.

13.6 (cont)

Rheological properties

Mooney viscosity, 100°C	51	57	46	43
Mooney scorch, 120°C, min	60	6	60	10
Monsanto *Rheometer*, 180°C				
M_{HR}, torque units	27	26	23	16
M_L, torque units	7	10	6	6
scorch, t_{s1}, min	2	0.5	2	0.8
cure, $t_c'(95)$, min	4.8	3.0	3.3	2.3
cure, $t_c'(100)$, min	6	4	4.5	3.5
time to 5% reversion, min	8.5	6.2	7.2	5.0

Vulcanizate properties, unaged

Formulation	1	2	3	4
Cure: 5min at 180°C				
Hardness, IRHD	51	50	53	39
Density, Mg/m³	1.22	1.22	1.35	1.28
MR100, MPa	1.04	0.62	1.01	0.75
Resilience, Lupke, %	70	51	58	58
Tensile properties				
M100, MPa	1.1	0.8	1.9	1.0
M300, MPa	3.25	1.8	4.4	2.4
TS, MPa	20.5	10.5	15.0	10.6
EB, %	695	785	645	670
Tear, ISO trouser				
23°C, median, kN/m	4.2	4.4	7.8	4.8
high/low ratio	1.3	1.1	1.1	1.2
100°C, median, kN/m	6.8	7.3	11.1	6.1
high/low ratio	1.6	2.4	1.3	1.2
Ring fatigue life, 0–100% strain				
median, kc	100	205	46	240
high/low ratio	1.8	3.6	3.7	2.5
Compression set, %				
1 day at −26°C	21	33	22	48
3 days at 23°C	9	22	10	25
1 day at 70°C	39	40	47	50

13.6 (cont)

Environmental ageing data

Formulation	1	2	3	4
Air-oven ageing for 7 days at 70°C				
change in hardness, IRHD	+4	+8	−1	0
change in M100, %	+50	+16	+10	+40
change in M300, %	+60	+20	+10	+50
change in TS, %	+5	−21	−5	+9
change in EB, %	−14	−18	−4	−3
Air-oven ageing for 3 days at 100°C				
change in hardness, IRHD	+3	+8	0	−4
change in M100, %	+60	−4	+5	+60
change in TS, %	−30	−40	−10	−28
change in EB, %	−28	−15	−4	−32
Low-temperature storage at −26°C				
time to				
5 point IRHD rise, days	3	28	3	21
10 point IRHD rise, days	>28	>28	>28	>28
Ozone resistance, 50pphm, 40°C, 20% strain				
time to first crack, days	>7	>7	>7	>7

13.7 *Novor*-vulcanized curing bag — 55 IRHD

High resistance to tearing and cutting and the thermal stability provided by *Novor* vulcanization give natural rubber curing bags service lives that can exceed those of chlorobutyl bags.

Formulation

SMR L	100
Lampblack[a]	58
Process aid[b]	3
Zinc oxide	5
Stearic acid	1
Antioxidant, TMQ[c]	2
Antioxidant, ZMBI[d]	2
Novor 924[e]	6.7
ZDMC	2
Desiccant[f]	3

a. *eg Magecol 888* (Columbian Carbon), or equivalent.
b. *eg Aktiplast* (Rhein–Chemie).
c. *eg Flectol H* (Monsanto).
d. *eg Vulkanox ZMB2* (Bayer).
e. Urethane crosslinker (Durham Chemicals). *Novor 950* will give substantially the same results.
f. *eg Caloxol W5G* (John & E Sturge).

Rheological properties

Mooney scorch, 120°C, min	17
Monsanto *Rheometer*, 160°C	
M_{HR}, torque units	35.5
M_L, torque units	6
scorch, t_{s1}, min	1.6
cure, $t_c'(95)$, min	35
cure, $t_c'(100)$, min	60

Further information on *Novor* vulcanization may be obtained from NR Technical Bulletin *Vulcanization with urethane reagents* and *NR Technology*, 1983, **14**, 17.

13.7 (cont)

Vulcanizate properties, unaged

Cure: 35min at 160°C	
Hardness, IRHD	62
MR100, MPa	1.88
Resilience, Lupke, %	64
Tensile properties	
M100, MPa	2.2
M300, MPa	11.5
TS, MPa	17.0
EB, %	445
Tear, ISO trouser	
23°C, median, kN/m	6.9
high/low ratio	1.8
100°C, median, kN/m	14
high/low ratio	2
Ring fatigue life, 0–100% strain	
median, kc	32
Compression set, %	
3 days at 23°C	15
1 day at 70°C	21
1 day at 100°C	32
1 day at 125°C	49

Environmental ageing data

Air-oven ageing for 7 days at 100°C	
change in hardness, IRHD	+4
change in M100, %	+20
change in M300, %	+10
change in TS, %	−25
change in EB, %	−30
ring fatigue life, kc	83

13.8 Truck and bus inner tubes **50–55 IRHD**

In some countries, natural rubber inner tubes are preferred for ease of repair. Formulation 4 gives improved air permeability; the zinc oxide should be added late in the mixing cycle and the dump temperature kept below 140°C.

Formulation

	1	2	3	4
SMR LV	100	100	80	50
SBR 1502			20	
Chlorobutyl[a]				50
N550, FEF black	20	30	30	
N762, SRF-LM-NS black				40
Whiting	20		10	
Process oil[b]			5	
Zinc oxide	5	5	5	5
Stearic acid	3	2	1	2
Antioxidant, TMQ[c]	1	2		2
Antioxidant, MBI[d]		2		
Antioxidant, IPPD[e]			1	
Wax blend[f]	2	2	2	
Sulphur	2.2	0.6	1.3	
DTDM				0.5
MBTS	0.75			1
CBS		1.5	0.8	
TMTD		0.5	0.1	
TETD	0.25			1.2

a. *eg Exxon Chlorobutyl HT1066* (Exxon).
b. *eg Dutrex 729UK* (Shell).
c. *eg Flectol H* (Monsanto).
d. *eg Vulkanox MB* (Bayer).
e. *eg Permanax IPPD* (Vulnax).
f. *eg Sunproof Improved* (Uniroyal).

Rheological properties

	1	2	3	4
Mooney viscosity, 100°C	34	48	39	44
Mooney scorch, 120°C, min	19	12	16	20
Monsanto *Rheometer*, 160°C				
M_{HR}, torque units	33	27	21	25
M_L, torque units	7	8.5	5	8.2
scorch, t_{s1}, min	2.2	2.2	3.7	3.2
cure, $t_c'(95)$, min	4.8	5.2	5.7	20
cure, $t_c'(100)$, min	7	9	8	30
time to 5% reversion, min	30	35	25	>40

Reference: Technical Information Sheet D122:1983

13.8 (cont)

Vulcanizate properties, unaged

Formulation	1	2	3	4
Cure time at 160°C, min	5	5	6	16
Hardness, IRHD	55	55	52	50
Density, Mg/m^3	1.12	1.07	1.11	1.11
MR100, MPa	1.31	1.18	1.13	0.93
Resilience, Lupke, %	79	70.6	66	32
Abrasion, DIN, mm^3	260	250	260	265
Tensile properties				
M100, MPa	1.3	1.25	1.2	1.2
M300, MPa	4.9	5.2	4.9	4.9
TS, MPa	20	24.5	21.5	10.5
EB, %	575	645	665	550
Tear, ISO trouser				
23°C, median, kN/m	10.8	14.8	12.6	8.8
high/low ratio	1.2	1.8	1.2	1.4
100°C,median, kN/m	6.2	16.4	9.3	2.3
high/low ratio	1.4	1.2	1.2	2
Ring fatigue life, 0–100% strain				
median, kc	52	57	93	269
high/low ratio	1.1	1.5	1.4	1.7
Compression set, %				
1 day at −26°C	25	80	39	68
3 days at 23°C	8	18	8	36
1 day at 70°C	29	31	31	34
1 day at 100°C	52	49	60	52
Air permeability, 30°C, m^2/Pa.s$x10^{-17}$	8.3	8.7	8.7	2.7

13.8 (cont)

Environmental ageing data

Formulation	1	2	3	4
Air-oven ageing for 7 days at 70°C				
change in hardness, IRHD	+8	+3	+7	+5
change in M100, %	+25	+22	+40	+20
change in M300, %	+40	+20	+45	+15
change in TS, %	−4	+3	0	+11
change in EB, %	−13	−6	−14	−6
Air-oven ageing for 3 days at 100°C				
change in hardness, IRHD	+8	+1	+7	+6
change in M100, %	+40	+16	+45	+34
change in TS, %	−40	−11	−25	+26
change in EB, %	−38	−11	−28	−15
Air-oven ageing for 3 days at 125°C				
change in hardness, IRHD		−10		−4
change in M100, %		+3		+13
change in TS, %		−50		+6
change in EB, %		−30		−7
Low-temperature storage at −26°C				
time to				
5 point IRHD rise, days	3	1	1	3
10 point IRHD rise, days	>28	2	3	5
20 point IRHD rise, days	>28	5	7	7

Section 14 Miscellaneous

14.1 Rubber-coated fabric
14.2 Thermoplastic natural rubber blends
14.3 Moulded sponge
14.4 Air-cured sponge
14.5 Waffle sponge carpet underlay
14.6 Expanded rubber

14.1 Rubber-coated fabric **60 IRHD**

For very demanding applications involving severe flexing and abrasion, *eg* hovercraft skirts. An RFL bonding system is included; best adhesion is obtained to RFL-treated fabric.

Formulation

SMR 5	80
Low-*cis* polybutadiene[a]	20
N330, HAF black	25
Precipitated silica[b]	15
Process oil[c]	4
Zinc oxide	5
Stearic acid	2
Antidegradant, HPPD[d]	3
Wax blend[e]	1
Bonding agent[f]	5
Sulphur	2.25
TBBS	1.2
TETD	0.1

a. Solution-polymerized low-*cis* polybutadiene, *Intene 55 NF* (Enichem).
b. *eg Ultrasil VN3* (Degussa).
c. *eg Dutrex 729UK* (Shell).
d. *eg Santoflex 13* (Monsanto).
e. *eg Sunproof Improved* (Uniroyal).
f. Solution of resorcinol in formaldehyde donor, *Cohedur RL* (Bayer).

Rheological properties

Mooney viscosity, 100°C	83
Mooney scorch, 120°C, min	28
Monsanto *Rheometer*, 140°C	
M_{HR}, torque units	34
M_L, torque units	12.5
scorch, t_{s1}, min	8.5
cure, $t_c'(95)$, min	18
cure, $t_c'(100)$, min	25
time to 5% reversion, min	41

Reference: Technical Information Sheet D40:1978

14.1 (cont)

Vulcanizate properties, unaged

Cure: 25min at 140°C	
Hardness, IRHD	59
Density, Mg/m^3	1.10
MR100, MPa	1.50
Resilience, Lupke, %	73
Abrasion, DIN, mm^3	185
Tensile properties	
M100, MPa	1.5
M300, MPa	7.7
TS, MPa	25
EB, %	585
Tear, ISO trouser	
23°C, median, kN/m	14
high/low ratio	1.9
100°C, median, kN/m	7
high/low ratio	1.4
Ring fatigue life, 0–100% strain	
median, kc	125
high/low ratio	1.6
Compression set, %	
1 day at −26°C	15
3 days at 23°C	6
1 day at 70°C	35
1 day at 100°C	54
Peel strength to nylon fabric, kN/m	
untreated fabric	2.5–5
RFL-treated fabric	12–20

Environmental ageing data

Air-oven ageing for 7 days at 70°C	
change in hardness, IRHD	+5
change in M100, MPa	+25
change in M300, MPa	+25
change in TS, %	−10
change in EB, %	−10
Air-oven ageing for 3 days at 100°C	
change in hardness, IRHD	+7
change in M100, MPa	+45
change in TS, %	−30
change in EB, %	−30
Ozone resistance, 50pphm, 40°C, 20% strain	
time to first crack, days	2

14.2 Thermoplastic natural rubber blends **35–70 Shore D**

Formulation 1 is suitable for cable insulation; formulations 2 and 3 are for general-purpose use; formulation 4 is a natural colour grade suitable for outdoor use; formulation 5 is recommended for complex injection mouldings; formulations 6–8 are high modulus impact-resistant materials.

Formulation

	1	2	3	4	5	6	7	8
Colour	White	White	Black	Natural	Black	Natural	Black	Black
Nominal hardness, Shore D	35	45	45	45	50	60	65	70
SMR L	70	50	50	55	42	35	30	15
Propathane GWM 101[a]	30	50	50					85
RMT 6100[b]				45	60			
KMT 6100[b]						65	70	
Oil[c]	15				8			
Precipitated silica[d]	15							
Hard clay[e]		85						
Zinc oxide	4							
Stearic acid	1							
TMTD	1							
Paraffin wax		3						
N550, FEF black					8			
N330, HAF black			1				10	1
Titanium dioxide	1	1						
Phenolic antioxidant		0.3		0.5		0.3		
Antioxidant blend[f]	0.5							
Antioxidant, TMQ[g]			0.2		0.5		0.5	0.5
Antioxidant synergist[h]				0.2	0.2	0.2	0.2	0.2
UV absorber[i]				0.2	0.2	0.2	0.2	0.2

a. Pelletized polypropylene (ICI).
b. Polypropylene copolymer (Shell).
c. *eg Sunpar 2280* (Sun Oil).
d. *eg Ultrasil VN3* (Degussa).
e. *eg Stockalite* (English China Clays).
f. *eg Permanax CNS* (Vulnax).
g. *eg Flectol H* (Monsanto).
h. Dilauryl thiodiproprionate, *Irganox PS 800* (Ciba Geigy).
i. *eg Tinuvin 327* (Ciba Geigy).

Reference: *NR Technology* 1981, **12,** 59.

14.2 (cont)

Physical properties

Formulation	1	2	3	4	5	6	7	8
Hardness, Shore A	80	95	96	96	97	98	99	100
Hardness Shore D	34	46	47	46	50	60	65	68
Density, Mg/m^3	1.02	1.28	0.91	0.91	0.94	0.91	0.95	0.91
MFI (230°C, 50N), g/10min	2.7	5	6	10	25	10	7	20
Flexural modulus[a], MPa		200	300	290	260	600	700	800
Tensile properties								
M50, MPa	5	9	10	9	10	17	17	
TS, MPa	8	11	12	11	11	16	18	
EB, %	300	300	350	350	325	400	400	
Tensile yield stress, MPa						17	18	23
Tear strength, crescent, kN/m	40	75	80		92	150		

a. ASTM D790.

Note: stiffness may be varied by altering the ratio of natural rubber to polypropylene: tensile strength generally increases with polypropylene content; EB is very variable.

14.3 Sponge rubber
Moulded fine-pore blown sponge

Formulation

SMR 20[a]	100
Whiting	25
China clay	20
Process oil[b]	30
Zinc oxide	5
Stearic acid	5
Antioxidant[c]	1
Blowing agent[d]	4
Sulphur	3.5
CBS	0.25
Salicylic acid	2

a. Masticated to 15–20 Mooney.
b. Low viscosity paraffinic or naphthenic oil.
c. Non-staining phenolic type.
d. Nitroso type, *eg Vulcacel BN94* (Vulnax).

Properties

Mooney viscosity, 100°C		5	
Cure: 35min at 153°C			
Mould loading, %	33		45
Bulk density, Mg/m^3	0.44		0.50

14.4 Sponge rubber

Hot-air cured sponge

Formulation

SMR 20[a]	100
Whiting	300
Process oil[b]	30
Zinc oxide	5
Stearic acid	4
Antioxidant[c]	1
Blowing agent[d]	2
Sulphur	2.5
Accelerator[e]	1

a. Masticated to 20 Mooney.
b. Low-viscosity paraffinic or naphthenic oil.
c. Non-staining phenolic type.
d. Benzene sulphonyl hydrazide *eg Porofor BSH* (Bayer).
e. Dithiocarbamate/thiazole blend, *Vulcafor 5* (Vulnax).

Properties

Cure: 45min at 120°C	
Expansion, %	100
Bulk density, Mg/m^3	0.79

14.5 Waffle sponge carpet underlay

Formulation

SMR 20[a]	100
Aluminium silicate	20
Whiting	150
Process oil[b]	10
Zinc oxide	5
Stearic acid	5
Paraffin wax	1
Antioxidant[c]	1
Sulphur	2.5
Accelerator[d]	1
DPG	0.5
Blowing agent[e]	3

Cure: 3min at 145°C in hot air

a. Masticated to 25–40 Mooney.
b. Low-viscosity paraffinic or naphthenic oil.
c. Non-staining phenolic type.
d. Thiazole/thiuram disulphide blend.
e. Benzene sulphonyl hydrazide *eg Porofor BSH* (Bayer).

Reference: Technical Information Sheet D10:1976

14.6 Expanded rubber

Expanded rubbers are cured in a 2-stage process: a partial cure under pressure gives sufficient crosslinking to prevent rupture of the cell walls as the product expands out of the mould; the second stage inserts crosslinks in the expanded state, improving dimensional stability. Hardness and density vary with time and temperature of the stages.

Blowing agent BSH is active at a lower temperature than OBSH. Pore sizes are determined by the balance of rates of cure and decomposition of the blowing agent and the second stage conditions: formulation 1 gives cells of diameter about 0.1–0.4 mm, and formulation 3 gives 0.1mm or less, depending on cure conditions. A mould release agent is essential.

Formulation

	1	2	3
OENR 75/25N[a]	100	100	100
Talc[b]	100	100	100
Process aid[c]		3	3
Zinc oxide	5	5	5
Stearic acid	2	2	2
Antioxidant[d]	1	1	1
Sulphur	2	2	3
MBTS	1	1	1
BSH[e]	7		
OBSH[f]		7	7
Desiccant[g]	1	1	1
Pigment		as required	

a. Oil-extended natural rubber, 25% naphthenic oil.
b. *eg Steamic OOS* (Talc de Luzanac).
c. *eg Struktol W33* (Schill & Seilacher).
d. *eg Permanax EXP* (Vulnax).
e. *eg Genitron BSH* (Fisons).
f. *eg Celogen OT* (Uniroyal).
g. *eg Caloxol CP2* (John & E Sturge).

Rheological properties

	1	2	3
Mooney viscosity, 100°C	14	20	24
Mooney scorch, 120°C, min	4	41	44
Monsanto *Rheometer*, 160°C			
cure, $t_c'(60)$, min	3.2	4.7	3.8
cure, $t_c'(95)$, min	8	12	13

14.6 (cont)

Physical properties

Measured on press-cured sheets from a 4mm-thick mould lubricated with a mould release agent *eg Promol PK*; mould loading 103%.

Formulation	1	2	3
Cure 1			
first stage: 6min at 160°C			
second stage: 1h at 70°C			
Hardness, Shore OO	75	70	75
Density, Mg/m^3	0.58	0.39	0.52
Resilience, Lupke, %	70	69	69
Compression set[a], %			
1 day at 23°C	31	31	31
Cure 2			
first stage: 6min at 160°C			
second stage: 1h at 125°C			
Hardness, Shore OO	70	63	70
Density, Mg/m^3	0.37	0.28	0.4
Resilience, Lupke, %	73	68	68
Compression set[a], %			
1 day at 23°C	19	32	23
Cure 3			
first stage: time at 160°C, min	3		4
second stage: 1h at 70°C			
Hardness, Shore OO	65		75
Density, Mg/m^3	0.28		0.46
Resilience, Lupke, %	70		69
Compression set[a], %			
1d at 23°C	27		30
Cure 4			
first stage: time at 160°C, min	3		4
second stage: 1h at 125°C			
Hardness, Shore OO	60		65
Density, Mg/m^3	0.22		0.27
Resilience, Lupke, %	73		68

a. Compression set, 50% compression. Measurements made after 24h recovery.

Part B

Latex formulary

Natural rubber latex concentrate

Natural rubber latex concentrates differ in the preservative systems and the methods of concentration used in their preparation. There are three methods of concentration: centrifugation, creaming, and evaporation. Over 90% of all commercial latex is prepared by centrifugation, but creamed and evaporated latices are available for special applications. Creamed latex, which has a rubber content of 65–66%, is used in latex thread production, and evaporated latex, which has a rubber content in the range 60–66%, is used in various binder applications.

Centrifuged latex is available with high- or low-ammonia preservation systems. High-ammonia (HA) latex contains 0.7% ammonia on the weight of latex. The various low-ammonia (LA) latices contain 0.2% ammonia with secondary preservative systems such as zinc oxide/tetramethylthiuram disulphide (LA–TZ latex) or boric acid (LA–BA latex). In many applications either HA or LA latex can be used, but the ammonia content of HA latex is normally reduced to 0.1–0.2% before use. For special-quality dipped products such as baby feeding teats and soothers, or in certain adhesive applications, HA latex is preferred. In general dipping operations, carpet backing and thread production, LA latices, especially LA–TZ, are becoming increasingly popular, largely because of lower ammonia levels in the factory atmosphere.

Natural rubber latex is used predominantly in latex dipping where its high uncured gel strength, rapid vulcanization and excellent physical properties are essential. It is also used in latex thread manufacture. In carpet backing and moulded latex foam, blends of natural rubber and SBR latex may be used to meet particular processing and economic requirements. Products may be dipped to give a natural rubber layer with a NBR or CR latex layer on the outside, or *vice versa*.

Prevulcanized natural rubber latex does not require further compounding, and gives strong, vulcanized films on drying. It is suitable for dipping and adhesive applications, and is frequently used in smaller factories because of the absence of additional compounding.

Preparation of dispersions and emulsions for latex concentrate

Unless otherwise stated, the formulations are designed for 50% of the active ingredient. They relate to ball-milling, but are generally applicable to other milling techniques with minor adjustments. For information on the influence of particle size, refer to *NR Technology*, 1981, *12*, 1 and 21, and to *Plastics and Rubber Processing and Applications*, 1983, **3**, 71–76. The dispersant used throughout is that described in the first formulation.

General-purpose formulation for an aqueous dispersion

Suitable for a variety of insoluble solid compounding ingredients.

Compounding ingredient	50
Dispersant[a]	2
Water	48

Ball mill for 24–48h, avoiding excessive foaming

a. Sulphonate type. Suitable examples include *Anchoid* (Anchor), *Belloid TD* (Geigy), *Darvan* (Vanderbilt), *Daxad* (Dewey and Almy), *Vulcastab LR* (Vulnax) and *Vultamol* (BASF).

Zinc oxide dispersion

Zinc oxide	50
Bentonite clay	1
Dispersant	1
Water	48

Ball mill for 2–4h

Sulphur dispersion

Sulphur	50
10% Casein solution	30
Bentonite clay	1
Dispersant	1
Water	18

Ball mill for 36–48h

Dithiocarbamate accelerator dispersion

Dithiocarbamate	50
Dispersant	1.5
Bentonite clay	0.5
Water	48

Ball mill for 4h[a]

a. In the case of ZDBC it is advisable to grind the dry powder for 2h, then add water, etc and complete the milling.

Zinc 2-mercaptobenzothiazole (ZMBT) accelerator dispersion

ZMBT	50
Bentonite clay	0.25
Dispersant	1
10% Potassium hydroxide solution	0.5
Water	48.25

Ball mill for 2–4h[a]

a. It is advisable to maintain the stored dispersion at pH 9 or above using dilute alkali solution.

Antioxidant dispersion

In many cases the general-purpose formulation is suitable. For substituted phenols the following is suggested.

Antioxidant	50
Dispersant	2
Bentonite clay	0.5
Polyvinyl pyrollidone	1
Sodium dodecylsulphate	0.1
Water	46.4

Ball mill for 2–6hrs

Pigment dispersion (20% active)

Pigment	20
Bentonite clay	0.5
10% Non-ionic surfactant solution[a]	2
Water	77

Ball mill for 12–24h

a. *eg Vulcastab LW* (Vulnax).

Emulsion suitable for extender oils

Extender oil	50
20% Potassium oleate solution[a]	7.5
Water	42.5

Mix under high shear until satisfactory particle size distribution (5–20 microns) is obtained. If the oil is viscous, heat both oil and water to 60–70°C before mixing.

a. Or potassium laurate or ricinoleate. Alternatively, use an equal weight of a non-ionic surfactant of the polyoxyethylene type, *eg Vulcastab LW* (Vulnax) or *Texofor FN30* (ABM Chemicals), or the sulphated polyoxyethylene type, *eg Solumin FS 85SD* (ABM Chemicals).

Emulsion suitable for paraffin wax (33% active)

Part A		Part B	
Wax	50	Water	82.3
Oleic acid	3.75	Triethanolamine	2.5
		10% Casein solution	12.5

Part A: heat wax to 10–15°C above its melting point, then add oleic acid.
Part B: heat water to similar temperature to wax, then add triethanolamine and casein. Blend A and B and homogenize whilst maintaining the temperature above the melting point of the wax.

Section 15 Adhesives

15.1 Carpet installation backing adhesives
15.2 Tufted carpet secondary backing adhesives
15.3 Envelope self-seal adhesive
15.4 Quick-grab adhesives
15.5 Tile adhesives, ceramic tiles
15.6 Tile adhesives, vinyl tiles

See also: Solution adhesives (Section A1).

15.1 Carpet installation backing adhesives

Formulations for peelable and non-peelable types

Formulation

	1	2
	Peelable	Non-peelable
60% NR latex, LA-TZ type	167	167
25% Surfactant[a]	1	8
50% Resin emulsion[b]		100
Tetrasodium pyrophosphate[c]	0.2	0.1
China clay	50	25
50% ZDEC	2	2
50% Antioxidant[d]	2	
10% Thickener[e]	5	10

a. Sulphated alkyl phenol-ethylene oxide condensate, *eg Solumin FX85SD* (ABM Chemicals).
b. Hydrogenated rosin ester, eg *Staybelite Ester 10* (Hercules).
c. *eg Tetron* (Albright and Wilson).
d. Non-staining phenolic type.
e. Polyacrylate or cellulosic type. Minor adjustment of thickener dosage may be required to achieve the desired viscosity.

Reference: Technical Information Sheet L30:1978

15.2 Tufted-carpet secondary backing adhesives
Formulations for lick-roll application

The formulations are designed to give good adhesion of the second backing, provide tuft anchorage and give the desired 'hand' to the carpet.

Formulation

	1	2	3	4
	General purpose	Soft 'hand'	Stiff 'hand'	Maximum bond strength
60% NR latex, LA-TZ type	167	167	167	167
50% *Heveaplus MG 49* latex			60	60
25% Surfactant[a]	3	3	3	3
Tetrasodium pyrophosphate[b]	1	1	1	1
Water		to 68–75% total solids		
Filler[c]	300	100	300	100
50% ZDEC	2	2	2	2
50% Antioxidant[d]	2	2	2	2
10% Thickener[e]	5	5	5	5

a. Sulphated alkyl phenol-ethylene oxide condensate, *eg Glofoam HE* (ABM Chemicals).
b. *eg Tetron* (Albright and Wilson).
c. Whiting, limestone, or clay. Moderately fine particle size grades generally give best results.
d. Phenolic or amine types are suitable.
e. Polyacrylate type, *eg Rohagit S-MV* (Rohm and Haas), but cellulose derivatives may be used if desired. Minor adjustment of thickener dosage may be required to achieve the desired viscosity.

Notes on processing

Drying conditions are difficult to specify because they depend on the type of carpet and the efficiency of the oven, but might typically be 5–10min at 130°C.

Reference: Technical Information Sheet L7:1976

15.3 Self-seal envelope adhesive
General-purpose formulation

Formulation

60% NR latex, LA-TZ type	167
10% Potassium hydroxide	2
50% ZDEC[a]	1

a. Provides protection against degradation, particularly metal-catalysed oxidation.

Reference: Technical Information Sheet L35:1979

15.4 Quick-grab adhesives

Quick-grab adhesives are used for light-duty applications, the most common being the bonding of insoles and labels into shoes. Formulations are given using unmodified and hydroxylamine-modified latices.

Formulation

	1	2
60% NR latex, LA-TZ type	167	
66% HRH latex[a]		152
Toluene	3–5	
50% ZDEC	2	2

a. Centrifuged latex modified with 0.15% hydroxylamine immediately after concentration.

Notes on processing

The formulations have been designed with appropriate reduced mechanical stability for 'grab' charcteristics. If the stability needs further adjustment to suit processing conditions, increasing or reducing the water content will increase or reduce the stability. Increased stability may alternatively be obtained by adding thickeners.

Reference: Technical Information Sheet L34:1979

15.5 Ceramic tile adhesives

Suitable for bonding ceramic tiles to concrete, plaster, wood or hardboard. The filler level may be increased (as in the second formulation) but this reduces bond strength.

Formulation

	1	2
60% Hydrocarbon resin[a] solution[b]	167	167
Oleic acid	3	3
10% Potassium hydroxide	7.5	7.5
15% Casein	20	20
65% Clay slurry	233	388
60% NR latex, HA or LA-TZ type	167	167
Water	18	18
50% ZDEC	2	2
Cellulose thickener[c]	0.4	0.4

a. Aliphatic resin, softening point 100°C, *eg Escorez 1102B* (Exxon Chemicals).
b. White spirit or other suitable solvent.
c. High viscosity grade, *eg Celacol HPM 5000* (British Celanese) or *Methofas PM 4500* (ICI).

Notes on mix preparation

Add the materials in the order given. A water-in-oil dispersion of the clay slurry is formed initially, and inverts during the later stages of adding the slurry or latex. Adjust the thickener level to give the required viscosity. The conventional technique of adding resin and filler to the stabilized latex may not give such high bond strength.

Test results

Tile-to-concrete adhesion: 50x50mm overlap, tested in shear.		
7 days after bond preparation shearing force to rupture, N	1370	980
After further 7 days immersion in water, tested wet shearing force to rupture, N	440	370

15.6 Vinyl tile adhesive

Suitable for bonding vinyl tiles to concrete plaster, wood or hardboard.

Formulation

Terpene-phenolic resin[a]	100
Pale liquid coumarone resin	50
Process oil[b]	50
Oleic acid	22.5
Solvent[c]	25
10% Potassium hydroxide	40
15% Casein	20
Water	75
50% ZDEC	4
60% NR latex, HA or LA-TZ type	167
Clay	100
Cellulose thickener[d]	as required

a. *eg Schenectady SP560* (Schenectady).
b. Aromatic oil, *eg Dutrex 729* (Shell).
c. White spirit or other suitable solvent.
d. High-viscosity grade, *eg Celacol HPM 5000* (British Celanese) or *Methofas PM 4500* (ICI).

Notes on mix preparation

Dissolve the resins, oil and oleic acid in the solvent by heating and allow to cool. Add the potassium hydroxide and half the casein to the solution, followed by the water and ZDEC. Add the remainder of the casein to the latex before adding this to the mix. The clay may be added dry or may be slurried first with some of the water.

Test results

Vinyl-to-vinyl adhesion: 75x35mm ovelap.	
Tested 7 days after bond preparation	
Shearing force to rupture, N	300
180° peel force, N	19

Reference: Technical Information Sheet L50:1982

Section 16 Carpet backing applications

16.1 Anchor coats, tufted carpet, for foam application
16.2 Anchor coats, tufted carpet
16.3 Anchor backings, washable rug
16.4 Backings, carpet tile
16.5 Blown foam backings
16.6 Foam backings, flame retardant to ASTM D2859
16.7 Foam backings, non-gel, flame retardant to BS 4790:1972
16.8 Foam backings, tufted carpet
16.9 Foam backings, tufted carpet, non-gel
16.10 Sizings, woven carpet backing

16.1 Tufted carpet anchor coats for foam application

Formulation

	1	2
	Unfilled	Filled
60% NR latex, LA-TZ type	167	167
50% *Heveaplus MG 49* latex	30	30
20% Ammonium oleate	5	5
Tetrasodium pyrophosphate[a]		1
Filler[b]		50
50% ZDEC	2	2
50% Antioxidant[c]	2	2
10% Thickener[d]	4	4

a. *eg Tetron*, (Albright and Wilson).
b. Whiting, limestone or clay. Finer particle size grades generally give better tuft-bonding.
c. Phenolic or amine types are suitable.
d. Polyacrylate type, *eg Rohagit S-MV*, (Rohm and Haas), but cellulose derivatives may be used if desired. Minor adjustment of thickener dosage may be required to achieve the desired viscosity.

Notes on processing

Drying conditions are difficult to specify because they depend on the type of carpet and the efficiency of the oven, but might typically be 5–10min at 130°C.

Reference: Technical Information Sheet L6:1976

16.2 Tufted carpet anchor coats

Formulations for lick-roll applications

Formulation

	General-purpose	Soft 'hand'	Stiff 'hand'	Maximum bond strength
60% NR latex, LA-TZ type	167	167	167	167
50% *Heveaplus MG 49* latex			60	200
25% Surfactant[a]	3	3	3	3
Tetrasodium pyrophosphate[b]	1	1	1	1
Water		to 72–75% total solids		
Filler[c]	400	100	400	100
50% ZDEC	2	2	2	2
50% Antioxidant[d]	2	2	2	2
Anti-foam agent		as necessary		
10% Thickener[e]	4	4	4	4

a. Sulphated alkyl phenol-ethylene oxide condensate, *eg Solumin FX85SD* (ABM Chemicals).
b. *eg Tetron* (Albright and Wilson).
c. Whiting, limestone or clay. Finer particle size grades generally give better tuft-bonding.
d. Phenolic or amine type anioxidants are suitable.
e. Polyacrylate type, *eg Rohagit* S-MV (Rohm and Haas), but cellulose derivatives may be used if desired. Minor adjustment of thickener dosage may be required to achieve the desired viscosity.

Notes on processing

Drying conditions are difficult to specify because they depend on the type of carpet and the efficiency of the oven, but might typically be 5–10min at 130°C.

Reference: Technical Information Sheet L6:1976

16.3 Washable rug anchor backings

General-purpose formulation

Formulation

60% NR latex, LA-TZ type	167
25% Surfactant[a]	3
Filler[b]	50
50% Zinc oxide	6
50% Sulphur	4
50% ZDEC	2
50% ZMBT	2
50% Antioxidant[c]	2
10% Thickener[d]	10

a. Sulphated alkyl phenol-ethylene oxide condensate, *eg Solumin FX85SD* (ABM Chemicals).
b. Whiting, limestone or clay.
c. An effective antioxidant is essential for adequate ageing/washing resistance. Suitable non-staining phenolic types include *Antioxidant 2246* or *425* (Cyanamid), *Permanax WSP* (Vulnax).
d. Polyacrylate or cellulosic type. Minor adjustment of the thickener level may be required to obtain the desired viscosity.

Notes on processing

Apply the mix by a lick-roll technique. Suitable drying and curing conditions are 15min at 130°C, but minor adjustments may be necessary, depending on the oven capacity and throughput rate. Oven temperatures above 150°C are not recommended.

Reference: Technical Information Sheet L31:1979

16.4 Carpet tile backings

Formulations for foamed and unfoamed types

Formulation

	1	2
	Unfoamed	Foamed
60% NR latex, LA-TZ type	167	167
25% Surfactant[a]	2	2
20% Potassium oleate		20
Tetrasodium pyrophosphate[b]	1	1
Water	to 70–75% total solids	
Filler[c]	250	400
50% Sulphur	4	4
50% ZDEC	2	3
50% ZMBT	2	3
50% Antioxidant[d]	2	2
10% Thickener[e]	7.5	10
50% Zinc oxide	8	8
20% Ammonium acetate	12.5	12.5

a. Sulphated alkyl phenol-ethylene oxide condensate, *eg Glofoam HE* (ABM Chemicals).
b. *eg Tetron*, (Albright and Wilson).
c. Whiting, limestone or clay.
d. *eg* Polymerized 2,2,4-trimethyl-1,2-dihydroquinoline.
e. Polyacrylate type, *eg Rohagit S-MV* (Rohm and Haas), but cellulose derivatives may be used if desired.

Notes on processing

Zinc oxide and ammonium acetate are not added with the other ingredients. In the unfoamed formulation, they are added to the mix immediately before use. In foam formulation, they are metered in *via* a blender unit after the base mix has been foamed.

The gelled foam should be crushed to increase its density. Drying and curing conditions are difficult to specify because they depend on the thickness of the backing, the type of carpet and the efficiency of the oven; they might typically be 20min at 130°C for a 5mm thick backing.

Reference: Technical Information Sheet L11:1976

16.5 Blown foam carpet backing

The formulation is especially suitable for thin dense backings, such as for carpet tiles. The latex mix can be applied by a simple lick-roll technique.

Formulation

60% NR latex, LA-TZ type	167
20% Potassium oleate	5
20% Surfactant[a]	2.5
Filler[b]	50
Blowing agent[c]	5
50% Zinc oxide	6
50% Sulphur	4
50% ZDEC	2
50% ZMBT	2
50% Antioxidant[d]	2
20% Ammonium acetate	5
10% Thickener[e]	10

a. Non-ionic type; alkyl phenol-ethylene oxide condensate containing *ca* 30 moles ethylene oxide per mole, *eg Texofor FN30* (ABM Chemicals).
b. Whiting, limestone or clay.
c. Nitroso type, *eg Vulcacel BN94* (Vulnax).
d. Phenolic or amine types are suitable.
e. Polyacrylate or cellulosic type.

Notes on processing

Drying and curing conditions are difficult to specify because they depend on the thickness of foam, the type of carpet and the efficiency of the oven; they might typically be 20min at 130°C for a 5mm thick foam.

Reference: Technical Information Sheet L29:1978

16.6 Foam backings, flame retardant to ASTM D2859

This formulation meets the compositional and general property requirements of the American Carpet and Rug Institute specification for high density backing foam and passes the flammability test of ASTM D2859.

Formulation

60% NR latex, LA-TZ type	167
20% Potassium oleate	20
50% Sulphur	5
50% ZDEC	2
50% ZMBT	2
50% Antioxidant[a]	3
50% Chlorinated wax[b]	10
50% *Tetrabromobisphenol A*[c]	15
Water	to 67% total solids
Hydrated alumina[d]	45
Filler[e]	50
5% Thickener[f]	as required
50% Zinc oxide	5
20% Ammonium acetate	12.5

a. *eg* Polymerized 2,2,4-trimethyl-1,2-dihydroquinoline.
b. Solid chlorinated paraffin wax containing 70% chlorine, *eg Cereclor 70* (ICI).
c. Great Lakes Chemical Corp.
d. *eg Baco FRFS* or a finer grade, *eg Baco FRF40* (British Aluminium Co).
e. Whiting, limestone or clay.
f. Polyacrylate type, *eg Rohagit S-MV* (Rohm and Haas), but cellulose derivatives may be used if desired.

Notes on processing

Drying and curing conditions are difficult to specify because they depend on the thickness of foam, the type of carpet and the efficiency of the oven; they might typically be 20min at 130°C for a 5mm thick foam.

Reference: Technical Information Sheet L12:1976

16.7 Foam backings, non-gel, flame retardant to BS 4790:1972

The formulation passes the flammability test (hot metal nut method) of BS4790.

Formulation

60% NR, LA-TZ type	167
25% Surfactant[a]	18.0
28% Sodium dodecyl sulphate	3.6
20% Potassium laurate	10
Tetrasodium pyrophosphate[b]	1
50% Sulphur	4
50% ZDEC	3
50% ZMBT	3
50% Antioxidant[c]	3
50% Zinc oxide	6
Water	to 75% total solids
Hydrated alumina[d]	180–200
5% Thickener[e]	as required

a. Alkyl sulphosuccinamate type, *eg Alcopol FA* (Allied Colloids).
b. *eg Tetron*, (Albright and Wilson).
c. *eg* Polymerized 2,2,4-trimethyl-1,2-dihydroquinoline.
d. *eg Baco FRF5* or finer grade *Baco FRF40* (British Aluminium Co).
e. Polyacrylate type, *eg Rohagit S-MV* (Rohm and Haas), but cellulose derivatives may be used if desired.

Notes on processing

Drying and curing conditions are difficult to specify because they depend on the thickness of foam, the type of carpet and the efficiency of the oven; they might typically be 20min at 130°C for a 5mm thick foam.

Reference: Technical Information Sheet L12:1976

16.8 Tufted carpet foam backings

Gelled foams

Formulation

	1	2
	Flat backing	Embossed backing
60% NR latex, LA-TZ type	167	167
20% Potassium oleate	15	15
30% Foam stabilizer[a]	1.5	1.5
Tetrasodium pyrophosphate[b]	1	1
Water		16
Filler[c]	100	150
50% Sulphur	5	5
50% ZDEC	2	2
50% ZMBT	2	2
50% Antioxidant[d]	2	2
10% Thickener[e]	5	5
50% Zinc oxide	8	6
10% Ammonium acetate	20	20

a. Alkyl sulphosuccinamate type surfactant, *eg Alcopol FA* (Allied Colloids).
b. *eg Tetron*, (Albright and Wilson).
c. Whiting, limestone or clay.
d. Polymerized 2,2,4-trimethyl-1,2-dihydroquinoline.
e. Polyacrylate type, *eg Rohagit S-MV* (Rohm and Haas), but cellulose derivatives may be used if desired.

Notes on processing

The last two components are metered in after foaming the base mix. Drying and curing conditions are difficult to specify because they depend on the thickness of foam, the type of carpet and the efficiency of the oven; they might typically be 20min at 130°C for a 5mm thick foam.

Reference: Technical Information Sheet L9:1976

16.9 Non-gel tufted carpet foam backings

Formulation

	1	2
	General purpose	Heavy duty
60% NR latex, LA-TZ type	167	167
30% Foam stabilizer[a]	18	12
28% Sodium dodecyl sulphate	7.2	3.6
20% Potassium oleate	5	5
20% Secondary foam stablizer[b]		5
Tetrasodium pyrophosphate[c]	1	1
Water	to 72–75% total solids	
Filler[d]	150–200	100
50% Zinc oxide	6	6
50% Sulphur	4.5	4.5
50% ZDEC	3	3
50% ZMBT	3	3
50% Antioxidant[e]	2	2
10% Thickener[f]	10	10

a. Alkyl sulphosuccinamate type surfactant, *eg Alcopol FA* (Allied Colloids).
b. Cetyl/oleyl alcohol-ethylene oxide condenstate, *eg Vulcastab LW* (Vulnax).
c. *eg Tetron*, (Albright and Wilson).
d. Whiting, limestone or clay.
e. *eg* Polymerized 2,2,4-trimethyl-1,2-dihydroquinoline.
f. Polyacrylate type, *eg Rohagit S-MV* (Rohm and Haas), but cellulose derivatives may be used if desired. Minor adjustment of thickener dosage may be required to achieve the desired viscosity.

Notes on processing

Drying and curing conditions are difficult to specify because they depend on the thickness of foam, the type of carpet and the efficiency of the oven; they might typically be 20min at 130°C for a 5mm thick foam.

Reference: Technical Information Sheet L8:1976

16.10 Woven carpet backing sizings
Translucent and opaque formulations

Formulation

	1	2	3
	Soft translucent	Stiff translucent	Stiff opaque
60% NR latex, LA-TZ type	167	167	167
50% *Heveaplus MG 49* latex		60	
25% Surfactant[a]	3	3	3
Tetrasodium pyrophosphate[b]			1
Water		as necessary	
Filler[c]			300
50% ZDEC	2	2	2
50% Antioxidant[d]	2	2	2
10% Potassium hydroxide	1	1	1
Antifoam agent		as necessary	
10% Thickener[e]			5

a. Sulphated alkyl phenol-ethylene oxide condensate, *eg Solumin FX85SD* (ABM Chemicals).
b. *eg Tetron* (Albright and Wilson).
c. Whiting, limestone or clay.
d. Phenolic or amine types are suitable.
e. Polyacrylate type, *eg Rohagit S–MV* (Rohm and Haas), but cellulose derivatives may be used if desired.

Notes on processing

Drying conditions are difficult to specify because they depend on the type of carpet and the efficiency of the oven, but might typically be 5–10min at 130°C.

Reference: Technical Information Sheet L10:1976

Section 17 Dipped Products

17.1 Adhesive, flocking
17.2 Gloves, household, detergent-resistant
17.3 Gloves, electricians to BS 697:1977, 1100 volt rating
17.4 Gloves, household, coagulant-dipped
17.5 Gloves, laminated
17.6 Heat-sensitive latex formulations
17.7 Teats, high transparency
17.8 Toy balloons
17.9 Gloves, surgeons'
17.10 Condoms

17.1 Flocking adhesive

The formulation is designed for low drainage (hence the incorporation of thickener) and to resist premature gelation which would otherwise reduce adhesion.

Formulation

60% NR latex, LA-TZ type	167
20% Surfactant[a]	2.5
10% Potassium hydroxide	2
50% Sulphur	2
50% ZDEC	2
50% Zinc oxide	2
50% Antioxidant[b]	2
Antifoaming agent[c]	0.1
10% Thickener[d]	2.0

a. Non-ionic type, *eg Texofor FN30* (ABM Chemicals) or *Lubrol PF* (ICI).
b. Non-staining phenolic type.
c. *eg* Trimethyl hexanol or silicone type.
d. Polyacrylate type, *eg Rohagit S–MV* (Rohm and Haas), but cellulose derivatives may also be used if desired. Minor adjustment of thickener dosage using the required to achieve the desired viscosity.

Reference: Technical Information Sheet L19:1977

17.2 Detergent-resistant household gloves

Formulation for coagulant dipping

Resistance to ageing after exposure to detergent is improved by using a vulcanizing system containing sulphenamide, morpholine or guanidine accelerators.

Formulation

	1	2	3	4
60% NR latex, LA-TZ type	167	167	167	167
10% Potassium hydroxide	2.5	2.5	2.5	2.5
20% Potassium laurate	1.3	1.3	1.3	1.3
50% Sulphur	2.5	2.5	2.5	2.5
50% Zinc oxide	2.0	2.0	2.0	2.0
50% ZDEC	0.4	0.4	0.4	0.4
50% ZMBT	2	2	2	2
50% TBBS	3			
10% Thiourea	10	10		10
50% DTDM[a]			2	
20% DPG			6	6
50% Antioxidant[b]	3	3	3	3

a. *eg Sulfasan R* (Monsanto).

b. An effective antioxidant is essential for detergent resistance. Suitable non-staining phenolic types include *Antioxidant 2246* or *425* (Cyanamid), or *Permanax WSP* (Vulnax). The results shown above were obtained using polymerized 2,2,4-trimethyl-1,2-dihydro- quinoline.

Properties

Cure: 30–60min at 120°C				
TS, MPa	32.5	36.6	40.9	41.9
EB, %	800	765	840	835
M300, MPa	1.33	2.09	1.83	1.95
Immersed 1h at 100°C in 1% detergent (*Omo*, Unilever): after air-oven ageing for 14 days at 70°C				
TS, MPa	19.9	26.5	25.5	30.9
EB, %	745	715	805	830

Reference: Technical Information Sheet L40:1980, and Gorton A.D.T., *Plastics and Rubber Materials and Applications*, 1979, **4**, 119.

17.3 Electricians' gloves to BS 697:1977, 1100-volt rating

Formulation

60% NR latex, HA or LA-TZ type[a]	167
20% Potassium laurate	1
10% Potassium hydroxide	2
50% Sulphur	2.4
50% ZDEC	3
50% Antioxidant[b]	2
40% Formaldehyde	to give pH 9.3
15% Polyvinyl methyl ether[c]	6
50% Zinc oxide	2

a. Special latices, such as doubly centrifuged and sub-stage types, may also be used with advantage since they have lower non-rubber solids than normal grades and thus give products containing lower quantities of water-soluble materials.
b. Any effective antioxidant may be used.
c. *eg Gantrez M154*, (General Aniline and Film Co) or *Lutanol M40* (BASF).

Notes on processing

During dipping, maintain latex pH between 9.0 and 9.5. The product must be thoroughly leached in water, as its electrical resistance is primarily dependent on leaching efficiency. Use a short wet-gel leach followed by a prolonged leach after stripping from the former. Suggested drying and curing conditions are 50min at 70°C followed by 45min at 120°C.

Reference: Technical Information Sheet L27:1978

17.4 Coagulant-dipped household gloves

Prevulcanized and vulcanizable formulations

Formulation

	1	2
	Prevulcanized	Vulcanizable
60% Prevulcanized NR latex	167	
60% NR latex, LA-TZ type		167
10% Potassium hydroxide	2	4
20% Potassium laurate		2
50% Sulphur		2.5
50% ZDEC		2
50% Antioxidant[a]	2	2
50% Zinc oxide		2
Colour[b]	as required	as required

a. Non-staining phenolic type.
b. To obtain a white base for pigmentation, titanium dioxide or lithopone are commonly used, either alone or in combination with *eg* whiting. Small amounts of filler and/or oils may be added if desired.

Notes on processing

The coagulant, usually calcium nitrate in alcohol or an alcohol/water mixture, is applied to the warm former. Vulcanization is normally in a hot-air oven at 110°C–140°C; at 130°C the vulcanizable mix will dry and cure in about 30min. Adequate leaching is necessary if prevulcanized latex is used.

Reference: Technical Information Sheet L18:1977

17.5 Laminated gloves

NR/chloroprene rubber latex blends for coagulant dipping

Formulation

NR layer	
60% NR latex, HA or LA-TZ type	167
10% Surfactant[a]	2
10% Potassium hydroxide	0.25
50% Zinc oxide	6
33% TMTD	9
10% Thiourea	10
50% ZDEC	2
50% Antioxidant[b]	2
50% Lithopone	10
Colour	as required

CR layer	
60% CR latex[c]	167
10% Casein	3.25
10% Surfactant[a]	2
50% Sulphur	2
47% Sodium dibutyldithiocarbamate[d]	2
33% TMTD	3
50% Antioxidant[b]	4
50% Zinc oxide	10
50% Filler slurry[e]	60
Colour	as required

a. Sulphated alkyl phenol-ethylene oxide condensate, *eg Solumin FX85SD* (ABM Chemicals).
b. Styrenated phenol type.
c. *eg Neoprene 650* (DuPont).
d. *eg Tepidone* (DuPont).
e. Prepared by adding 25 parts lithopone, 50 parts clay and 75 parts whiting to 150 parts of 1% sodium alkyl naphthalene sulphonate solution.

Notes on processing

Dry glove for 1h at 70°C and cure for 1h at 120°C.

Reference: Technical Information Sheet L32:1979

17.6 Heat-sensitive latex formulations

In these formulations the heat-sensitive system is based on low cloud-point, non-ionic surfactants. The formulation containing glycol has the greater heat sensitivity.

Formulation

	1	2
60% NR latex, LA-TZ type	167	
60% NR latex, HA type		167
25% Surfactant[a]		0.8
50% Zinc oxide	2	3
50% ZDEC	1	1
50% Sulphur	2	2
50% Antioxidant[b]	1	1
25% Low cloud point, non-ionic surfactant[c]	10	5
25% Polypropylene glycol[d]		5

a. Non-ionic type, *eg Texofor FN30* (ABM Chemicals) or *Vulcastab LW* (Vulnax).
b. *eg* Non-staining phenolic type.
c. Alkyl phenol-ethylene oxide adducts and fatty alcohol-ethylene oxide adducts having 'cloud points' in the range 40–60°C are suitable, *eg Texofor V27* (ABM Chemicals), *Empilan NP9* (Albright and Wilson) and *Triton CF21* (Rohm and Haas).
d. *eg* Propylan D702 (Lankro Chemicals).

Properties

	1	2
Gelation temperature, °C	>30	40
Minimum storage life at 25°C, weeks	2	2
Cure	30min at 100°C	

Reference: Technical Information Sheet L44:1981

17.7 High transparency teats

Formulations for coagulant and heat-sensitive dipping.

Formulation

	1	2
	Coagulant dipping	Heat-sensitive dipping
60% NR latex, LA-TZ type	167	167
70% Potassium laurate	2	
10% Potassium hydroxide	2	
20% Surfactant[a]		2
40% Formaldehyde		to pH 7.5–8.0
50% ZDBC	2	2
50% Sulphur	2	2
10% Polyvinyl methyl ether[b]		10

a. Non-ionic type: an alkyl phenol-ethylene oxide condensate containing *ca* 30moles ethylene oxide per mole, *eg Texofor FN30*, (ABM Chemicals).

b. *eg Gantrez M154* (General Aniline and Film Co) or *Lutanol M40*, (BASF).

Notes on processing

Prevulcanize mix 1 for 2h at 60°C. Dip the teats, dry at 70°C and leach thoroughly. A solution of cyclohexylamine acetate (*Coagulant CAA*, Bayer) is sometimes preferred for dipping instead of calcium nitrate for maximum transparency.

Users must ensure that the formulations meet the health requirements of the country in which the product will be sold. These requirements vary widely and are subject to frequent changes.

Reference: Technical Information Sheet L41:1981

17.8 Toy balloons

Prevulcanized and vulcanizable formulations

Formulation

	1	2
	Prevulcanized	Vulcanizable
60% Prevulcanized NR latex	167	
60% NR latex, LA-TZ type		167
10% Potassium hydroxide	2	4
20% Potassium laurate		2
50% Sulphur		1
50% ZDEC		1.5
50% Antioxidant[a]	2	2
50% Zinc oxide		0.5
Water	3	
Colour	as required	

Dry and cure: 20–25min at 120°C

a. Some countries do not allow antioxidants in toy balloons. If used, the antioxidant should be a low-toxicity type; suppliers should be consulted.

Notes on processing

Where prevulcanized latex is used, the product should be thoroughly leached if the best strength/elongation properties are required.

Reference: Technical Information Sheet L20:1977

17.9 Surgeons' gloves

Formulations for disposable and sterilizable gloves

The formulation for sterilizable gloves uses a low-sulphur EV system designed to give good ageing properties. For good transparency the level of zinc oxide has been kept as low as possible and the rubber-soluble zinc dibutyldithiocarbamate has been used.

Formulation

	1	2
	Disposable	Sterilizable
60% Natural rubber latex, LA-TZ type	167	167
20% Potasium laurate solution[a]	1	1
10% Potasium hydroxide solution	3	3
50% Sulphur	1	0.4
50% TMTD		1
50% ZDBC	1.5	2
Zinc oxide	0.5	0.5
50% Antioxidant[b]	1	2

a. Potasium caprylate is also suitable.
b. Non-staining phenolic *eg Antioxidant 2246* (Cyanamid) or *Permananx WSL* (Vulnax).

Notes on processing

The coagulant applied to the former is usually calcium nitrate in aqueous methylated spirit. A drying and cure time of 15min at 120°C is suitable for both formulations.

Reference: Technical Information Sheet L51:1982

17.10 Condoms

These formulations are designed for stripping of condoms in the dry, using rotating brushes, or in the wet, using air and pressurized water sprays.

Formulation

	1	2
	Dry strip	Wet strip
60% NR latex, LA-TZ type	167	167
10% Potassium hydroxide	2	2
20% Potassium laurate	0.5	10
50% Sulphur	1.8	1.5
50% Zinc oxide	0.5	0.5
50% ZDBC	1	1.5
50% ZMBT	2.5	1.5
50% Antioxidant[a]	1	1
Water	24	15

a. Non-toxic, non-staining phenolic type.

Notes on processing

The mix should be matured before use, suitable conditions being 36h at 25°C for formulation 1 and 4h at 55°C for formulation 2. On withdrawal from the mix, the formers are rotated to even the deposit at the end and partially dried at 60–80°C before being given a second dip. Suitable cure conditions are 20min at 110°C prior to stripping.

Reference: *NR Technology*, 1983, **14**, 66.

Section 18 Latex Foam

18.1 Flame-retardant foam
18.2 Moulded foam, heat-sensitive formulation
18.3 Moulded foam, silico-fluoride formulation
18.4 Spread foam

18.1 Flame-retardant foam

Flame-retardant formulation to Federal Motor Vehicle Safety Standard 302.

Formulation

60% NR latex, LA-TZ type	167
20% Potassium oleate	7.5
50% Sulphur	5
50% ZDEC	2
50% ZMBT	2
50% Antioxidant[a]	2
50% Chlorinated wax[b]	5
50% *Tetrabromobisphenol A*[c]	10
50% Hydrated alumina[d]	20
50% Secondary gelling agent[e]	2
50% Zinc oxide	6
20% Sodium silicofluoride	5

Dry and cure: 30min at 100°C in steam

a. *eg* Polymerized 2,2,4-trimethyl-1,2-dihydroquinoline.
b. Solid chlorinated paraffin wax containing 70% chlorine, *eg Cereclor 70* (ICI).
c. Great Lakes Chemical Co.
d. *eg Baco FRF5* or *Baco FRF40* (British Aluminimum Co).
e. Ethyl chloride-formaldehyde-ammonia reaction product, *eg Trimene Base* (Uniroyal) or *Vulcafor EFA* (Vulnax).

Properties

Density, Mg/m3	0.1
FMVSS burn rate, mm/min[a]	50

a. A foam made to the same formulation without the flame-retardant additives gave a burn rate of 150mm/min.

Reference: Technical Information Sheet L22:1978

18.2 Moulded foam

Heat-sensitive formulation using polypropylene glycol

This formulation is recommended for articles of relatively thin section.

Formulation

60% NR latex, HA type	167
20% Potassium ricinoleate[a]	1
50% Antioxidant[b]	2
50% ZDEC	2
50% ZMBT	2
50% Sulphur	5
50% Filler slurry[c]	as required
50% Colour	as required
25% Polypropylene glycol[d]	10
10% Secondary gelling agent[e]	1
50% Zinc oxide	6

Cure: 30min at 100°C in steam or hot water

a. Castor oil soap.
b. Non-staining phenolic type.
c. Whiting, clay, talc, lithopone, etc.
d. *eg Propylan D702* (Lankro Chemicals).
e. *eg* Cetyl trimethylammonium bromide or similar cationic surfactant.

Notes on processing

Mix the latex with the ricinoleate, antioxidant, accelerators and sulphur, and then foam to the required volume before adding a mixture of the remaining ingredients. Pour the foam into a mould preheated to 55–65°C, close and allow to gel for 5–10min. To cure, heat the mould in steam or hot air at 100°C for *ca* 30min. This heat-sensitive gelling system is more easily controlled than the silico-fluoride system.

Reference: Technical Information Sheet L33:1979

18.3 Moulded foam
Formulation for silico-fluoride (Dunlop) method

This formulation is suitable for any type of foam product.

Formulation

60% NR latex, LA-TZ type	167
50% Sulphur	4
20% Potassium oleate	7.5
50% ZDEC	2
50% ZMBT	2
50% Antioxidant[a]	2
50% Secondary gelling agent[c]	1.6
50% Zinc oxide	10
20% Sodium silicofluoride	6

a. Non-staining phenolic type.
b. Ethyl chloride-formaldehyde-ammonia reaction product, *eg Trimene Base* (Uniroyal) or *Vulcafor EFA* (Vulnax).

Notes on processing

Careful control of mix temperature is important. Suitable curing conditions are 20–30min at 100°C in open steam or 60min at 120°C in hot air.

Reference: Technical Information Sheet L42:1981

18.4 Spread foam

Heat-sensitive formulation using polypropylene glycol

Applications of spread foam include carpet backings and underlays.

Formulation

60% NR latex, HA type	167
20% Potassium ricinoleate (castor oil soap)	6
50% Antioxidant[a]	2
10% Casein	10
50% ZDEC	2
50% ZMBT	2
50% Sulphur	5
China clay	70–100
50% Colour	as required
25% Polypropylene glycol[b]	4
10% Secondary gelling agent[c]	6
50% Zinc oxide	6

a. Non-staining phenolic type.
b. *eg Propylan D702* (Lankro Chemicals).
c. *eg* Cetyl trimethylammonium bromide or similar cationic surfactant.

Notes on processing

Mix the latex with the ricinoleate, antioxidant, casein, accelerators and sulphur, and then foam to approximately six times its original volume before adding a mixture of the remaining ingredients. Gel in a hot-air stream at 90°C or using an infra-red heating unit. Dry and cure in a hot-air oven at 100–130°C. This heat-sensitive gelling system is more easily controlled than the silico-fluoride system.

Reference: Technical Information Sheet L33:1979

Section 19 Prevulcanized Latices

19.1 Prevulcanized latices, general-purpose
19.2 Prevulcanized latices, heat resistant
19.3 Prevulcanized latices, copper ageing-resistant
19.4 Prevulcanized latices, transparent products

19.1 General-purpose prevulcanized latices

Formulation

	1	2	3
	Low modulus	Medium modulus	High modulus
60% NR latex, HA or LA-TZ type	167	167	167
20% Potassium laurate	1.3	1.3	1.3
10% Potassium hydroxide	2.5	2.5	2.5
50% Sulphur	0.4	2	4
50% ZDEC	0.4	1	2
50% Zinc oxide	0.4	0.4	0.4

Recommended conditions for prevulcanization : 4h at 60°C

Properties

Typical properties of dried films after leaching for 16h at 20°C:

	1	2	3
TS, MPa	30.7	35.0	31.0
EB, %	970	875	785
M300, MPa	1.10	1.52	1.87

Reference: *NR Technology*, 1979, **10**, 9 and Technical Information Sheet L53:1982.

19.2 Heat-resistant prevulcanized latices

Heat resistance is obtained by using a 'sulphurless' prevulcanizing system.

Formulation

60% NR latex, HA or LA-TZ type	167
10% Casein	5
25% Surfactant[a]	2
10% Potassium hydroxide	2.5
50% ZDBC	2
50% Zinc oxide	2
30% TETD	9
10% Thiourea	10

Recommended conditions for prevulcanization: 2h at 60°C

a. Non-ionic type: alkyl phenol-ethylene oxide condensate containing *ca* 30moles of ethylene oxide per mole, *eg Texofor FN30* (ABM Chemicals).

Reference: *NR Technology*, 1979, **10**, 9 and Technical Information Sheet L54:1982.

19.3 Prevulcanized latices resistant to copper-catalysed ageing

Improved protection against metal-catalysed oxidation is given by increased levels of zinc dithiocarbamate relative to sulphur. At least 1.5 parts phr of the accelerator should be used.

Formulation

	1	2
	Medium modulus	High modulus
60% NR latex, HA or LA-TZ type	167	167
20% Potassium laurate	1.3	1.3
10% Potassium hydroxide	2.5	2.5
50% Sulphur	2	4
50% ZDEC[b]	4	4
50% Zinc oxide	0.4	0.4

Recommended conditions for prevulcanization: 4h at 60°C

a. ZDBC may also be used.

Reference: *NR Technology*, 1979, **10**, 9 and Technical Information Sheet L54:1982.

19.4 Prevulcanized latices for transparent products

Transparency is obtained by eliminating zinc oxide from the prevulcanizing system and using zinc dibutyl dithiocarbamate (ZDBC) as accelerator.

Formulation

60% NR latex, HA or LA-TZ type	167
20% Potassium laurate	1.3
10% Potassium hydroxide	2.5
50% Sulphur	2
50% ZDBC	1

Recommended conditions for prevulcanization: 4h at 60°C

Reference: *NR Technology*, 1979, **10**, 9.

Section 20 Miscellaneous products

20.1 Cast products, flame-retardant
20.2 Cast products, general-purpose
20.3 Cast products, heat-sensitized
20.4 Coating compounds, flame-retardant
20.5 Latex thread, general-purpose
20.6 Latex thread, heat-resistant
20.7 Non-woven fabric binder
20.8 Non-woven fabric binder, general-purpose
20.9 Rubberized hair/fibre binder
20.10 Rubberized hair/fibre binder, flame retardant
20.11 Rubberized sports surfaces
20.12 Extruded latex tubing
20.13 Latex-modified cement

20.1 Flame-retardant cast products

For cast products made in porous plaster of paris mould for use in theatre stage scenery.

Formulation

60% NR LA-TZ type	167
20% Potassium oleate	2.5
70% Hydrated alumina[a,b]	190
70% Clay[b]	95
50% Sulphur	2.6
50% Zinc oxide	1.9
50% ZDEC	1.3
50% ZMBT	1.3
50% Antioxidant[c]	1.3
5% Thickener[d]	10

a. *eg Baco FRF5* (British Aluminium Co).
b. Prepared as a slurry by subjecting the following mix to high shear dispersion for 10min: 200 parts alumina or clay, 84 parts water and 1 part dispersant (*Dispex N40*, Allied Colloids).
c. Non-staining phenolic type.
d. Cellulosic type, *eg Celacol HPM500DS* (British Celanese).

Notes on processing

After forming the deposit in the cold mould, heat the mould to 100°C to dry/cure the casting until it is sufficiently strong to remove from the mould without distortion. Final drying/curing is carried out at 70°C after removal from the mould.

Reference: Technical Information Sheet L46:1981

20.2 General-purpose cast products

For the production of hollow cast latex articles in pourous plaster of paris moulds.

Formulations

	1	2	3
	Soft	Semi-rigid	Rigid
60% NR latex, HA or LA-TZ type	167	167	167
10% Surfactant[a]			5
50% Sulphur	2	3	5
50% Zinc oxide	2	3	10
50% ZDEC	2	2	3
Whiting[b]		100	300
Tetrasodium pyrophosphate[c]		0.5	1
Water		30	90

a. *eg* Casein, but other surfactants are suitable.
b. Some grades of whiting may cause flocculation and thickening of the latex; check each batch of whiting for flocculation tendency before full-scale use.
c. *eg Tetron* (Albright and Wilson).

Notes on processing

After forming the deposit in the cold mould, heat the mould to 100°C to dry/cure the casting until it is sufficiently strong to remove from the mould without distortion. Final drying/curing is carried out at 70°C after removal from the mould.

Reference: Technical Information Sheet L36:1979

20.3 Heat-sensitive cast products

Heat-sensitive formulations using polypropylene glycol

The formulations are intended for general-purpose use but are also suitable for the rotational casting of completely closed hollow articles such as play-balls. Antioxidants, colouring agents and small amounts of filler may be added as required. Fillers reduce the cost of the mix but also reduce the degree of heat sensitivity and the wet-gel strength.

Formulations

	1	2
	Prevulcanized	Vulcanizable
60% NR latex, HA type		167
60% Prevulcanized latex	167	
20% Surfactant[a]	0.5	0.5
50% Sulphur		2
50% Zinc oxide	2	2
50% ZDEC		2
25% Polypropylene glycol[b]	10	10

a. Non-ionic type: cetyl/oleyl alcohol-ethylene oxide condensate, *eg Vulcastab LW* (Vulnax). Only necessary if long storage periods are required. Without surfactant, mixes are stable for a minimum of 2–3 days provided they are kept below 20°C.

b. *eg Propylan D702* (Lankro Chemicals).

Notes on processing

Allow the mix to gel in the warm mould (60–70°C), and dry/cure *in situ* in an oven at 100°C until the casting is sufficiently strong to remove from the mould without distortion. Final drying/curing is carried out at 70°C after removal from the mould.

Reference: Technical Information Sheet L28:1978

20.4 Flame-retardant coating compounds
Un-vulcanized formulation

This formulation is designed for use in theatre stage scenery. It has been used to coat polystyrene foam with a flexible flame-retardant film. Coatings can be painted and decorated.

Formulation

60% NR latex, LA-TZ type	167
25% Surfactant[a]	8
28% Sodium dodecyl sulphate	3.6
Hydrated alumina[b]	400
50% ZDEC	2
40% Formaldehyde	2.2
5% Thickener[c]	17

a. Non-ionic sulphated type, *eg Solumin FX85 SD*, (ABM Chemicals).
b. *eg Baco FRF5* (British Aluminium Co).
c. Cellulosic type, *eg Celacol HPM500DS* (British Celanese).

Notes on processing

The mix may be applied by hand using brushing or roller techniques or by spray gun.

Reference: Technical Information Sheet L45:1981

20.5 Latex thread

General-purpose formulation

The formulation is designed to minimize copper staining.

Formulation

60% NR latex, LA-TZ type[a]	167
20% Potassium laurate	2.5
10% Potassium hydroxide	4
50% Sulphur	3.5
50% ZMBT	3
50% ZDBC	0.5
50% Antioxidant[b]	3
50% Titanium dioxide	10
50% Zinc oxide	5

a. May be replaced by 152 parts of 66% creamed latex.
b. An effective antioxidant is essential for adequate laundering resistance and because of the high surface area of thread. Suitable non-staining phenolic types include *Antioxidant 2246* or *425* (Cyanamid), *Permanax WSP* (Vulnax) and *Naugard 445* (Uniroyal).

Notes on processing

Because the diameter of thread is usually small, care must be taken to ensure that all dispersions are free of coarse particles; a particle size of less than 5 microns is advised. The mix should be matured, *eg* for 4 days at 25°C, then homogenized, de-aerated and filtered before use. Suitable drying and curing conditions are 10–15 min at 130°C. Alternatively the thread can be given sufficient cure to enable it to be handled without distortion, *eg* 3 min at 135°C, and then given a post cure, often at a lower temperature, *eg* 16h at 70°C.

Reference: *NR Technology*, 1979, **10**, 80 and Technical Information Sheet L55:1982

20.6 Heat-resistant latex thread

The formulation is designed for use in garments laundered at high temperature.

Formulation

60% NR latex, LA-TZ type[a]	167
20% Potassium laurate	2.5
10% Potassium hydroxide	4
50% DPTT[b]	4
50% ZMBT	3
50% ZDBC	1
50% Antioxidant[c]	3
50% Titanium dioxide	10
50% Zinc oxide	4

a. May be replaced by 152 parts of 66% creamed latex.
b. Dipentamethylene thiuram tetrasulphide, *eg Robac P25* (Robinson Bros).
c. An effective antioxidant is essential for adequate heat/laundering resistance and because of the high surface area of thread. Suitable non-staining phenolic types include *Antioxidant 2246* or *425* (Cyanamid), *Permanax WSP* (Vulnax) and *Naugard 445* (Uniroyal).

Notes on processing

Because the diameter of thread is usually small, care must be taken to ensure that all dispersions are free of coarse particles; a particle size of less than 5 microns is advised. The mix should be matured, *eg* for 4 days at 25°C, then homogenized, de-aerated and filtered before use. Suitable drying and curing conditions are 10–15min at 135°C. Alternatively the thread can be given sufficient cure to enable it to be handled without distortion, *eg* 3min at 135°C, and then given a post cure, often at a lower temperature, *eg* 16h at 70°C.

Reference: *NR Technology*, 1979, **10**, 80 and Technical Information Sheet L55:1982

20.7 Non-woven fabric binder
Delamination-resistant

This formulation relies on heat-sensitive gelling of the latex mix for improved bonding of the fibres.

Formulation

60% NR latex, LA-TZ type	167
20% Surfactant[a]	1.3
40% Formaldehyde	to pH 7.5–8.0
50% Sulphur	4
50% Zinc oxide	6
50% ZDEC	3
50% ZMBT	1.5
50% Antioxidant[b]	2
10% Polyvinylmethyl ether[c]	20
Water	to ca 20% total solids

a. Non-ionic type; alkyl phenol-ethylene oxide condensate containing *ca* 30moles ethylene oxide per mole, *eg Texofor FN30* (ABM Chemicals).
b. *eg* Non-staining phenolic type.
c. *eg Gantrez M154* (General Aniline and Film Co) or *Lutanol M40* (BASF).

Properties

Gelling temperature:	about 32°C
Minimum shelf life at 20°C:	1 week

Reference: Technical Information Sheet L43:1981

20.8 General-purpose binder for non-woven fabrics

Formulation

60% NR latex, HA or LA type	167
20% Surfactant[a]	2
50% Sulphur	4
50% ZDEC	3
50% ZMBT	1.5
50% Antioxidant[b]	2
50% Zinc oxide	6
Water	as required

Cure: 3–8min at 120°C in hot air

a. *eg* Potassium laurate, sodium dodecyl sulphate or sulphated alkyl phenol-ethylene oxide condensate.
b. *eg* Non-staining phenolic type.

Reference: Technical Information Sheet L43:1981

20.9 Binders for rubberized hair/fibre

For animal hair and coir

Compression modulus may be increased by including a water-soluble thermosetting resin such as melamine-formaldehyde resin. Small amounts of fillers may also be added, but excessive amounts adversely affect some properties.

Formulation

	1	2
	Animal hair	Coir
60% NR latex, HA or LA-TZ type	167	167
20% Surfactant[a]	4	4
20% Potassium hydroxide	2	2
50% Antioxidant, TMQ[b]	3	3
50% ZDEC	2	2
50% ZMBT	3	3
50% Sulphur	8	5
50% Zinc oxide	10	10
Water		to 50–55% total solids

a. Sulphated alkyl phenol-ethylene oxide condensate, *eg Glofoam HE* (ABM Chemicals).
b. *eg Flectol H* (Monsanto).

Notes on processing

Dry at 60–70°C, and then cure for 30min at 100°C in hot air. Alternatively use a high-velocity air oven and dry and cure for 5min at 140°C.

Reference: Technical Information Sheet L24:1978

20.10 Flame-retardant binders for rubberized hair/fibre Flame-retardant to Federal Motor Vehicle Safety Standard 302

Formulation

	1	2	3
		blend ratio	
Animal hair	100	80	50
Coir	0	20	50
60% NR latex, HA or LA-TZ type	167	167	167
25% Surfactant[a]	6	6	6
50% Sulphur	7	7	7
50% ZDEC	2	2	2
50% ZMBT	3	3	3
50% Antioxidant, TMQ[b]	3	3	3
50% Chlorinated wax[c]	10	10	10
50% *Tetrabromobisphenol A*[d]	20	30	40
50% Hydrated alumina[e]	50	50	50
50% Antimony trioxide	4	6	12
50% Zinc oxide	6	6	6
Water		to 50–55% total solids	

Dry and cure: 20min at 120°C in hot air

a. Sulphated alkyl phenol-ethylene oxide condensate, *eg Glofoam HE* (ABM Chemicals).
b. *eg Flectol H* (Monsanto).
c. Solid chlorinated paraffin wax containing 70% chlorine, *eg Cereclor 70* (ICI).
d. Great Lakes Chemical Co. Note that vegetable fibres, such as coir, require higher proportions of flame-retardants than animal hair.
e. *eg Baco FRF5* or *Baco FRF40* (British Aluminium Co).

Properties

Density, Mg/m3	0.048	0.048	0.048
FMVSS burn rate, mm/min	25–38	40–56	50–75

Reference: Technical Information Sheet L22:1978

20.11 Rubberized sports surfaces

Latex-bonded tyre crumb/cement composition

Formulation

60% NR latex, LA-TZ type	167
25% Surfactant[a]	8
Vulcanizing/protectant paste*	68
Tyre crumb	175
Portland cement	150
*Vulcanizing/protectant paste:	
50% Sulphur	3
50% ZDBC	3
50% ZMBT	3
50% Zinc oxide	2
50% Antioxidant, TMQ[b]	4
50% UV absorber[c]	4
Thiourea	1
25% Surfactant[a]	8
20% Glycine	15
10% Thickener[d]	5
10% Casein	20

a. Non-ionic type; alkyl phenol-ethylene oxide condensate containing *ca* 30moles ethylene oxide per mole, *eg Texofor FN30* (ABM Chemicals).
b. *eg Flectol H* (Monsanto).
c. Benzotriazole derivative, *eg Tinuvin P* (Geigy).
d. Polyacrylate type, *eg Rohagit S–MV* (Rohm and Haas), but cellulose derivatives may be used if desired.

Notes on processing

This mix is prepared as a two-part, self-setting composition, the tyre crumb and cement being added to the stabilized latex on site. The latex must be adequately stabilized, stability being enhanced if required by adding 1–3% glycine.

Reference: Technical Information Sheet L25:1978

20.12 Extruded latex tubing

High-quality rubber tubing can be made from latex by a simple heat-sensitive extrusion process. Two formulations are given, one requiring vulcanization and the other using prevulcanized latex. Fillers may be added if required. Formulations containing up to 100 parts clay per 100 parts of dry rubber have been successfully extruded.

Formulation

	1	2
60% NR latex, LA-TZ type	167	
60% Prevulcanized NR latex		167
25% Stabilizer[a]	1	1
40% Formaldehyde	to pH 7.5–8.0	
Water	30	30
50% Sulphur	2.5	
50% ZDMC	2	
50% Zinc oxide	2	
50% Antioxidant[b]	1	
10% Polyvinyl methyl ether[c]	20	20

a. Non-ionic type, *eg Emulvin W* (Bayer), *Texofor FN30* (ABM Chemicals) or *Vulcastab LW* (Vulnax.).
b. Non-staining phenolic.
c. *eg Gantrez M154* (General Aniline and Film Co) or *Lutanol M40* (BASF).

Notes on processing
The latex mix is stored in a header tank jacketed to keep the latex below 20°C. It passes from the tank through a constant level device or pressure regulator to the extruder, which consists of two water-jacketed concentric glass tubes. The upper part of the water jacket is maintained at 15–20°C to prevent premature gelation in the supply tube. The lower part is usually maintained at 50–70°C depending on the cross-section of the tube. The latex flows between the glass tubes, gels in the heated zone and is then slowly extruded.

The extruded wet gel is passed through a detackifying bath containing talc slurry or other suitable materials, leached and finally dried and vulcanized in a hot-air oven.

Unless great care is taken to set up the extruder so that the glass tubes are concentric, tubing of irregular wall thickness will be produced.

Extrusion rate is controlled partly by the hydrostatic head of the latex reservoir above the extruder and partly by the length of gelled tubing hanging from it. An extrusion rate of 200–300mm/min will typically be given by a head of 500–600mm and a hanging length of 500mm. The hydrostatic head may be replaced by a pressurized pumping system, although this does not give a faster extrusion rate. Overall output can be increased by attaching several extruders to the same reservoir of latex.

Reference: Technical Information Sheet L58:1983 and NR Technology, 1982, **13**, 94

20.13 Latex-modified cement

Formulations for use with Portland cements

Addition of NR latex increases adhesion to steel, concrete and glass, improves wear resistance and reduces water permeability. Applications include flooring and ship and bridge decks.

Formulation

	1	2
73% NR latex, evaporated type[a]	143	
60% NR latex, centrifuged type		167
10% Casein		25
25% Surfactant[b]	20	20
Water (giving 40% rubber content)	87	38

a. *Standard Revertex* (Revertex).
b. Non-ionic type, alkyl phenyl-ethylene oxide condensate containing *ca* 30 moles ethylene oxide per mole, *eg Texofor FN30* (ABM Chemicals).

Notes on processing

Suitable NR/cement mortar compositions are as follows (in parts by weight):

low rubber content: sand, 300; Portland cement, 100; water, 30; NR latex mix, 25
high rubber content: sand, 300; Portland cement, 100; water, 10; NR latex mix, 50.

The sand and cement are batched together and wetted before adding the latex mix. Alternatively the water may be premixed with the latex mix. The latex should not be added to the cement before the water, otherwise it may destabilize. The optimum water content will depend largely on the sand or aggregate used.

Reference: *NR Technology*, 1983, **14**, 65

Part C

Dry Rubber Vulcanizate Property Index

Notes on Property Indexes

These indexes enable dry rubber formulations to be selected to meet particular physical property requirements. Each index contains single line coded entries giving a list of physical properties for an individual formulation in Part A of the Formulary. One index is for vulcanizates cured at 140–165°C, the other for cures at 180–200°C. The following physical properties, where available, are given in sequence from left to right using the codes shown; hardness, TS and EB are indexed in increasing numerical value.

Heading	Property
IRHD	Hardness, IRHD
TS	Tensile strength, MPa
EB	Elongation at break, %
Comset 70	Compression set, 1 day at 70°C, %
100	Compression set, 1 day at 100°C, %
Resilience	Lupke resilience, %
Fatigue[a]	Ring fatigue life, 0–100% strain, kc to failure
Tear	Tear, ISO trouser, 23°C, as indicated by codes:
	1 = tear strength <10kN/m
	2 = tear strength >10<20kN/m
	3 = tear strength >20kN/m
Ozone	Ozone resistance, as indicated by codes:
	1 = marginal protection
	2 = well protected (time to first crack >3 days at 50pphm ozone, 40°C, 20% strain)
$t_c'95$[b]	*Rheometer* $t_c'95$, min, at indicated temperature, °C
Cure[b]	Cure time, min, at indicated temperature, °C
Class	Class and colour, as indicated by codes:
	A = conventional vulcanization system
	B = semi-EV system
	C = EV or peroxide system
	T = Thermoplastic rubber
	/N = non-black
Method[c]	Cure method as indicated by codes:
	PC = press cure
	INJ = injection moulding
	LCM = liquid cure method, using salt bath
Reference	Formulation reference, as Section/formulation number

a. Fatigue resistance is profoundly affected by antidegradants; incorporation of a *p*-phenylenediamine antidegradant will improve fatigue life.

b. The *Rheometer* over-estimates the cure time required at high temperatures, and the actual cure time is substantially less than the *Rheometer* $t_c'95$, even for press cures. For injection moulding and continuous curing the discrepancies are larger.

c. For high temperature cures only.

Section 21 Dry rubber vulcanizate property indexes

21.1 Vulcanization at 140–165°C
21.2 Vulcanization at 180–200°C

21.1 Vulcanization at 140–165°C

IRHD	TS	EB	Comset 70	Comset 100	Resilience	Fatigue	Tear	Ozone	t_c'95	Class	Reference
18	5	725	49				1			A/N	9.1/2
18	11	995	54				1			A/N	9.1/1
22	3	630	50	63	78		1		6.5/150	A/N	11.2/1
25	14	850	39				1			A/N	9.1/4
25	16	850	36				1			A/N	9.1/3
29	17	785	29				1			A/N	9.2/2
30	8	640	24	57	84	85	1		7.5/150	B/N	11.2/2
30	17	775	33				1			A/N	9.2/3
30	20	905	36				1			A/N	9.2/1
35	22	880	32	50	79	140	1		9.0/140	A/N	6.11/4
36	23	910	34	61	82	110	1		7.0/140	A/N	6.11/2
36	24	910	28	53	83	115	1		11/140	A/N	6.11/1
37	20	775								A	9.9/3
38	10	705								A	9.9/1
38	23	840	35	62	79	175	1		8.6/150	A/N	11.3/2
38	23	860	30	54	79	190	2		9.2/150	A/N	11.3/1
38	24	740	15	26	87	96	2		11/160	C	10.6/1
38	27	800	18	42	87	145	1		10/150	A/N	9.6/1
39	13	740								A	9.9/2
39	14	660	26							C/N	6.2/4
39	23	700	16	35	82	180	1	2	11/150	C	12.2/1
39	23	740	22							B/N	6.2/1
39	23	750	22							B/N	6.2/2
39	25	700	17	40	84	90	1		24/140	C/N	6.11/5
39	29	825	33	55	86	89	1		11/140	B/N	6.11/3
40	13	720	33	62	87	115	1		7.0/150	B/N	11.2/3
40	15	690	61		54	66	1		13/150	A	5.1/3
40	18	680								C	2.4/2
40	18	765	30							A	9.9/8
40	24	720	24							B/N	6.2/3
41	21	725	50		66	130	1		14/150	A	5.1/2
41	24	740	36	50	85	330	1	2	15/150	A	9.3/1
42	8	625								A	9.9/4
42	23	740	58		81	122	1		27/140	A/N	8.5/1
42	24	705	19	27	53	66	2	2	12/150	C	5.2/2
42	25	680	27	45	86	95	1		6.2/150	A	9.7/1
42	25	785	39		78	120	1		14/150	A	5.1/1
43	25	655	20	39	72	78	1	2	14/150	C	5.2/1
44	11	680								B	9.9/5
44	20	700	19	40	32	63	2	2	13/150	C	5.2/4
44	21	685	11							B	9.9/9
44	22	675	18	35	42	79	2	2	12/150	C	5.2/3
44	27	695	20	40	80	67	1		6.0/160	B/N	12.4/2

21.1 (cont)

IRHD	TS	EB	Comset 70	Comset 100	Resilience	Fatigue	Tear	Ozone	$t_c'95$	Class	Reference
45	17	665	20	34	20	91	2	2	15/150	C	5.2/6
45	24	655	20	39	83	68	1		5.8/160	B/N	12.4/1
45	24	745	38		79	190	1		28/140	A/N	8.5/2
45	26	650	10	21	75	83	1	2	8.7/153	C	5.6/1
45	26	700								C/N	6.6/1
46	23	670	36	51	80	120	1	2	14/150	A	9.3/2
46	14	715	11							B	9.9/6
46	15	750	27							A/N	6.10/1
46	20	645	16	31	25	77	2	2	13/150	C	5.2/5
47	18	660	11							B	9.9/7
48	18	665	32	61	86	60	1		6.0/150	B/N	11.2/4
48	20	705	50		52	230	3		15/150	A	5.1/5
48	25	715	44		70	210	2		15/150	A	5.1/4
48	27	720	19	39	77	68	2		10/150	A/N	9.6/2
49	25	605	18	28	85	59	2		8.0/160	C	10.6/2
49	27	630	17	37	79	67	1	2	11/150	C	12.2/2
50	11	550	34	52	32	269	1	2	20/160	C	13.8/4
50	21	595								A	2.4/1
50	21	795	27	43	73	97	2		5.1/160	A/N	10.1/1
50	23	725	12	18	71	39	3		13/160	C/N	10.1/3
50	25	600	19	44	81	59	1		6.3/150	A	9.7/2
51	18	710	33	62	80	56	1	2	18/140	A/N	8.2/1
51	21	640	31		50	135			4.0/160	A	10.2/1
51	23	635	36		42	88			4.7/160	A	10.2/2
51	27	645								C/N	6.6/2
51	29	640	18	44	81	187	1	2	20/140	B	5.8/1
51	30	670	34	57	78	272	2	2	29/140	A	5.5/1
52	7	550	32							B	9.10/1
52	9	560	25							B	9.10/2
52	15	530	22		61	83			6.5/160	A	10.2/3
52	15	615	54		40	128	3		12/150	A	5.1/6
52	17	675								A/N	2.4/3
52	22	665	31	60	66	93	2	1	5.7/160	B	13.8/3
52	23	590	41	52	79	100	2	2	14/150	A	9.3/3
52	29	690	32	51	83	236	1	2	29/140	A	5.10/1
53	11	500	35		70		2		2.6/160	B/N	7.2/1
53	24	710	26	47	79	73	2		6.5/160	A/N	10.1/2
53	25	665	45		87	70	1		20/140	A/N	2.3/1
53	26	590	23	56	84	155	1	2	28/140	A	5.5/2
53	26	750	20	33	76	61	2		2.8/160	B/N	10.1/4
54	21	630	41	60	80	30	1		8.2/150	B/N	11.2/5

21.1 (cont)

IRHD	TS	EB	Comset 70	Comset 100	Resilience	Fatigue	Tear	Ozone	$t_c'95$	Class	Reference
55	11	575	24							B	9.10/3
55	14	595	23							B	9.10/4
55	20	575	29	52	79	52	2	1	4.8/160	A	13.8/1
55	21	655	30	60	80	65	1	2	16/140	A/N	8.2/4
55	23	570	14							B	9.10/6
55	25	645	31	49	71	57	2	1	5.2/160	C	13.8/2
55	29	650	27	49	74	134	2	2	25/140	A	5.10/3
56	20	505	14	24	71	41	1		35/160	C	10.4/1
56	23	550	10	21	68	63	2	2	8.3/153	C	5.6/2
57	17	585	37		69	24	3		3.3/160	B/N	7.1/2
57	18	580	20							B	9.10/5
57	20	635	24	46	71	63	2		8.0/150	A/N	9.6/3
58	23	520	14	28	73	60	2		10/150	C	5.4/1
58	30	645	17	34	61	56	3		24/140	C	2.1/2
58	20	600	42	59	83	25	1		7.9/150	B/N	11.2/6
59	5	370	43							A	9.11/1
59	11	550	19							A	9.11/6
59	14	660	26	48	75	24	1	2	21/140	A/N	8.2/2
59	15	570	36							A	9.11/7
59	18	395	12	20	72	56	1		25/160	C	5.4/4
59	19	640	42		74	45	3		30/140	A/N	2.3/2
59	20	595	58		44	285	3		32/140	A	2.2/2
59	22	540	27	48	79	150	2		9.0/150	A	5.3/1
59	23	540	17	31	67	55	2		19/150	C	5.4/2
59	24	540	20	43	76	46	1		5.5/150	A	9.7/3
59	25	585	35	54	73	125	2	1	18/140	A	14.1/1
60	6	525	29							B	9.11/2
60	7	460	32							A	9.11/3
60	10	550	22							A	9.11/5
60	17	540	53		70	22	3		4.0/160	B/N	7.1/1
60	18	590	50		43	210	3		12/150	A	5.1/8
60	21	610	29		59	758	2	1	5.5/165	B	13.4/3
60	23	535	24	47	80	120	1		7.5/150	A	5.3/2
60	24	520	18	38	66	47	2	2	10/150	C	12.2/3
60	26	560	33	51	73	207	2	2	27/140	A	5.5/3
60	29	575	28							A	9.11/10
60	29	640	28	47	74	197	3	2	28/140	A	5.10/2
61	19	530	31							A	9.11/8
61	22	510	28							A	9.11/9
61	23	560	44		58	130	3		14/150	A	5.1/7
61	26	490	22	36	88	55	1	2	22/160	C/N	12.3/1

21.1 (cont)

IRHD	TS	EB	Comset 70	Comset 100	Resilience	Fatigue	Tear	Ozone	$t_c'95$	Class	Reference
62	12	430								A	2.5/2
62	13	560	25	48	77	16	1	2	19/140	A/N	8.2/6
62	17	445	21	32	64	32	1		35/160	C	13.7/1
62	17	535	22	37	58	73	2		40/140	C	8.6/3
62	20	480	42	55	74	130	2	2	15/150	A	9.3/4
62	21	570	29		51	405	2	1	4.5/165	B	13.4/2
62	21	620	59						2.3/160	A/N	7.5/3
62	22	685	48						2.7/160	A/N	7.5/2
62	26	565	19	44	72	104	2	2	17/140	B	5.8/2
63	8	475	29							A	9.11/4
63	12	650	31	54	73	14	1	2	22/140	A/N	8.2/3
63	25	515	19	47	73	70	2		6.0/150	B	5.9/2
63	27	540	18	41	57	74	3		5.9/160	C	12.1/1
64	15	535	41		65	21	2		3.0/160	B/N	7.1/4
64	21	450	20	53	85	65	1		7.5/150	A	5.3/3
64	24	475	26	46	74	65	2		7.0/150	B	5.3/4
64	29	560	14	33	64	45	2		18/150	C	5.9/3
65	19	395	30	57	60	164	2		14/150	A	13.1/2
65	20	515	48		72	26	1		31/140	A	8.4/1
65	20	525	45	70	41	270	3	2	20/140	B	13.3/1
65	21	445	12	26	74	47	1		9.0/150	C	5.9/4
65	29	575	34	60	64	160	3		22/140	A	2.1/1
65	11	535	31	48	60	25	1		45/140	C	8.6/1
65	16	515	48		72	14	1		33/140	A	8.4/2
65	17	370	29	52	58	100	2		13/150	A	13.1/2
65	18	580	30	45	58	71	1		40/140	C	8.6/2
66	19	490								C/N	6.6/3
66	20	455	11	20	56	46	3	2	7.2/153	C	5.6/3
66	20	545	32	55	45	178	3		26/140	B	2.2/3
66	22	550	43	71	45	255	3		29/140	A	2.2/1
66	25	455	24	44	61	86	2	1	10/150	B	13.3/2
66	25	530	24	39	73	40	2		9.0/150	C	5.9/5
66	26	505	33	53	63	150	2	1	10/150	B	13.3/2
66	27	515	30	54	66	105	2		13/150	A	5.9/1
67	14	500	42		65	14	2		4.0/160	B/N	7.1/3
67	21	425	44	71	66	166	2		14/150	A	13.1/1
67	21	495	25	41	40	185	2	2	20/140	B	13.3/1
67	23	495	22	52	77	144	2	2	25/140	A	5.5/4
67	24	575	35		62	100	3		29/140	A	8.5/3
68	20	400	39		65	103	2	2	14/150	A	9.3/5
68	23	555	25	41	69	36	2		13/150	C	5.4/3
68	26	470	23	33	82	52	1	2	22/160	C/N	12.3/2
68	26	590	24	47	55	82	3		6.2/160	C	12.1/2

21.1 (cont)

IRHD	TS	EB	Comset		Resilience	Fatigue	Tear	Ozone	$t_c'95$	Class	Reference
			70	100							
69	7	400	49		33	24	1		31/140	A	8.4/4
69	16	560	29	54	76	8	1	2	16/140	A/N	8.2/5
69	17	500	16	22	59	66	2		40/140	C	8.6/5
69	20	375	24		63	59	2	2	8.5/150	B	9.5/1
69	22	400	23	49	64	123	2	2	25/140	A	8.3/1
69	25	660	53						3.0/160	A/N	7.5/1
70	16	420	14	22	60	68	1		40/140	C	8.6/6
70	18	380	40	65	60	170	2		13/150	A	13.1/2
70	18	450	15	20	59	46	1		45/140	C	8.6/4
70	20	375	18	43	66	25	1		4.8/150	A	9.7/4
70	20	520	30		44	314	3	1	4.0/165	B	13.4/1
70	22	410	16	44	64	73	2	2	24/140	B	8.3/2
70	22	445	21	44	63	120	2	2	15/140	B	5.8/3
71	10	490	37		47	17	1		24/140	A	8.4/3
71	18	385	19	27	71	33	1		8.5/160	C	13.2/1
71	21	505	35		66	60	2		12/140	A	13.5/1
71	27	550	29	48	63	218	3	2	28/140	A	5.10/4
72	7	390	25							A	9.12/5
72	10	535	34	61	67	6	1	2	16/140	A	8.2/7
72	13	440	14	33	53	23	3		33/140	B	8.1/1
72	16	365	25							A	9.12/8
72	17	340	18	35	61	10	2	2	8.5/150	C	12.2/4
72	25	395	22	27	55	122	2		30/160	C	10.5/1
73	9	365	26							A	9.12/6
73	10	295	23	50	51	14	1	2	40/140	B	8.1/2
73	13	335								A	2.5/1
73	19	355	18						7.2/160	C	6.9/1
73	21	390	26	27	53	174	3	2	30/160	C	10.5/2
73	5	400	44							A	9.12/2
73	5	405	34							A	9.12/1
73	6	390	28							A	9.12/3
74	11	345	23							A	9.12/7
75	12	455	49		60				3.3/160	A/N	7.2/2
76	18	440	30	39	42	98	3	2	25/160	C	10.5/3
76	25	350	19							A	9.12/10
77	7	330	41							A	9.12/4
77	19	310	30		57	37	3	2	9.2/150	B	9.5/2
79	5	320	30							A	9.13/1
79	10	280	32							A	9.13/3
79	13	405	30						16/150	B/N	9.8/1
79	20	450	37						9.0/150	B/N	9.8/2
79	21	340	21							A	9.12/9
79	21	340	21							A	9.13/6
79	25	430	24	41	71	62	1	2	23/160	C/N	12.3/3

21.1 (cont)

IRHD	TS	EB	Comset		Resilience	Fatigue	Tear	Ozone	t_c'95	Class	Reference
			70	100							
80	8	300								T/N	14.2/1
80	11	510	50	50	34	195	3	2	30/160	C	10.5/5
80	14	240	29							A	9.13/4
80	16	235	19	47	55	29	1		5.7/150	A	9.7/5
80	17	510	36	37	53	290	1	2	28/160	C	10.5/4
80	18	255	24							A	9.13/5
80	18	325	27		53	64	1	2	10/150	A	9.3/7
81	14	250	15	31	50	4	1	2	8.2/150	C	12.2/5
81	16	240	41		51	77	1	2	11/150	A	9.3/6
82	21	315	32			68	3		6.2/160	A	7.3/1
83	9	270	25							A	9.13/2
84	16	410	31						18/150	B/N	9.8/4
87	15	210	26		36	100	2	2	8.2/150	B	9.5/3
87	17	395	36						21/150	B/N	9.8/3
88	16	340	41			66	3		11/160	A	6.1/3
88	19	330	45			290	3	2	14/150	A	9.4/2
88	19	370	31	49		105	2		13/150	C	13.2/2
88	20	350	31			62	2		5.0/160	A	7.3/2
88	20	370	31	49		105	2		13/150	C	10.6/3
89	15	495			40	40	3		4.6/160	A/N	7.4/3
89	16	170	42			72	2	2	15/150	A	9.4/1
90	16	250	42			99	2		10/160	A	6.1/1
90	17	315	48			120	3	2	15/150	A	9.4/4
90	17	400	36			84	3	2	7.0/150	B	9.5/4
91	11	235	23	44	42	2	1	2	14/150	C	12.2/6
91	13	395	22						14/150	B/N	9.8/5
92	5	290	40							A	9.14/1
92	8	245	31							A	9.14/2
92	11	350			43	22	1		6.2/160	A/N	7.4/1
92	14	225	29							A	9.14/3
92	15	350	41			60	3	2	7.0/150	B	9.5/5
92	17	290	63			340	3	2	13/150	A	9.4/3
93	14	215	43			46	1		11/160	A	6.1/2
93	9	355			58	23	2		6.2/160	A/N	7.4/2
95	11	300								T/N	14.2/2
95	11	350								T/N	14.2/4
95	12	350								T	14.2/3
97	15	380	21						18/150	B/N	9.8/6
98	13	300	18						17/150	B/N	9.8/8
98	13	345	16						18/150	B/N	9.8/7
99	14	355	26						22/150	B/N	9.8/9
>95										T	14.2/8
>95	15	285	55			200	2	2	19/150	A	9.4/5
>95	11	325								T	14.2/5
>95	18	400								T	14.2/7
>95	16	400								T/N	14.2/6

21.2 Vulcanization at 180–200°C

IRHD	TS	EB	Comset 70	Ozone	Cure	Class	Method	Reference
39	11	670	50	2	5.0/180	B/N	PC	13.6/4
39	18	715			1.8/190	C	INJ	9.16/1
42	17	745	32		2.0/180	B/N	INJ	10.3/2
48	12	710		2	1.4/200	B/N	LCM	6.3/1
50	11	785	40	2	5.0/180	B/N	PC	13.6/2
51	21	695	39	2	5.0/180	A/N	PC	13.6/1
52	24	590			0.8/190	C	INJ	9.16/2
53	13	650		2	1.0/200	B/N	LCM	6.3/2
53	15	645	47	2	5.0/180	B/N	PC	13.6/3
53	18	590	17		3.0/180	C/N	INJ	10.3/1
54	17	420		2	0.4/202	B	LCM	6.4/4
58	18	460	19	2	1.2/200	B	LCM	6.7/4
58	24	495		2	0.5/197	B	LCM	6.4/6
60	16	505	19	2	1.2/200	B	LCM	6.7/1
60	19	475			1.5/180	C	INJ	9.16/3
60	21	430		2	1.0/199	C	LCM	6.5/1
60	21	440		2	0.5/196	B	LCM	6.4/2
60	21	645	31	1	4.0/180	B/N	INJ	9.15/5
60	24	450		2	0.3/199	B	LCM	6.4/5
62	24	460		1	0.4/199	B	LCM	6.4/7
63	24	450		2	0.4/195	B	LCM	6.4/3
64	16	475	24	2	1.0/200	B	LCM	6.7/3
64	22	450		2	0.4/202	B	LCM	6.4/1
64	23	465		2	0.9/200	C	LCM	6.5/3
66	17	510	25	2	1.1/200	B	LCM	6.7/2
67	21	405		2	0.7/199	C	LCM	6.5/2
68	14	405	19	2	1.0/200	B	LCM	6.7/5
69	25	650	46	2	1.5/180	A/N	INJ	9.15/2
70	23	725	38	2	1.0/180	A/N	INJ	9.15/1
70	24	640	40	1	1.5/180	B/N	INJ	9.15/4
71	24	700	47	1	1.3/180	B/N	INJ	9.15/3
72	17	290			1.0/180	C	INJ	9.16/4
82	15	235			1.3/180	C	INJ	9.16/5
89	16	290			2.5/180	A	INJ	9.17/2
90	18	280			2.5/180	A	INJ	9.17/1
91	11	230			4.0/180	A	INJ	9.17/3

Part D

Additional information and applications indexes

Physical test methods

The various International and British Standard test methods used to obtain the data in this Formulary are listed below. The conditions of test referred to are those normally used; deviations from these conditions are indicated as appropriate in the tables of properties. The standard laboratory temperature is 23+/−2°C.

Raw and unvulcanized rubber

Mooney viscosity
ISO/R289 Determination of viscosity of natural and synthetic rubber by the shearing disk viscometer

Reported as ML1+4, in torque units, indicating a preheat time of 1min and a reading time of 4min. Test temperature 100°C.

Mooney scorch
ISO 667 Compounded rubber – Determination of the rate of cure using the shearing disk viscometer

Reported as the time for the Mooney viscosity to reach 5 units above the minimum reading. Test temperature 120°C.

Vulcanization characteristics
ISO 3417 Rubber – Measurement of vulcanization characteristics with the oscillating disk curemeter

Monsanto *Rheometer 100*, using an oscillation amplitude of 1°, an oscillation frequency of 1.7Hz and no pre-heat time.

Analysis and presentation of curemeter data:

Torque values
M_L records the minimum torque
M_{HR} records the maximum torque
These are reported in torque units, 1 unit being equal to 1lbf.in (0.113N.m).

Scorch time
scorch, t_{s1}, records the time taken to reach 1 torque unit above the minimum torque value M_L.

Cure time
$t_c'(90)$ records the time for the torque value to increase to $M_L + 0.9(M_{HR} - M_L)$.
$t_c'(95)$ records the time for the torque value to increase to $M_L + 0.95(M_{HR} - M_L)$.
$t_c'(100)$ records the time to 100% cure.
time to 5% reversion records the total time for the torque value to decrease by 5% of $(M_{HR} - M_L)$.

Vulcanized rubber

Hardness International scale (IRHD)
ISO 48 Vulcanized rubbers – Determination of hardness (Hardness between 30 and 85 IRHD)
ISO 1400 Vulcanized rubbers of high hardness (85–100 IRHD) – Determination of hardness
ISO 1818 Vulcanized rubbers of low hardness (10–35 IRHD) – Determination of hardness
The micro hardness test described in *BS 903 Part A26* is also used.

Hardness Shore A durometer scale
ASTM D2240 Rubber property – durometer hardness

Density
ISO 2781 Vulcanized rubbers – Determination of density
Method A, the test-piece being weighed in air and in water.

Tensile strength, elongation at break and modulus (or stress)
ISO 37 Vulcanized rubber – Determination of tensile stress-strain properties
Measured using the 'type 2' dumb-bell test-piece in the MRPRA Automatic Tensile Tester. Modulus is the stress (calculated on the original test-piece cross-section) at a given elongation.

Relaxed modulus (relaxed tensile stress)
BS 903 Methods of testing vulcanized rubber Part A41 – Determination of relaxed tensile stress (In course of preparation: based on BS 1673, Part 4, now withdrawn)
Tensile stress at 100% elongation after 1min relaxation (MR100), using a specially-designed instrument, the Wallace-MRPRA Relaxed Modulus (MOD) Tester. See *Rubber Developments*, 1973, **26**, 40.

Tension set
ISO 2285 Vulcanized rubbers – Determination of tension set under constant elongation at normal and high temperatures
Measured using strip test-pieces with enlarged ends and a 30min recovery period.

Compression set
ISO 815 Vulcanized rubber – Determination of compression set under constant deflection at normal and high temperatures
Measured using small test-piece (13.0mm diameter, 6.3mm thick), at 25% compression, with lubrication and 30min recovery period.

Tear strength (trouser and crescent methods)
ISO 34 Vulcanized rubber – Determination of tear strength (Trouser, angle and crescent test-pieces)
Median values of maximum force per unit thickness are reported for 5 test-pieces. The high/low ratio is the ratio of the highest to the lowest result and is a measure of the normal scatter in the results.

Resilience
Lupke: *ISO 4662 Rubber – Determination of rebound resilience of vulcanizates*

Dunlop *Tripsometer*: *BS 903 Methods of testing vulcanized rubber Part A8 – Determination of rebound resilience*

Measured using method A with the Type 1 test-piece, normally 4mm thick.

Ring fatigue
ISO 6943 Rubber, vulcanized – Determination of tension fatigue

Measured using the Wallace–MRPRA ring fatigue machine (see *Rubber Developments*, 1972, **25**, 63) on which ring test-pieces (external diameter 52.6mm, internal diameter 44.6mm, thickness 1.5mm) are cycled 0–100% to break at a frequency of 5Hz. The median result of 5 test-pieces is reported. The high/low ratio given is the ratio of the highest to the lowest results and is a measure of the normal scatter.

Goodrich *Flexometer*
ISO 4666/3 Rubber, vulcanized – Determination of temperature rise and resistance to fatigue in flexometer testing – Part 3 Compression flexometer

Temperature rise and set are measured; test conditions are always reported.

Abrasion resistance
Akron method: *BS 903 Methods of testing vulcanized rubber. Part A9 – Determination of abrasion resistance*

A slip angle of 15° is used. The abrasive wheel is dusted throughout the test with a mixture of fuller's earth and carborundum powder, to prevent clogging of the wheel by abraded rubber. Result reported as volume loss, mm^3/500 rev.

DIN method: *ISO 4649 Rubber, vulcanized – Determination of abrasion resistance*

The sample is allowed to rotate during abrasion against a standard emery cloth. The volume loss of a vulcanizate prepared to reference formulation B of the ISO standard is 191mm^3.

Ozone resistance
ISO 1431/1 Rubber, vulcanized – Resistance to ozone cracking – Part 1: Static strain tests

A Hampden-Shawbury Ozone Cabinet is used with an ozone concentration of 50 parts per hundred million (pphm) at 40°C and strip test-pieces at 20% strain.

Resistance to liquids
ISO 1817 Vulcanized rubbers – Resistance to liquids – Methods of test

The volumetric method is used.

Accelerated ageing and heat resistance
ISO 188 Vulcanized ruber – Accelerated ageing or heat resistance tests
Air-oven method, using multi-cell and normal ovens.

Low temperature crystallization
ISO 3387 Rubbers – Determination of crystallization effects by hardness measurements
Also applied as appropriate to raw and unvulcanized rubbers. There are many other tests for crystallization resistance as well as for glass hardening.

Conversion table for stress values

To convert a stress value in MPa (MN/m^2) to kgf/cm^2 multiply by 10.197.
To convert a stress value in MPa to lbf/in^2 multiply by 145.04.

Stress values

MPa	kgf/cm^2	lbf/in^2	MPa	kgf/cm^2	lbf/in^2
3.5	35.7	508	17	173.4	2466
4	40.8	580	18	183.5	2611
4.5	45.9	653	19	193.7	2756
5	51.0	725	20	203.9	2901
5.5	56.1	798	21	214.1	3046
6	61.2	870	22	224.3	3191
6.5	66.3	943	23	234.5	3336
7	71.4	1015	24	244.7	3481
7.5	76.5	1088	25	254.9	3626
8	81.6	1160	26	265.1	3771
8.5	86.7	1233	27	275.3	3916
9	91.8	1305	28	285.5	4061
9.5	96.9	1378	29	295.7	4206
10	102.0	1450	30	305.9	4351
11	112.2	1595	31	316.1	4496
12	122.4	1740	32	326.3	4641
13	132.6	1885	33	336.5	4786
14	142.8	2031	34	346.7	4931
15	153.0	2176	35	356.9	5076
16	163.2	2321	36	367.1	5121

Pressure-temperature equivalents for saturated steam

The following table gives the gauge pressure of saturated steam at mean sea level for various temperatures. It is assumed that atmospheric pressure is 101.325kPa (14.696lb/in^2; 1.0335kgf/cm^2).

Temperature		Steam gauge pressure		
°C	°F	kPa	kgf/cm^2	lb/in^2
100	212	0	0	0
105	221	19.5	0.20	3
110	230	42	0.43	6
115	239	68	0.69	10
120	248	97	0.99	14
125	258	131	1.34	19
130	266	169	1.72	25
135	275	212	2.16	31
140	284	260	2.65	38
145	293	314	3.20	46
150	303	374	3.81	54
155	311	442	4.51	64
160	320	516	5.26	75
165	329	599	6.11	87
170	338	690	7.03	100
175	347	791	8.07	115
180	356	901	9.19	131
185	365	1021	10.4	148
190	379	1153	11.8	167
200	392	1452	14.8	211

Useful conversion factors

A	B	To convert A to B multiply by	To convert B to A multiply by
Length			
millimetre	inch	0.0394	25.4
metre	foot	3.2808	0.3048
kilometre	mile	0.6214	1.6093
Area			
centimetre^2	inch^2	0.1550	6.4516
metre^2	foot^2	10.7639	0.0929
hectare	acre	2.471	0.4047
Volume			
centimetre^3	inch^3	0.0610	16.3871
metre^3	foot^3	35.3147	0.0283
millilitre	Imperial fluid ounce	0.0352	28.4131
litre	Imperial gallon	0.2200	4.5461
litre	US gallon	0.2642	3.7853
Mass			
gram	ounce	0.0353	28.3495
kilogram	pound	2.2046	0.4536
tonne	Imperial ton (2240lb)	0.9842	1.0161
tonne	US ton (2000lb)	1.1023	0.9072
Density			
megagram/metre^3	pound/inch^3	0.0361	27.68
Force			
Newton	kilogram-force	0.1020	9.807
Newton	pound-force	0.2248	4.448
Newton	dyne	10^5	10^{-5}
Stress			
megaPascal	kilogram-force/centimetre^2	10.197	0.0981
magaPascal	pound-force/inch^2	145.04	0.0069
kilogram-force/centimetre^2	pound-force/inch^2	14.223	0.0703
Tear strength			
Newton/millimetre	kilogram-force/centimetre	1.109	0.981
Newton/millimetre	pound-force/inch	5.709	0.1751
Frequency			
Hertz	cycle/minute	60	0.0167
Temperature			
degree Celsius	degree Fahrenheit	1.8 before adding 32	0.5556 after subtracting 32

Densities of rubbers and compounding ingredients

Ingredient	Density, Mg/m^3
Polymers	
Natural rubber	0.92
NR latex (60% drc)	0.95
Butadiene rubber	0.92
Butyl rubber	0.92
Chloroprene rubber	1.23
Ethylene-propylene rubber	0.86
Isoprene rubber	0.92
Nitrile rubber (33% AN)	0.98
Styrene-butadiene rubber	0.94
High styrene resin	0.98–1.00
Fillers	
Aluminimum silicate	2.0
Barytes	4.45
Blanc fixe	4.3
Calcium carbonate	2.65
Calcium silicate	2.1
Carbon black	1.8
China clay	2.6
Ebonite dust	1.17–1.2
Lithopone	4.15
Magnesium carbonate	2.2
Magnesium oxide	3.2–3.6
Pumice	2.4
Silica	1.95
Talc	2.8
Titanium dioxide, anatase	3.9
Titanium dioxide, rutile	4.2
Whiting *etc*	2.7
Zinc oxide	5.6

Ingredient	Density, Mg/m^3
Process aids, oils and plasticizers	
Coumarone-indene resin	1.1
Dibutyl phthalate	1.04
Diethylene glycol	1.12
Dioctyl phthalate	0.98
Dioctyl sebacate	0.91
Factice	1.05–1.1
Mineral rubber	1.04
Pine Tar	1.08
Polyethylene glycol	1.21
Petroleum oils, paraffinic	0.86–0.88
naphthenic	0.92–0.95
aromatic	0.98–1.01
Whole tyre reclaim	1.16–1.20
Vulcanizing ingredients	
Accelerators	1.0–1.5
Dicumyl peroxide	1.02
Stearic acid	0.85
Sulphur	2.05
Zinc-2-ethylhexanoate	1.16
Zinc stearate	1.05
Protective agents	
Antidegradants	0.9–1.5
Wax	0.90–0.95

Physical constants of vulcanized rubber

The values given are typical of a soft, gum vulcanizate containing vulcanizing ingredients only and of a harder, black-filled vulcanizate containing 50 parts phr carbon black.

Physical constants

Property	Unit	Gum vulcanizate	Black-filled vulcanizate
Density	Mg/m^3	0.95	1.12
Young's modulus	MPa	2	6
Bulk modulus	MPa	2000	2200
Poisson's ratio		0.4998	0.4995
Sound transmission velocity	m/s	54	37
Glass transition temperature	°C	−70	−70
Specific heat	J/(g°C)	1.83	1.50
Thermal conductivity	W/(m°C)	0.15	0.28
Cubical expansion coefficient	10^{-5}/°C	67	56
Volume resistivity	ohm.m	10^{14}	10^{10}
Dielectric constant		3	15
Power factor		0.002	0.1

Notes
1. For comparison the specific heat, thermal conductivity and cubical expansion coefficient of mild steel are respectively 0.48J/(g°C), 46W/(m/°C) and $3.5x10^{-5}$/°C.
2. Electrical resistivity depends on filler type and concentration; using specially conductive carbon black, a volume resistivity of 10ohm.m can be achieved.

Abbreviations

The common abbreviations used in this Formulary are listed below.

Accelerators

BA	butraldehyde-aniline condensate
BiDMC	bismuth dimethyldithiocarbamate
CBS	N-cyclohexylbenzothiazole-2-sulphenamide
CdDEC	cadmium diethyldithiocarbamate
DDTS	dimethyl-diphenylthiuram disulphide
DOTG	di-o-tolylguanidine
DPG	diphenylguanidine
DPTT	dipentamethylenethiuram tetrasulphide
DTDM	4,4′-dithiodimorpholine
HMT	hexamethylenetetramine
MBD	4-morpholinyl-2-benzothiazyl disulphide
MBS	2-morpholinothiobenzothiazole-2-sulphenamide N-oxydiethylenebenzothiazole-2-sulphenamide
MBT	2-mercaptobenzothiazole
MBTS	2,2′-benzothiazole disulphide 2,2′-benzothiazyl disulphide
TBBS	N-*t*-butylbenzothiazole-2-sulphenamide
TBTD	tetrabutylthiuram disulphide
TETD	tetra-ethylthiuram disulphide
TMTD	tetramethylthiuram disulphide
TMTM	tetramethylthiuram monosulphide
ZBDC	zinc dibutyldithiocarbamate
ZDEC	zinc diethyldithiocarbamate
ZDMC	zinc dimethyldithiocarbamate
ZMBT	zinc-2-mercaptobenzothiazole

Other ingredients

CTP	N-cyclohexylthiophthalimide
DEG	diethylene glycol
DHPPD	N,N′-bis-(1,4-dimethylpentyl)-*p*-phenylenediamine
DOP	dioctyl phthalate
DOPPD	dioctyl-*p*-phenylenediamine
HPPD	N-(1,3-dimethylbutyl)-N′-phenyl-*p*-phenylenediamine
IPPD	N-isopropyl-N′-phenyl-*p*-phenylenediamine
MBI	mercaptobenzimidazole
PEG	polyethylene glycol
TEA	triethanolamine
TMQ	poly-2,2,4-trimethyl-1,2-dihydroquinoline
ZEH	zinc-2-ethylhexanoate
ZMBI	zinc-2-mercaptobenzimidazole

Trade Names Index

This index gives the chemical names of proprietary materials used in this Formulary. Where chemical equivalents are available, they would normally be expected to give equivalent results.

Accelerators, peroxide vulcanization agents, *etc*

Butyl Eight (Vanderbilt)	activated dithiocarbamate
Dicup R (Hercules)	dicumyl peroxide
Ethyl Cadmate (Vanderbilt)	cadmium diethyldithiocarbamate
Hexa (Degussa)	hexamethylene tetramine
Morfax (Vanderbilt)	4-morpholinyl-2-benzothiazyl disulphide
Novor 924 (Durham Chemicals)	urethane crosslinker
Novor 950 (Durham Chemicals)	urethane crosslinker
Rhenocure Hexa (Rhein Chemie)	hexamethylene tetramine
Robac P25 (Robinson Bros)	dipentamethylene-thiuram tetrasulphide
Santogard PVI (Monsanto)	N-cyclohexylthiophthalimide
Sulfasan R (Monsanto)	4,4′-dithiodimorpholine
Telloy (Vanderbilt)	tellurium
Vulcafor 5 (Vulnax)	dithiocarbamate/thiazole blend
Vulkacit 1000 (Bayer)	*o*-tolylbiguanide
Vulkacit H30 (Bayer)	hexamethylene tetramine
Vulkacit J (Bayer)	dimethyl-diphenyl-thiuram disulphide

Activators

ATM 16 (Ancomer)	acrylate monomer coagent
Hexa (Degussa)	hexamethylene tetramine
Maglite D (Merck)	light calcined magnesium oxide
PEG 4000 (Shell)	polyethylene glycol, molecular weight 4000
Rhenocure Hexa (Rhein Chemie)	hexamethylene tetramine
Vulkacit H30 (Bayer)	hexamethylene tetramine
Zinc Octoate (Tenneco)	zinc-2-ethylhexanoate
Zinkoxyd aktiv (Bayer)	collodial zinc oxide
Zinc Oxide, Transparent (Bayer)	basic zinc carbonate

Antidegradants

Agerite Resin D (Vanderbilt)	poly-2,2,4-trimethyl-1,2-dihydroquinoline
Antioxidant 425 (Cyanamid)	2,2′-methylene-bis-(4-ethyl-6-*t*-butylphenol)
Antioxidant 2246 (Cyanamid)	2,2′-methylene-bis-(4-methyl-6-*t*-butyl phenol)
Antiozonant AFS 50 (Bayer)	cyclic acetal, 50% active.
BLE 25 (Uniroyal)	acetone-diphenylamine condensate
BLE 75 (Uniroyal)	acetone-diphenylamine condensate, 75% active
Flectol H (Monsanto)	poly-2,2,4-trimethyl-1,2-dihydroquinoline

Flexzone 4L (Uniroyal)	N,N′-bis-(1,4-dimethylpentyl)-*p*-phenylene-diamine
Irganox PS 800 (Ciba-Geigy)	dilaurylthiodipropionate
Naugard (Uniroyal)	tris-(nonylated-phenyl)-phosphate
Naugard 445 (Uniroyal)	styrenated diphenylamine
Perkanox P15/60 (Akzo Chemie)	di-alpha-methylstyrenated nonylphenol (60% active)
Permanax BL (Vulnax)	acetone-diphenylamine condensate
Permanax CNS (Vulnax)	blend of MBI and *Permanax WSP*
Permanax IPPD (Vulnax)	N-isopropyl-N′-phenyl-*p*-phenylenediamine
Permanax WSL (Vulnax)	methylcyclohexyl xylenols
Permanax WSP (Vulnax)	2,2′-methylene-bis-6-(alpha-methylcyclohexyl)-*p*-cresol
Polygard (Uniroyal)	tris-(nonylated-phenyl)-phosphate
Santoflex 13 (Monsanto)	N-(1,3-dimethylbutyl)-N'-phenyl-*p*-phenylene-diamine
Santoflex 77 (Monsanto)	N,N'-bis-(1,4-dimethylpentyl)-*p*-phenylene-diamine
Santovar A (Monsanto)	2,5-di-*t*-amylhydroquinoline
Sunproof Improved (Uniroyal)	wax blend
Tinuvin 327 (Ciba-Geigy)	2-(2′-dihydroxy-3,5-di-*t*-butyllphenyl)-5-chlorobenztriazole
UOP 88 (Universal Oil Products)	N,N′-dioctyl-*p*-phenylenediamine
Vulkanox KSM (Bayer)	styrenated/methylstyrenated cresols
Vulkanox MB (Bayer)	2-mercaptobenzimidazole
Vulkanox TSP (Bayer)	alkyl/aryl phenol blend
Vulkanox ZMB (Bayer)	zinc mercaptobenzimidazole
Vulkanox ZMB2 (Bayer)	methyl derivative of zinc-mercaptobenzimidazole
Wingstay L (Goodyear)	butylated *p*-cresol/dicyclopentadiene
Wingstay 100 (Goodyear)	diaryl-*p*-phenylenediamine

Blowing agents

Genitron CR (Fisons)	blend of azodicarbonamide and benzene sulphonyl hydrazide
Porofor BSH (Bayer)	benzene sulphonylhydrazide
Vulcacell BN (Vulnax)	dinitrosopentamethylenetetramine

Fillers

Britomya Violet (Croxton & Garry)	fine ground whiting
Calofort S (John & E Sturge)	coated calcium carbonate
Devolite Clay (English China Clays)	soft clay
Extra Steamic OOS (Talc de Luzanac)	fine talc
Glass Fibre (Owens-Corning Fibreglass)	rubber-impregnated chopped strand, 0.25in
Hexafil (English China Clays)	hard alkaline clay
Hi-Sil 233 (PPG)	reinforcing precipitated silica
Magecol 888 (Columbian Carbon)	lampblack
Pole Star 200R (English China Clays)	calcined clay
Santoweb D (Monsanto)	celluose fibre
Silane D (PPG)	semi-reinforcing precipitated silica
Silteg AS7 (Degussa)	synthetic aluminium silicate
Snowcal 2ML (Cement Marketing Board)	coarse ground whiting

Natural Rubber Formulary

Stockalite Clay (English China Clays)	hard primary clay
Ultrasil VN3 (Degussa)	reinforcing precipitated silica
Winnofil S (ICI)	coated calcium carbonate

Process aids, oils, *etc*

Aktiplast (Rhein-Chemie)	zinc soaps of higher fatty acids
Ancoplas ER (Vanderbilt)	sulphonated oil blend
Dutrex 729 (Shell)	high-viscosity aromatic oil
Escorez 1102 (Esso)	aliphatic hydrocarbon resin
MRX (Rubber Regenerating)	mineral rubber
Petrofina 2059 (Petrofina Oils)	light naphthenic/paraffinic oil
Piccolyte S105 (Hercules)	beta-pinene polyterpene resin
Plastogen (Vanderbilt)	sulphonated oil blend
Struktol A60 (Schill & Seilacher)	zinc soaps of higher fatty acids
Sunpar 2280 (Sun Oils)	paraffinic oil, low volatility
Whitbro 844 (Anchor Chemicals)	sulphur vulcanized glyceride oil
White factice (Anchor Chemicals)	sulphur monochloride vulcanized oil

Miscellaneous dry rubber compounding ingredients

Caloxol W5G (John & E Sturge)	calcium oxide dispersion
Cellobond J1113H (BP Chemicals)	novolak phenol-formaldehyde resins containing 10% hexamine
Cellobond J1115H (BP Chemicals)	novolak phenol-formaldehyde resins containing 10% hexamine
Cereclor 42 (ICI)	chlorinated wax, 42% chlorine
Cofill 11 (Degussa)	blend of resorcinol and silica
Cohedur RL (Bayer)	solution of resorcinol in formaldehyde donor
Manobond CN10 (Monsanto)	cobalt naphthenate
Resimene 3520 (Monsanto)	melamine formaldehyde resin
Si 69 (Degussa)	bis-(3-triethoxylsilylpropyl)-tetrasulphide

Latex surfactants and stabilizers

Alcopol FA (Allied Colloids)	alkyl sulphosuccinamate
Anchoid (Anchor Chemicals)	sulphonated surfactant
Belloid TD (Geigy)	sulphonated surfactant
Darvan (Vanderbilt)	sulphonated surfactant
Daxad (Dewy & Almy)	sulphonated surfactant
Empilan NP9 (Albright & Wilson)	alkylphenol-ethylene oxide condensate
Glofoam HE (ABM Chemicals)	sulphonated alkylphenol-ethylene oxide condensate
Lubrol PF (ICI)	alkylphenol-ethylene oxide condensate
Solumin FX85SD (ABM Chemicals)	sulphonated alkylphenol-ethylene oxide condensate
Texofor FN30 (ABM Chemicals)	alkylphenol-ethylene oxide condensate
Texofor V27 (ABM Chemicals)	alkylphenol-ethylene oxide condensate
Triton CF21 (Rohm & Haas)	alkylphenol-ethylene oxide condensate
Vulcastab LR (Vulnax)	sulphonated surfactant
Vulcastab LW (Vulnax)	cetyl/oleyl alcohol-ethylene oxide condensate
Vultamol (BASF)	sulphonated surfactant

Latex thickeners and resins

Celacol HPM 5000 (British Celanese)	cellulose
*Escorez 1102*B (Exxon Chemicals)	aliphatic resin
Methofas PM 5400 (ICI)	cellulose
Rohagit S-MV (Rohm & Haas)	polyacrylate
Schenectady SP 560 (Schenectady)	terpene-phenolic resin
Staybelite Ester 10 (Hercules)	hydrogenated resin ester

Miscellaneous latex compounding ingredients

Baco FRF5 (British Aluminium)	hydrated alumina
Baco FRF40 (British Aluminium)	hydrated alumina
Gantrez M1454 (General Aniline)	polyvinyl methyl ether
Lutanol M40 (BASF)	polyvinyl methyl ether
Propylan D702 (Lankro Chemicals)	polypropylene glycol
Tetron (Albright & Wilson)	tetrasodium pyrophosphate
Trimene Base (Uniroyal)	ethylchloride-formaldehyde-ammonia condensate
Vulcastab EFA (Vulnax)	ethylchloride-formaldehyde ammonia condensate

Dry rubber applications index

Abrasion-resistant vulcanizates, 2.1, 5.10
  belting, 2.1
  fabric coatings, 14.1
  fork-lift truck tyres, 13.1
  hose linings, 8.5
  retreads, 13.3, 13.4
Acrylonitrile-isoprene copolymer, blends, 5.2, 10.2
Adhesion, fabric, 14.1
Adhesives ebonite linings, 3.2
  solution, 1
  two-part, 1.4
  vulcanizable, 1.3–1.4
Adhesive tapes, pressure-sensitive, 1.1–1.2
Air permeability (low), 13.8
ASTM D2000, 9.9–9.14
ASTM D4014, 5.5, 5.8
Automotive components, 6.7
  body insulators, 5.2
  brake seals, 12.1
  bumpers, 9.17
  bushes, 5.2, 5.7, 5.9
  engine mounts, 5.3–5.4, 5.7
  hose, 8.1

Bands, elastic, 11.3
Barwell extruders, 13.4
Batteries boxes, 3.1
  injection-moulded, 4.3
  separator plates, 4.1
Bearings, bridges, 5.5, 5.8
Belting, 2
Blankets, printing, 11.2
Blends
  bromobutyl rubber, 13.6
  chlorobutyl rubber, 13.6, 13.8
  EPDM, 6.3, 10.5, 13.6
  EVA, 10.5
  isoprene-acrylonitrile copolymer, 5.2, 10.2
  nitrile rubber, 5.2, 10.2
  ozone-resistant, 10.5, 13.6
  trans-polyoctenamer, 6.1
  polybutadiene
    high-*cis*, 13.4
    low-*cis*, 13.3, 14.1
  polypropylene, 14.2
Body insulators, 5.2
Bonded bushes, 5.2, 5.9
Bonding, vulcanized rubber, 1.4
Boot soles, heavy-duty, 7.3
Brake seals, 12.1
Bridge bearings, 5.5, 5.8
Bromobutyl rubber, blends, 13.6
BS 490 Part 1, 2.1–2.3
BS 1154 W40 grade, 12.4
BS 1154 (Y series), 9.6
BS 1154 (Z series), 9.7
BS 1970, 10.3
BS 2494, 12.2
BS 2775, 6.10
BS 5400 Part 9, 5.8
Bumpers, 9.17
Bundesgesundheitsamt (BGA), 6.11, 10.1
Bungs, 6.10
Bushes, 5.2, 5.9
  bonded, 5.9
  injection mouldings, 5.7
Bus tyres, inner tubes, 13.8

Cable insulation, thermoplastic rubber, 14.2
Carpet underlay, waffle sponge, 14.5
Casual shoes, soles, 7.1
Chemical plant linings
  ebonite, 3.1–3.2
  soft rubber, 3.3
Chlorobutyl rubber, blends, 13.6, 13.8
Cisterns, lavatory, 4.3
Cold-feed extrusion, winter retreads, 13.4
Compression set, *see Section 21*
Containers, ebonite, 3.1
Continuous vulcanization, 6.3–6.9
Conveyor belts
  covers
    food-contact, 2.3
    high-quality, 2.1
    oil-extended, 2.2
    white, 2.3
  friction formulations, 2.4
    synthetic fabrics, 2.5
Couplings, injection mouldings, 5.7
Creep (low), 5.6
  high damping, 5.2
  injection mouldings, 5.7
Curing bags, 13.7
Cushion gum, pre-cured treads, 13.5

Dairying, 10.2
Damping
  high, low creep, 5.2
  moderate, 5.1

Delayed-action peroxide vulcanization, 10.5
Detergent-resistant vulcanizates, 12.4
Drains, seals, 12.2

Ebonite
  battery separator plates, 4.1
  extruded, 4.2
  hand-built, 4.2
  injection mouldings, 4.3
  lining adhesives, 3.2
  linings, 3.1
  moulded, 4.2
Efficient vulcanization *see* EV systems
Elastic bands, 11.3
Electrical insulation tapes, 1.1
Engine mounts, 5.3
  heat-resistant, 5.4
  injection mouldings, 5.7
EPDM
  blends, 10.5, 13.6
    LCM vulcanization, 6.3
Erasers, 11.1
Ethylene-propylene terpolymers *see* EPDM
EVA, blends, 10.5
EV systems, 5.4, 5.9, 6.5
  soluble, 5.2, 5.4, 5.6
Expanded rubber, 14.6
Extrusions
  automotive, 9.9–9.11
  heat-resistant, 6.5
  high hardness, 6.1
  light-coloured, 6.2, 6.6
  LCM vulcanization, 6.3–6.8
  microwave vulcanization, 6.9
  sponge rubber, 6.8
  tubing, 6.10, 6.11
  windscreen seals, 6.7

Fabrics
  adhesion, 2.5
  rubber coatings, 14.1
Fibre reinforcement, 9.17
Filters, ebonite, 3.1
Food and Drugs Administration (FDA), 2.3, 6.11, 10.2
Food contact
  conveyor belt covers, 2.3
  milk liners, 10.2
  mouldings, 10.1
  tubing, 6.11
Footwear, 7
Fork-lift truck tyres, 13.1
Friction formulations, 2.4
  synthetic fabrics, 2.5

Gaskets, *see also* Seals
  washing machines, 12.4
German Federal Republic, BGA, 6.11, 10.1
Grit blasting, hose linings, 8.5

Halobutyl rubber, blends, 13.6, 13.8
Hand-built ebonite, 4.2
Hard rubber, *see* Ebonite
Heating pads, 10.4
Heat-resistant vulcanizates, 10.5
  brake seals, 12.1
  bushes, 5.9
  conveyor belt covers, 2.1
  friction formulations, 2.4
  hose, covers, 8.3
  hose linings, 8.6
  low creep, 5.6
  mountings, 5.4
  rollers, 10.6
  solid tyres, 13.2
  tubing, 6.11
Heavy duty boot soles, 7.3
Heveaplus MG, 9.4
  hard flexible materials, 9.17
High-hardness vulcanizates, 6.1, 9.8, 9.17
  extrusions, 6.1
  mouldings, 9.4
High-styrene resins, 7.1–7.4, 9.3, 9.4, 9.8
High-temperature curing, 6.2–6.8, 10.3, 13.8
Hose, automotive, 8.1
  covers
    heat-resistant, 8.3
    high-quality, 8.3
    light-coloured, 8.2
  linings, 8.4
    abrasion-resistant, 8.5
    grit blasting, 8.5
    heat-resistant, 8.6
Hot-air curing, sponge rubber, 14.4
Hot-water bottles, injection mouldings, 10.3
Hovercraft skirts, 14.1

Identification tapes, 1.1
Injection mouldings
  boot soles, 7.3
  ebonite, 4.3
  hard flexible materials, 9.17
  hot-water bottles, 10.3
  low creep vulcanizates, 5.7
  shoe soles, 7.1–7.2
  silica-filled vulcanizates, 9.15
  soluble EV systems, 9.16
  thermoplastic rubber, 14.2
Ink erasers, 11.1

Inner tubes, truck and bus, 13.8
Insulation tapes, 1.1
Isoprene-acrylonitrile copolymer, blends, 5.2, 10.2
ISO 2023, 7.3

Laboratory tubing, 6.10
Lavatory cisterns, 4.3
LCM vulcanization
  heat-resistant, 6.5
  NR/EPDM blends, 6.3
  light-coloured, 6.3, 6.6
  sponge rubber, 6.8
  windscreen seals, 6.7
Light-coloured vulcanizates
  conveyor belt covers, 2.3
  extrusions, 6.2
    LCM vulcanization, 6.3, 6.6
  friction formulations, 2.4
  hose, covers, 8.2
  shoe soles, 7.5
  silica-filled mouldings, 9.15
  stereos, 11.2
  washing machine seals, 12.4
Linings, chemical plant, 3
Low-hardness vulcanizates, 9.1, 9.2, 9.9, 11.2
Low temperature-resistant vulcanizates, 5.3, 5.5, 9.3

Masking tapes, 1.1
Microwave vulcanization, 6.9
Milk liners, 10.2
Mouldings
  ASTM D2000, 9.9–9.14
  BS 1154, 9.6, 9.7
  classified by application, 10
  hardness-classified, 9
  thick, 5.8
Mountings, 5.3, 5.7
  heat-resistant, 5.4

Novor vulcanizates, 5.4
  curing bags, 13.7
  engine mountings, 5.4
  heating pads, 10.4
  LCM vulcanization, 6.5, 6.8
  rollers, 10.6
  solid tyres, 13.2
  sponge rubber, 6.8
  suspension bushes, 5.9
Nylon fabrics
  adhesion, 2.5
  rubber coatings, 14.1

Odourless vulcanizates, 10.1
Oil-extended vulcanizates, 9.1–9.2
  conveyor belt covers, 2.2
  damping, 5.1, 13.4
  expanded rubber, 14.6
  low hardness, 9.1, 9.2
  stereos, 11.2
Oil-resistant vulcanizates, 5.2, 10.2
On-site vulcanization, heating pads, 10.4
Orbitread extruders, 13.4
Ozone-resistant blends, 10.5

Packaging tapes, 1.2
Passenger tyres, winter retreads, 13.4
Pencil erasers, 11.1
Permeability, low air, 13.8
Peroxide vulcanization, 5.4
  coagent-modified, 10.5
Phenol formaldehyde resins, 9.4
Pickling baths, linings, 3.3
Pipes
  ebonite, 3.1
  sealing rings, 12.2
Plant linings
  ebonite, 3.1–3.2
  soft rubber, 3.3
Plating baths, linings, 3.3
Polybutadiene, blends, 13.3, 13.4, 14.1
trans-Polyoctenamer, blends, 6.1
Polypropylene, blends, 14.2
Pre-cured treads, cushion gum, 13.5
Pressure-sensitive adhesive tapes, 1.1–1.2
Printing stereos, 11.2
Profiles *see* Extrusions
Public service vehicles, inner tubes, 13.8
Pumps, ebonite, 3.1

Resin reinforcement, 7.4, 9.3–9.5
  light-coloured, 9.8
Retreads
  cushion gum, 13.5
  truck tyres, 13.3
  winter passenger tyres, 13.4
Reversion-resistant vulcanizates, 5.7, 5.8, 9.5
RFL system, 2.5, 14.1
Ring seals, 12.2
Rods, ebonite, 4.2
Rollers
  ebonite, 3.1
  heat-resistant, 10.6
Rolling resistance (low), 13.1

Sand blasting, hose linings, 8.5
Seals
 brake, 12.1
 non-black, 12.3
 pipe, 12.2
 washing machines, 12.4
 windscreens, 6.7
Semi-EV systems, 5.8, 5.9, 9.5
Separator plates, ebonite, 4.1
Sewers, seals, 12.2
Shoe soles
 high-quality casual, 7.1
 medium quality, 7.2
 transparent, 7.5
Sidewalls, white, 13.6
Sight shields, 9.17
Silane coupling agents, 9.15, 12.3, 13.4
Silica
 adhesion promotion to fabrics, 2.5
 filler
  injection mouldings, 9.15
  seals, 12.3
Skim rubber, 7.4
Soft vulcanizates, 9.1, 9.2, 11.2
 plant linings, 3.3
Solid tyres, 13.2
Soluble-EV systems, 5.2, 5.4, 5.6–5.7, 5.9
 injection mouldings, 9.16
Solution adhesives, 1
Sponge rubber, 14.3
 carpet underlay, 14.5
 heat-resistant, 6.8
 hot-air curing, 14.4
 LCM vulcanization, 6.8
  see also Expanded rubber
Sports shoes, soles, 7.1
Standards *see* ASTM, BS and ISO
Stationers bands, 11.3
Steam-resistant vulcanizates, 8.6
Stereo rubbers, 11.2
Stoppers, laboratory, 6.10
Surgical tapes, 1.2
Suspension bushes, 5.2, 5.9
 bonded, 5.9
 injection mouldings, 5.7
Swelling
 ASTM oils, 5.2, 10.2
 butter oil, 10.2
 brake fluids, 12.1

Tapes, pressure-sensitive adhesive, 1.1–1.2
Tasteless vulcanizates, 10.1
Tear-resistant vulcanizates, *see Section 21*
Thermoplastic rubber blends, 14.2
Thick mouldings, 5.8
Transparent vulcanizates
 shoe soles, 7.5
 tubing, 6.11
Trays, ebonite, 3.1
Truck tyres
 inner tubes, 13.8
 retreads, 13.3
Tubing
 ebonite, 4.2
 heat-resistant, 6.11
 laboratory, 6.10
 transparent, 6.11
Tyres
 curing bags, 13.7
 fork-lift trucks, 13.1
 inner tubes, 13.8
 solid, 13.2
 white sidewalls, 13.6
 winter passenger treads, 13.4
  see also Truck tyres

Underlay, waffle sponge, 14.5
United States Food and Drugs Administration (FDA), 2.3, 6.11, 10.2

Vacuum extrusion, LCM vulcanization, 6.3–6.7
Valves, ebonite, 3.1
Vehicle suspension bushes *see* Bushes
Vulcanizable adhesives, 1.3–1.4
Vulcanized rubber, bonding, 1.4
Vulcanizers, heating pads, 10.4

Waffle sponge, 14.5
Washing machines, seals, 12.4
Water mains, seals, 12.2
West Germany, BGA, 6.11, 10.1
White sidewalls, 13.6
Windscreen seals, 6.7
Winter tyres, passenger, 13.4

Zinc oxide reinforcement, 9.6

Latex applications index

Adhesives
  carpet installation, 15.1
  ceramic tiles, 15.5
  flocking, 17.1
  peelable, 15.1
  polyvinyl chloride tiles, 15.6
  quick-grab, 15.4
  self-seal envelopes, 15.3
  tufted carpeting, secondary backings, 15.2
  vinyl tiles, 15.6
Anchor coats
  tufted carpeting, 16.1-16.2
  washable rugs, 16.3

Backings (carpets)
  flame-retardant, 16.6-16.7
  foam, 16.7-16.8
  non-gelled, 16.9
  tiles, 16.4
  washable, 16.3
Balloons, toy, 17.8
Binders
  non-woven fabrics, 20.8
    delamination-resistant, 20.7
  rubberized hair, 20.9
    flame-retardant, 20.1
Blown foam, carpet backings, 16.5

Carpets
  backings
    blown foam, 16.5
    flame-retardant, 16.6-16.7
    foam rubber, 16.6-16.9
  installation adhesives, 15.1
  tile backings, 16.4
    foam, 16.5
  woven, sizings, 16.1
Cast products, 20.2
  flame-retardant, 20.1
  heat-sensitive systems, 20.3
Cement, Portland, 20.13
Ceramic tiles, adhesives, 15.5
Chloroprene rubber, laminated gloves, 17.5
Coatings, flame-retardant, 20.4
Coir, rubberized, 20.9
Condoms, 17.10
Copper-resistant prevulcanized latices, 19.3

Delamination-resistant binders, 20.7
Detergent-resistant, household gloves, 17.2
Dipped products, 17.1-17.10
Dunlop process, 18.3

Electricians gloves, 17.3
Envelopes, self-seal, adhesives, 15.3
Extrusion
  thread, 20.5
  tubing, 20.12

Fibres, rubberized, 20.9
Flame-retardant systems
  carpet backings, 16.6-16.7
  cast products, 20.1
  coatings, 20.4
  foam rubber, 18.1
    carpet backings, 16.7
  rubberized hair, 20.10
Flocking adhesives, household gloves, 17.1
Foam rubber
  carpet backings, 16.5-16.9
  flame-retardant, 18.1
    carpet backings, 16.6-16.7
  moulded, 18.2-18.3
  spread, 18.4

Gloves
  electricians, 17.3
  household, 17.4
    detergent-resistant, 17.2
    flocking adhesives, 17.1
  laminated, chloroprene rubber, 17.5

Hair, rubberized, 20.9
Heat-resistant systems
  prevulcanized latices, 19.2
  thread, 20.6
Heat-sensitive systems, 17.6-17.7
  cast products, 20.3
  extruded tubing, 20.12
  moulded foam, 18.2, 18.4
Hollow cast articles, 20.2
Household gloves, 17.4
  detergent-resistant, 17.2
  flocking adhesives, 17.1

Laminated gloves, chloroprene rubber, 17.5
Latex thread, heat-resistant, 20.6

Modified cement, 20.13
Moulded foam, 18.2-18.3

Non-gelled foams, tufted carpeting, 16.9
Non-woven fabrics
  binders, 20.8
    delamination-resistant, 20.7

Peelable adhesives, 15.1
Plaster of paris moulds, casting into, 20.1-20.2
Polyvinyl chloride tiles, adhesives, 15.6
Portland cement, 20.13
Prevulcanized latices, 19.1
  copper-resistant, 19.3
  heat-resistant, 19.2
  transparent products, 19.4
Prophylactics, 17.10

Quick-grab adhesives, 15.4

Rubberized cement, 20.13
Rubberized hair/fibre binders, 20.9
  flame-retardant, 20.1
Rubberized sports surfaces, 20.11
Rugs, washable, anchor backings, 16.3

Self-seal envelopes, adhesives, 15.3
Silico-fluoride process, 18.3
Sizings, woven carpets, 16.10
Sports surfaces, 20.11
Spread foam, 18.4
Stage scenery, 20.1, 20.4

Teats, 17.7
Theatrical scenery, 20.1, 20.4
Thread, 20.5
  heat-resistant, 20.6
Tiles
  carpet, backings, 16.4-16.5
  ceramic, adhesives, 15.5
  polyvinyl chloride, adhesives, 15.6
  vinyl, adhesives, 15.6
Toy balloons, 17.8
Transparent products, prevulcanized latices, 19.4
Tubing, 20.12
Tufted carpeting
  anchor coats, 16.1-16.2
  foam backings, 16.8
  non-gelled foams, 16.9
  secondary backings, adhesives, 15.2
Tyre crumb/cement compositions, 20.11

Vinyl tiles, adhesives, 15.6

Washable rugs, anchor coats, 16.3
Woven carpets, back sizings, 16.1